S.F.N.
34

Rocky Mountain Reader

IDAHO

George Snell 1
Vardis Fisher 2

MONTANA

Grace Stone Coates 1
Clyde F. Murphy 2
Mildred Walker 3
Lew Sarett 4
Norman Macleod 5
Joseph K. Howard 6
Jessie Treichler 7

WYOMING

Alan Swallow 1
Ted Olson 2

NEVADA

Walter Van Tilburg Clark 1
Richard G. Lillard 2
Edwin Corle 3

UTAH

Bernard DeVoto 1
Wallace Stegner 2
Dale Morgan 3
Brewster Ghiselin 4
Whit Burnett 5
Maurine Whipple 6
Jonreed Lauritzen 7

COLORADO

Rosamund D. Thomson 1
Hope Williams Sykes 2
Thomas Hornsby Ferril 3
Katharine Shattuck 4
Clyde Brion Davis 5

ROCKY
MOUNTAIN
READER

Edited by

Ray B. West, Jr.

1946

E. P. DUTTON & CO., INC.

NEW YORK

American Book–Stratford Press, Inc., New York

For . . .
LUCILLE
LELIA
JULIE

Acknowledgments

Brittin, Norman: *Spring Wind* by permission of the *Rocky Mountain Review.*

Burnett, Whit: *Sherrel* by permission of the author and *Story* Magazine.

Clark, Walter Van Tilburg: *A Western Incident* from *The Ox-Bow Incident,* copyright, 1940, Walter Van Tilburg Clark, by permission of Random House, Inc.

Clough, Wilson O.: *Regionalism* by permission of the *Rocky Mountain Review. On a Naked Hill in Wyoming* by permission of the author and the *Southwest Review.*

Coates, Grace Stone: *The Way of a Transgressor* from *Black Cherries,* copyright, 1931, by Alfred A. Knopf, Inc. by permission and special arrangement with the author and Alfred A. Knopf, Inc.

Corle, Edwin: *Desert Ghosts* from *Coarse Gold,* copyright, 1942, by Edwin Corle by permission of E. P. Dutton & Co., Inc.

Davis, Clyde Brion: *Payday* by permission of the author.

DeVoto, Bernard: *Jonathan Dyer: Frontiersman* by permission of the author.

Ferril, Thomas Hornsby: *Ghost Town* from *Westering* by permission of Yale University Press. *Writings in the Rockies* by permission of the author and the *Saturday Review of Literature.*

Fisher, Vardis: *Children of God,* copyright, 1939, by Vardis Fisher, by permission of Harper & Brothers.

Foote, Ellis: *Sad Hills* by permission of the *Rocky Mountain Review.*

Ghiselin, Brewster: *New World* from *Against the Circle* by permission of the author and E. P. Dutton & Co., Inc.

Hart, Edward: *Conclusions* by permission of the *Rocky Mountain Review.*

Howard, Joseph K.: *Boisterous Butte* from *Montana: High, Wide, and Handsome* by permission of Yale University Press.

Lake, Richard: *The Cradle of History* by permission of the *Rocky Mountain Review.*

Lauritzen, Jonreed: *Indian Boy* from *Arrows into the Sun,* copy-

7

right, 1943, by Alfred A. Knopf, Inc. by permission and special arrangement with Alfred A. Knopf, Inc.

Lillard, Richard G.: *Wild West in Neon* from *Desert Challenge,* copyright, 1942, by Richard G. Lillard by permission of Alfred A. Knopf, Inc.

Macleod, Norman: *Gunsight Trail: Glacier Park* from *Five Poets* by permission of the author.

Morgan, Dale L.: *Mormon Storytellers* by permission of the *Rocky Mountain Review. Rain* from *The Humboldt,* copyright, 1943, by Dale L. Morgan by permission of Farrar & Rinehart, Inc.

Murphy, Clyde F.: *Hogan of Dublin Gulch* from *The Glittering Hill,* copyright, 1944, by E. P. Dutton & Co., Inc. by permission of E. P. Dutton & Co., Inc.

Olson, Ted: *Cabin Fever* by permission of *Story* Magazine.

Sarett, Lew: *Breaker of Broncos* from *Slow Smoke* by permission of Henry Holt and Company, Inc.

Stegner, Wallace: *Arcadian Village* from *Mormon Country* by permission of Duell, Sloan & Pearce, Inc.

Shattuck, Katharine: *Journey to Denver* by permission of the author.

Snell, George: *Smoke on the Snow* by permission of the *Rocky Mountain Review.*

Swallow, Alan: *Two Rocky Mountain Poets* by permission of the *Rocky Mountain Review. Wyoming* by permission of *Voices.*

Sykes, Hope Williams: *Second Hoeing* by permission of the author.

Thompson, Rosamund Dargan: *And We Call Out* by permission of the *University of Kansas City Review.*

Thurston, Jarvis: *The One and Only Appearance of Jeez Christ on Sun Mountain* by permission of the author and the *Rocky Mountain Review.*

Treichler, Jessie: *Homecoming* by permission of the author and *The Antioch Review.*

Walker, Mildred: *Winter Wheat,* copyright, 1944, by Harcourt, Brace and Company, Inc. by permission of Harcourt, Brace and Company, Inc.

West, Ray B., Jr.: *The Blue Spring* by permission of *Interim.*

Whipple, Maurine: *Temple Builders* from *The Giant Joshua* by permission of Houghton Mifflin Company.

Table of Contents

Table of Contents

Introduction

IT MUST be realized—and this is a fact which often escapes the observer from an older, more settled section of America—that the Rocky Mountain region remains the youngest in our nation. It is young even in comparison with its neighbors to the south and west, whose cultures were, in part at least, established by the nature of their settlers long before the great Western migration of the nineteenth century began. The Rocky Mountain area was unknown before 1825. A few Spanish colonists had penetrated into southern Colorado, and a Catholic priest had come within thirty miles of Great Salt Lake seeking a shortcut from Santa Fe to Monterrey, Mexico. Lewis and Clark had skirted the area in their examination of the newly acquired Louisiana Purchase, while Father DeSmet had set up Indian missions in the North. The fur trappers of the Hudson's Bay Company, the Rocky Mountain Fur Company, and the American Fur Company knew the streams of eastern Colorado and Wyoming, Montana, and northern Idaho, but it was not until 1824 that one of them, Jim Bridger, traveled as far south as Great Salt Lake, and he thought for a full year that he had reached the shores of the Pacific. There was no Spanish or Mexican culture, and no Indian culture comparable to that in the Southwest except for a few small bands of Navajos in southern Colorado, southern Utah, and north of the Grand Canyon on the Arizona Strip, sections that even today are sparsely settled. Brigham Young's band of Mormon pioneers, who reached the shores of Great Salt Lake in July, 1847, were the first permanent settlers in the entire area—less than 100 years ago.

The historical background from this point on is well known: the gold rush in '49, which used the South Pass as a funnel to California; the discovery of gold in Colorado ten years later; the coming of the telegraph to displace the Pony Express; the transcontinental railroad

13

following the Civil War; then the discovery of copper at Butte and Bingham Canyon, the development of cattle and sheep grazing, and finally the homesteaders at the turn of the century. All of this has been, admittedly, material for the "regional" writer, and the wonder of American letters for many years was that such stories were not used seriously in prose or verse.

Some of them were told, of course—by writers who came into the area from outside. Washington Irving was impressed by the Western fur trade and the exploration of the West, and he wrote *The Adventures of Captain Bonneville* and *Astoria*. Mark Twain and Bret Harte recorded the humor, the color, and the melodrama of the Nevada gold camps. Living for a while in Colorado Springs, Helen Hunt Jackson was impressed by the romance of the Indians and the scenery. Walt Whitman visited briefly, as did Kipling, Arthur Conan Doyle, Richard Burton, and Oscar Wilde, and all wrote down their impressions of the people and of the country. Harry Leon Wilson, Owen Wister, and Zane Grey used the material of the Rocky Mountains in their novels, giving impetus to what has become as devastating an exploitation of the region's fictional resources as the incursions of Eastern finance have of its natural wealth. In addition there were a few semi-indigenous wits like Bill Nye and Eugene Field, newspapermen, who exploited the broad frontier type of humor and made something of a national reputation for themselves out of it. But all of this material has been collected and edited by Levette J. Davidson and Prudence Bostwick of Denver, and is available in a single volume (*The Literature of the Rocky Mountain West*, Caxton Printers, 1939). Aside from being an interesting collection of social data (including excerpts from pioneer journals and diaries as well as early reports of such geological investigations as that of Captain Howard Stansbury), the book represents an interesting and valuable introduction to the present anthology.

It is indicative that the first crop of genuine Rocky Mountain authors has sprung from the Mormon settlements of Utah, Idaho, Wyoming, and Arizona, and this is undoubtedly because the Mormons represented the single, early group of permanent settlers to come into the region already possessed of a single, unified belief, a cultural core against which the chaos of the frontier could be judged and set into some kind of order. Even then it was not easy for the Mormon writer to grasp the meaning of his environment. Speaking of Salt Lake City, Dale Morgan has written recently in the *Rocky Mountain Review:* "In the very presence of the fact, it is difficult to believe. You have to deal with the Kingdom of God—fashioned in the form of a Yankee town, set down at a Western crossroads, and subjected to a fifty-year sand-blasting by the American frontier."

Again it was the outsider, the "gentile," who first grasped the psychological and dramatic possibilities of the Mormon story. As late as 1935, the most complete and sensible portrayal was made by an English writer, Susan Ertz, in *The Proselyte*. But the floodgates were about to burst. George Snell's *Root, Hog and Die* appeared the next year. Three years later came Vardis Fisher's Harper's Prize novel, *Children of God*, followed by Jean Woodman's *Glory Spent*, Paul Bailey's *For This My Glory*, Maurine Whipple's *The Giant Joshua*, Lorene Pearson's *The Harvest Waits*, and Virginia Sorenson's *A Little Lower than the Angels*, all of these from native authors, in addition to such novels as Hoffman Birney's *Ann Carmeny* and Elinor Pryor's *And Never Yield*, by writers from outside the region. Bernard DeVoto had touched upon the subject as early as 1926 in his novel *The Chariot of Fire*, and he published his brief but excellent biographical study *Jonathan Dyer: Frontiersman* in 1933. In 1943 Jonreed Lauritzen published *Arrows into the Sun*, a novel dealing with the relations between Indians and Mormons in southern Utah and northern Arizona; while Wallace Stegner's valuable volume, *Mormon Country*, in the "American Folkways" series, appeared the same year. Dale Morgan was also concerned with the Mormon story in his "Rivers of America" series book, *The Humboldt*, published in 1943. Thus, this first phase of pioneer settlement, a fictional treatment of which had not been attempted ten years before, had by 1945 become almost a glut on the publisher's market. Bernard DeVoto's fears that the story, because of its extravagant and anomalous character, could never be told, have been proved unfounded.

The most significant of the Mormon novels to have appeared to date is undoubtedly Vardis Fisher's *Children of God*. It is, essentially, the story of the Mormon migration west from Nauvoo, Illinois,

to Salt Lake City, though including in its scheme the early days of
the church in New York, Ohio, and Missouri, and continuing to the
time of the Mormon manifesto prohibiting polygamy, several years
after the death of Brigham Young. In its general tone and selection
of events it is an historical epic, and it succeeds admirably in cap-
turing the whole heroic atmosphere of the westward trek, its idealism, fanaticism, devotion, humor, and tragedy. Its action is concerned, for the most part, with the historical conflicts between the
Mormons and their enemies, the occasional disagreements among
the Mormons themselves, as well as the problems of polygamy,
political recognition, and social adjustment. There is a tone of high
seriousness and admiration permeating the novel which (despite
its opening somewhat "clinical" examination of the "divinity" of the
Mormon prophet, Joseph Smith) probably accounts for its unity, its
effectiveness, and perhaps its popularity. It definitely creates an
heroic stature for its chief figure, Brigham Young, and it treats the
major events of his life with epic seriousness, though turning often,
in minor events and with minor characters, to a gusty, frontier
humor for a kind of comic relief. For those who were familiar with
Mr. Fisher's early farm novels as well as his long tetralogy, it was a
surprising and pleasing performance. It might be said that if the
early novels were an examination of the author's environment, an
examination and an evaluation, *Children of God* was a celebration
of its historical background.

Other Mormon novels have been less pretentious, and the second
most popular of them, Maurine Whipple's *The Giant Joshua*, represents in many respects a contrast to *Children of God*. Its tone is
similar, differing however in degree, so that it might be called, for
want of a better word, lyrical. While Mr. Fisher was concerned with
the whole sweep of the Mormon westward movement, Miss Whipple
concentrated upon a single settlement: what has become known as
the Dixie Colony in southern Utah, which was, in the early days,
probably the most colorful of all Mormon settlements. The story
itself is focused upon a young woman convert to Mormonism who
very early becomes the only slightly unwilling bride to an older
church dignitary—his fourth wife. But the action fades into the
background. It is a variation of the local-color story, but with all

of the advantages and none of the falseness of the guide-book type produced by the professional journalists who wrote about the region knowing only the externals. The novel is rich in specialized incident, a result partly of the peculiarities of custom and doctrine and partly of the attempts of the settlers to achieve a measure of psychological protection against their environment. It is a folk crystallization, highly susceptible to exterior presentation, and we recognize its meaning even in the title: the giant cactus of the southern Utah desert—the Joshua tree—like the characters themselves, draws a meager sustenance from the arid soil, but its pronged arms are outstretched toward heaven.

In contrast to the Mormon settlements, the mining camps of Colorado, Nevada, and Montana were picturesque and isolated centers of disorder, unified at first only by the personalities of such men as "Silver Dollar" Tabor, Sandy Bowers, and Marcus Daly, and made up, for the most part, of transient wanderers whose dream of "striking it rich" was little more than a local variation of the false idealism of the Gilded Age. Likewise, the exploitation of the early cattle ranges and "free land" came as a result of the same dream, as did the building of the transcontinental railroad; but it was a point of view imposed upon the West by outside interests, and the men who held it did not, for the most part, come as settlers, nor did they come with any understanding of why they had come, beyond the desire to "make their pile" and return home. When they did strike pay-dirt, they often built fantastic and elaborate mansions in the hills or on the deserts and stocked them with the plunder of Europe. A few of them, like Denver's Tabor, had themselves elected members of Congress and returned to the East in style.

That their whole incredulous activity did have meaning, we are only now beginning to see and understand, though there were few among them with the desire to recognize this. As a result, little of their story has been written, and where it has been told it has been done by outsiders, by journalists who have understood the popular appeal the telling of such melodramatic tales would have. This accounts for such fictional biographies as David Karsner's *Silver Dollar* or Gene Fowler's *Timberline*. The native authors who have attempted to deal with the same material have had less technical ability and little more recognition of the total meaning behind the whole amazing phenomenon of greedy digging in the earth for wealth. Dorothy Gardner's *The Madonna of the Hills* and Frank Waters' *Below Grass Roots* are biographical novels, inept and sprawling, lacking the polish of the professional works, but they are, on the whole, more honest. Better are the novels of two Montana authors, *Singermann* and *Wide Open Town* by Myron Brinig and *The Glittering Hill* by Clyde F. Murphy, but they are better not because of any technical excellence or great talent, but because the subject has been approached from the point of view of an already coherent ethnic group transplanted to the Rocky Mountain scene. Undoubtedly the two best fictional treatments of the mining theme are Vardis Fisher's *City of Illusion* and Edwin Corle's *Coarse Gold,* though Mr. Fisher's book is far from being his best work and Mr. Corle's novel is, perhaps, too much a philosophic treatise in the guise of fiction.

The story of the Rocky Mountain cattle industry represents, in many ways, a repetition of the history of mining. Perhaps the most promising of all Rocky Mountain literary material, this subject matter has been exploited by outside writers until it has become, as T. K. Whipple has pointed out, a form of regional myth—but, as Mr. Whipple neglects to say, it is a false one. The typical "western" of Zane Grey, the moving pictures, and the pulp magazines have created an heroic figure of the American cowboy, which, it must be admitted, has much in common with the mythological heroes of antiquity. This popular concept has, as a matter of fact, become so firmly planted in the consciousness of the American reader that an honest literary craftsman of the region has difficulty in approaching it. If, as Lionel Trilling has said, "The value of any myth cannot depend upon its demonstrability as fact, but only on the value of the attitudes it embodies, the further attitudes it engenders and the actions it motivates," then there is something somehow pathetic in the spectacle of Western farmhands struggling to live up to this popular concept of them.

The success of the Western myth depends upon the measure of truth which exists in this portrayal of the lonely, self-reliant individual of the cow country. The popular story is possible because of the numerous actual conflicts between cattle men and "nesters," between the cattle men and sheep men, which provide a basis of truth and make it appear genuine. It is not only, however, that the myth is an oversimplification. All myth is that—a reduction of the truth to its lowest common denominator—but the popular myth is a simplification of all that was sentimental in character or fantastic in action. The real West was engaged in a gigantic struggle against nature. It rejected many of its inherited concepts, but retained enough to make the search for its own standards a very complicated one indeed, and evidences of both the struggle and the search are still apparent in legislation which demands Eastern aid in conservation and reclamation measures, on the one hand, but which literally thumbs its nose at Eastern morality from the divorce courts at Reno, on the other.

As a result there has been only one novel which has succeeded in dealing with the story both in its own terms and in terms of those elements of truth which the myth contains. Walter Van Tilburg Clark's *The Ox-Bow Incident* is a genuine interpretation of one of the major conflicts of frontier life—the struggle for justice in a society which found itself without the usual means of obtaining it. This is also a familiar theme of the "popular" story, which can be said to have a theme only in the sense that we may see the cowboy hero, the Western outlaw, and the beautiful "schoolmarm" as pale types in a simple, formulized allegory of absolute good and evil. Each of Mr. Clark's characters, on the other hand, is a human being with his own personal reaction to the situation, a reaction conditioned somewhat by his own relationship to the environment, but displayed against a general, humanistic backdrop—the concept of justice as a mean between the impulsive vengeance of the irrational man of action and the sentimental pity of the moralist.

The struggle in *The Ox-Bow Incident* is not for religious expression, not for the particular brand of spiritual salvation represented in the Mormon creed, but for an all-embracing, general concept of simple justice. One suspects that Mr. Clark began, not with the specific historical fact, as did the Mormon authors, but that he saw the moral fact in all its general implications and then set about to clothe it in an objective sequence of events. In so doing, however, he drew upon all of the physical and psychological resources of Western history; above all, he utilized the heterogeneity of character which the various success-seeking enterprises of the West supplied. In its rigid simplicity of structure, his novel is almost classical in design. Its style (despite the fact that it is a narrative in the first person) is almost coldly dispassionate. Its theme is heightened and emotionalized by the steady progression of events preceding and following the lynching of three supposed cattle thieves, and the author portrays the subtle but powerful ironies which operate among diverse characters under the stress of such an event. The narrator is a kind of chorus, a participator in the action, but certainly not the central figure. If there is a "hero" it is Davies, the store owner and unofficial moralist of Bridger's Wells, who is the spokesman for the idea of legal procedure because he believes that it is only through "due process of law" that injustice can be avoided. But it is not as simple as that either, because Davies is a pacifist.

> "Now do you see," he said triumphantly, like all he wanted to do was make himself out the worst he could. "I knew those men were innocent. I knew it as surely as I do now. And I knew Tetley could be stopped. I knew in that moment you were all ready to be turned. And I was glad I didn't have a gun."

Davies is not an heroic figure, except in a new sense. Even with his concept of justice, he was glad he could not use force to save the lives of three innocent men. The whole action might be said to represent a kind of multiple tragedy, with the degree and kind of emotion varying according to the worth and kind of the various characters, but with the burden of remorse falling upon the only figure capable of verbalizing his conflict.

But to say this is to say no more than that it is not a tragedy at all —in the traditional sense. It does, however, move the reader to an accumulated sense of horror by the steady and relentless movement of the act to its completion; to pity for the majority of the characters, who are seen to be motivated by a reasonable ethical cause, but who are defeated by the very intensity with which that cause is held.

In addition, the novel supplies, as in the case of Mr. Fisher and Miss Whipple, a juxtaposition of idealism and reality, which produces pleasure, finally, through the recognition of a simple pattern beneath a rather complex series of character relationships. The pattern itself represents a version of the most common of all Western themes, and one suspects that much of the sense of originality in the novel comes, exactly, from the fact that Mr. Clark felt the necessity to avoid the commonplaces of the popular Western story.

A third type of fiction, and one which has achieved a measure of genuine excellence, is the farm, or small-town, story. In a general way, much of this writing has been done in the tradition of the regionalists, particularly of the South and Midwest, which began shortly before World War I and continued into the 1930's. It is perhaps significant that most, though not all, of these stories from the Rocky Mountain area were pseudo-biographies, allowing their authors the opportunity of introspection and re-examination at a time when they felt, no doubt, incapable of the objectivity of the later historical fiction. The best examples of this type of writing are contained in the early novels of Vardis Fisher, particularly in such books as *Dark Bridwell* and *In Tragic Life*, set in the Antelope Hills country of southern Idaho where Fisher grew up, and in such novels as *Second Hoeing* by Hope Williams Sykes of Colorado, *The Great Adam* by George Snell, Norman Macleod's *The Bitter Roots*, and Max Miller's *The Beginning of a Mortal*. It is significant, too, that most of the work in the short story falls into this classification, such stories as Jessie Treichler's "Homecoming," Ted Olson's "Cabin Fever," and Grace Stone Coates' "The Way of the Transgressor."

There is a temptation to place Wallace Stegner with this group, remembering such stories as "The Bugle Song" and "Butcher Bird," but both are excerpts from his most recent novel, and it would be a mistake to think of *The Big Rock Candy Mountain* as representing no more than is available in the short stories which have been taken from it. It has more in common with *Children of God* and *The Ox-Bow Incident* (though unlike them) than it has with *Dark Bridwell* and *Second Hoeing*. While Mr. Fisher and Mr. Clark measured the frontier against traditional religious and ethical standards, Mr. Stegner has chosen a perspective which creates mythical significance for the frontier itself. Still retaining the epic framework, his theme is based upon the recognition that the West is no longer a scene for heroic action of the type celebrated by *Children of God*. In addition, Mr. Stegner makes use not of a single locale, not of a unique and special group, but displays his characters against a background which includes almost all of the Rocky Mountain area from Saskatchewan, Canada, to Reno and Salt Lake City.

The central figure in *The Big Rock Candy Mountain*, Bo Mason, begins life in the Middle West. Endowed naturally with every talent that usually makes for the successful man of action—curiosity, daring, and physical strength—he is pulled westward by the overwhelming desire to "strike it rich."

> He had a notion where home would turn out to be . . .
> —over the next range, on the Big Rock Candy Mountain,
> that place of impossible loveliness that had pulled the
> whole nation westward, the place where the fat land
> sweated up wealth and the heavens dropped lemonade.

This is Bo Mason's dream, and there is little recognition of moral problems in it, because that battle had been won before he was born. Bo was confronted only in his personal relations by the necessity which represented the special problem of the characters in *The Ox-Bow Incident*—the psychological necessity to replace chaos with order—and as a result there is in him no real struggle for moral integration. "He was a man who never knew himself, who was never satisfied, who was born disliking the present and believing in the future. . . . He wore out his wife and broke her heart, he destroyed one son and turned the other against him. At the end he degenerated into a broken old man, sponging a bare living and sustaining himself on a last gilded, impossible dream; and when he could no longer bear the indignities which the world heaped upon him, and when the dream broke like a bubble, he sought some way, out of an obscure and passionate compulsion to exonerate himself, to lay the blame onto another."

This is an astute examination of the character of Bo Mason, suggesting as it does the impossibility of the "gilded" dream, the false idealism for which Bo stood. They are the words of the author through the consciousness of Bo's one remaining link with the world in those days before he murdered an unfaithful mistress and took his own life in a cheap Salt Lake City hotel. Beginning as a foil and a contrast to his father, Bruce Mason has begun by the time of his father's death to recognize his own dream and to realize that it was compounded in part of his father's errors. The relationship of Bruce to Bo is the relationship of Walter Van Tilburg Clark's characters to their environment. Other authors might have called it the moralizing influence of the character's contact with evil, but it is significant that few Rocky Mountain authors have seen evil as anything other than a combination of environmental circumstances. Bruce, thinking back over his father's life, says:

> Perhaps that was what it meant, all of it. It was good to have been along and to have shared it. There were things he had learned that could not be taken away from him. Perhaps it took several generations to make a man, perhaps it took several combinations and re-creations of his mother's gentleness and resilience, his father's enormous energy and appetite for the new, a subtle blending of masculine and feminine, selfish and selfless, stubborn and yielding, before a proper man could be fashioned.

But the end is the same—to fashion a proper man, a proper society. The evil in Bo Mason consisted in his failure to achieve what he, with his great talents, felt that he was capable of achieving, his inability to compromise with the society which was emerging from the frontier, his confusion in defeat. Brigham Young and the settlers of the Dixie Mission might have said it otherwise. They would have said Bo was possessed of the devil. Their dream consisted in a heaven and a hell as well as the earth. But there were similarities. For Bruce and for the settlers of Bridger's Wells, the fulfillment of the dream lay not in the present, but in the future. The tragedy of *The Ox-Bow Incident* is that Mr. Clark's characters attempted to achieve a kind of perfection through their own individual and all-too-human judgment. Call it what you will—Heaven, the Big Rock

Candy Mountain, the idea of justice—it all amounts to the same thing: the struggle to fashion order out of chaos (in the case of Bo Mason it is an inversion of this process)—the chaos of the individual mind and of the natural universe, and it is significant that the novelists of the West recognized this as their proper fictional theme.

But the chief facts which stand out in a survey of Rocky Mountain writing is the predominance of the novel and the comparatively small—though growing—amount of poetry. This can be partially accounted for by literary fashion, by the fact that there is little market for poetry and almost no financial remuneration. More important, however, are the facts that the writing of poetry demands, particularly in the short lyrics which are the dominant fashion, a preoccupation with matters of style and technique which the region has had neither time nor inclination to supply, and, further, that the Western story has been seen primarily as an epic, while the American epic form is not verse, but the novel.

There has been an inclination on the part of Westerners to consider the area beyond the Mississippi River the effete East, particularly the cities of New York and Boston, and this attitude may have been partly responsible for the kind of writing which has come out of the West. In poetry, it betrays itself in a lack of sympathy with the best verse being written elsewhere, which results in a continued attempt, on the part of minor versifiers, to hitch their uncertain talents to an outmoded tradition. The better poets are more sensitive to the cultural climate of their age, and some of them, like Thomas Hornsby Ferril, Ted Olson, Ellis Foote, and Alan Swallow, seem to have taken upon themselves a problem even more difficult than that of the novelists: an integration of themselves with the unique aspects of Rocky Mountain scenery. This has resulted in such excellent lines as the following from Ferril's "Time of Mountains":

> But if I go before these mountains go,
> I'm unbewildered by the time of mountains,
> I, who have followed life up from the sea
> Into a black incision in this planet
> Can bring an end to stone infinitives.
> I have held rivers to my eyes like lenses,

> And rearranged the mountains at my pleasure,
> As one might change the apples in a bowl,
> And I have walked a dim unearthly prairie
> From which these peaks have not yet blown away.

But the result has been much the same as with the novelists—as it was bound to be. Brewster Ghiselin, who must be called a Rocky Mountain poet despite his Pacific Coast origins, has stated the problem with perceptive irony in the opening lines of his "New World":

> This is the land our fathers came to find:
> They found the old world only, they found the known
> Measures of the moods of their own minds:
> The blue mountains' dying, the plain's surmise,
> The bones and bountiful nakedness and thought
> Of barbarous rock, and the green peace of earth;
> They found the hostile forests of the heart.

That is probably as succinct a statement as can be made concerning the problem of the Western pioneer. Its meaning comes to us, however, with an added force, because it is an embodiment of the frontier myth. Mr. Ghiselin's "fathers" left the chaos, the economic, political, and social chaos of the period preceding and following the Civil War. They found only what they had never lost in a new mood. They found what they had come to escape: "the hostile forests of the heart." The ultimate value for the poets, as for the novelists, has been a discovery of this kind. Their discoveries were not unique or fantastic because they had come into a region filled with inexplicable extremes of beauty and ugliness, though it was enough to throw them temporarily off-balance. Sooner or later, the artist was to discover that he could rearrange the mountains at his pleasure. With this discovery has come, more and more, the ability to arrange according to a meaningful and artful design, but it is only recently that the measure of achievement has been such that it could stand comparison with other, and older, regions. The chief value of the Rocky Mountain author lies in the fact that he satisfies a need for the clarification of general ideals in the light of the particular nature of his environment, an important segment of the American frontier, and the remarkable thing about this body of writing is not, as has been long supposed, that it was late in arriving, but that what we have at the present time is as competent and aware of its obligations as the present body of material indicates it to be.

RAY B. WEST, JR.

Note

A WORD of explanation is due, I believe, for at least two omissions from this collection of selections which deserve, on all grounds except editorial expediency, to have been included. They are the novels *The Bitter Roots* by Norman Macleod and *The Harvest Waits* by Lorene Pearson. Both are recommended to readers of this collection, the first for its significant portrayal of a small boy in a Montana community during the first World War, the second as another interesting example of the Mormon story in fiction.

R. W.

Rocky Mountain Reader

CHILDREN OF GOD

Brigham camped at the foot of the mountain. When he entered the valley the next morning, the main camp had been told of his coming and now rushed in a body to meet him, a few of them wildly enthusiastic but most of them depressed and dismayed. They had preceded Brigham by three days and had already begun to dam creeks, dig trenches, and make small reservoirs; but this country appalled them. The earth, they said, was so dry that it had to be watered before it could be plowed; they had seen only one tree since entering the valley; the bottomlands westward were beds of alkali; and no matter where they went, they stepped on big ugly crickets that swarmed in millions. Bridger, declared one, had been right: this land had been abandoned by God to drouth and crickets and wolves, prickly pear and cheat grass and thistles, to time and desolation.

"Is this our new home?"

"Yes," said Brigham. "We'll build here."

"We can't. We'll all starve to death."

"Nonsense." Brigham looked westward across the valley and waved a hand. "We'll make that desert blossom like a rose."

He was still pale and weak from his sickness, but he walked through the camp, praising those who had labored, rebuking those who had not, and giving to all of them his vision of what this country would be like in ten years. Nobody had ever been able to resist his enthusiasm; nobody was able now. The men came to life as he strode among them. They seized shovels, harnessed teams, set plows to the earth, and brought forth the seed which they had hoarded on the long journey.

"You think this land will grow things?"

"Damn it," said Brigham, "I know it. We'll turn this valley into a garden. We'll make it one of the wonder spots of the world."

The one who had asked the question now gazed out over the alkali wastes. He looked around him at the sagebrush, the withered grass, the black crickets crawling up every stem and shrub.

"Will corn grow here?" asked another, who had set up his blacksmith shop and was busy.

"Anything will grow here that will grow in this latitude."

Some of the men looked dubious, but little by little they caught the dauntless spirit of their leader; and a week after Brigham walked into it, the camp was transformed. The men were singing again. Most of them were like lads in a strange playground: they set out in exploring parties, some entering the canyons to search for timber, others going up and down the valley or to the dead sea. This inland lake amazed them. The water was heavy with salt, the shores were salt beaches, and the islands in it seemed to be bird sanctuaries. Day by day the explorers returned to report their discoveries. There were dozens of excellent hot springs; there was a slow meandering river which they named the Jordan; there was a little timber in some of the canyons, as well as a fine quality of building stone; there seemed to be ample water for irrigation; and the soil was not so worthless as they had supposed.

Around campfires in the evenings they caught Brigham's faith, and planned and dreamed, though now and then one gazed solemnly at the eastern mountains, trying to realize that his family was twelve hundred miles away. Brigham called the camp together and laid down the law. "The law of this valley," he said, standing in a wagon, "shall be the law of God, and no person will live here who does not obey that law. You will not work or hunt or fish on Sunday, but will keep that day holy. Anyone who does not like the law here may dwell where he pleases but he shall not dwell among us. No man shall buy or sell land, for all land will be held in common.

Every man shall have land measured off to him, both in the city and for farming. He may have as much as he can till and may till as much as he pleases, but he must till all that he uses and take care of it. If he refuses to till his land, it shall be taken from him.

"All wood and timber and water will belong to the community, and all other natural resources: there will be no monopoly in this valley by any man of any such resources for his own wealth and power. Only dead timber is to be used now, for we must let the living timber grow for future use and carefully conserve it. All ditches, canals, reservoirs and other irrigation channels will be the common property of all; and any person trying to take greedy advantage of the materials which we must all use for our common welfare will be driven out of this valley. . . ."

Those bold and farsighted pronouncements flabbergasted some of the men: they had already explored and had intended to take this grove of timber, this stream, this land for their exclusive use. Brigham had said he intended to establish United Orders throughout the valley, and to make of the church a huge society of community enterprise, ownership and management.

"By God," said one, "how can a man get rich here?"

But Tim McBride was fired by this dream of socialism. "God gave the revelations to Joseph," he said. "We must obey them."

"You mean about the United Orders?"

"Yes. We are to own and share everything in common and work for one another. Then we'll have no rich men, no poor men, but will all be brothers in the gospel."

"I don't know about that. But will it work?"

"Of course it will," said Tim, "if we have love in our hearts."

When Brigham chose the site for the city at the foot of the eastern mountains, he took a block for his own use and another for the temple. He walked ahead with Orson Pratt, his engineer, and the crowd followed, going through sagebrush, crushing under feet the big black crickets, scaring up clouds of grasshoppers, and smelling the beds where wolves and catamounts had lain. The City of Great Salt Lake, Brigham said, would be in blocks of ten acres each, with streets eight rods wide and with twenty feet on either side given to sidewalks. There would be gardens and lawns, and every kind of

shade and fruit tree and flowering shrub that would grow here.
There would be no filth in this city, no petty shops, no ugliness of
any sort; nor would any man be allowed to divide his property into
lots for speculation. The temple and its grounds would cover forty
acres, and would be beautified with trees and shrubs, beds of
flowers, fountains and ponds.

As the men heard these statements one by one, they alternately
stared at Brigham and at the desolation around them; and a few
wondered if fever had affected his mind. They were all astonished
by his audacity. Here they were, a handful of pilgrims in a desert
of dust and insects and wild beasts; and yet he was talking of a city
that would be more beautiful than any they had ever seen. He was
talking of flowers and gardens and fountains upon this barren
mountainside where they could see only sagebrush and sand.

"Holy hell," said one. "The crickets will eat all the gardens up."

"And mice and rats will march in armies down the streets."

"Mice, good God. There was a thousand in my tent last night.
They crawled over me like lice."

"Yes, and when I woke up, my bed was full of crickets. They was
smashed all over the quilts."

"I think Brother Brigham is out of his mind."

"Well, Joseph made a beautiful city out of a swamp. Mebbe
Brigham sees things we don't see."

"But imagine a city here!"

Crickets and mice and rats, rattlesnakes and wolves were not
worrying Brigham. He sent one body of men to build a road up a
canyon, another to cut dead timber, and a third to erect a spacious
but tentative building for church services. This he called the Bowery. A fourth group went with wagons to the dead sea and returned
with hundreds of bushels of salt. He called for carpenters, lime
burners and masons. He rode everywhere to urge the men to
greater effort; and within ten days after he entered the Basin, adobe
and log houses were being set up. Within three weeks, the Bowery
was ready, and a huge stockade for defense against Indians had
been begun. He had read in Frémont and others that the Utah
Indians were cowardly and degenerate thieves who lived chiefly on
crickets and roots; and though he expected little trouble from them,

he was taking no chances. As the building progressed, he was the least amazed person in camp. Others now and then paused to marvel at the transformation taking place. It was incredible, it was a miracle, they said, little realizing that a great organizer was co-ordinating their efforts and driving them at top speed.

While many built, others plowed and planted, or dug canals to water the crops. A few under Porter Rockwell hunted wild game—for the daily fare now was chiefly of flesh. Blacksmiths hammered all day long, putting shoes on oxen, repairing axles, and setting wagon tires. It was little wonder that the men were astonished. They looked around them and saw lime kilns smoking, houses, a great bowery, piles of timber, and row on row of wagons ready for the return journey—they saw, indeed, a teeming village where only three weeks ago there had been nothing but sagebrush.

Soon Utah Indians, seeing the smoke of fires and hearing the industry, came to the settlement to trade or steal. They were dwarfed and ragged and half-naked creatures who looked craftily at everything in sight and tried to make off with anything they could get their dirty hands on. Shoshonis came too, with whom the Utahans seemed to be at war; and one afternoon Brigham saw a terrific fight between two painted braves. One of the Utah rascals had stolen a horse from a Shoshoni buck and then traded it for a rifle. Discovered in the theft, he was unwilling to yield the rifle or return the horse; whereupon his exasperated foe broke a gun over the Utahan's skull.

Brigham expected the blow to lay the fellow out. It did stagger him and make him grunt but it did not by any means vanquish him. With blood streaming down his face, he went for his enemy like a wild beast. While the two warriors fought, an old Indian came up with a whip and laid it impartially over the heads of both. A stinging lash across the Utahan's face made him turn from his foe to strike the old man. That made the old warrior mad. With murder in his eye, he seized a pole and broke it over the Utahan's head.

Did all Indians, Brigham wondered, have skulls as thick as that? The old man now turned to the other warrior, who was his own son, and knocked him down; and then he lectured both of them and told them to do their trading away from camp. The Utahan looked

abashed but he still plotted. When a few minutes later, he saw a
horse belonging to the Shoshonis, he leapt to its back and set off
into the mountains as if a hundred devils were after him. With a
howl of astonishment and rage, four Shoshoni warriors went in pur-
suit. A few hours later they returned with the horse and with blood
on one of their rifles.

Satisfied with that vengeance, they built a fire and made ready
for supper. When word of it went through the camp, all the men
came to stare in amazement; for these Indian warriors, sitting im-
perturbably around their fire, were catching the big-bellied crickets
and roasting them alive. They ate them from their fingers, and
licked their fingers and palms after each mouthful.

"By the God of Israel!" cried Porter. "I wonder what they taste
like."

"I don't think," said another, "I could ever make the riffle with
one of them things. Look how they wizzle up when they fry! My old
stomach would come up and stick right out of my mouth."

A few of the men turned away, sickened; but most of them stared,
fascinated, while the warriors, indifferent to curious eyes, thrust
sharp twigs through the writhing black bodies and held them above
the flame. After roasting a wriggling insect and shoving it into his
mouth, a buck would turn calmly and pick another off the sagebrush.

"By God, I'd eat roots first."

"Me, I'd eat my harness tugs."

"They might taste fine," said Porter. "We might be eatun some
ourselves before a year rolls by."

"Are they too dodgasted lazy to hunt deer or do they like them
things?"

"The way they waller them down I'd say they like them."

"Look, you see him over there? By God, he's et seventeen since I
been standun here and watchun him."

The Indians preferred sugar and bacon and flour. After midnight,
they would creep stealthily through the camp, intent on stealing not
only food but ammunition and guns; and they became such a pest
that Brigham told his men not to admit them to wagons or tents or
houses. Foreseeing possible trouble in the months ahead, he rushed
the building of the stockade. It was true, he reflected, that the

Lamanites were, as the Book of Mormon said, a degenerate people.

His chief concern now, his greatest worry, was the journey back to the Missouri before winter set in, as well as what would happen to those who remained here while he was gone. They had arrived too late to plant crops that could be harvested this fall. The men could, of course, exist on roots and wild flesh; but during his absence they might be ambushed by Indians and wiped out. He might return to find bowery, stockade and every house burned to the ground. But he had to go, no matter what happened here; and on the seventeenth of August, less than a month after his arrival, he sent the first company on its way. He would take with him half the men, most of the wagons and teams, but no provisions except salt; because the little he had would be needed by those who remained. Those returning, he said, would live on fish and meat.

To those commanded to remain in the valley, he spoke from a wagon one morning as if they were his children, telling them to guard against Indians and disease, to be industrious and frugal, to love one another and to remember their God. Full of grief and fear, they listened to him; and when he had finished they crowded around him, many of them with tears in their eyes.

"Brother Brigham, if you leave us a year you'll find just bones when you come back."

"God will watch over you."

"But you're the one who has been watching over us."

"Brigham, let us go with you."

Brigham looked at the tears in the eyes of strong men. He turned away for a moment a little overcome; and then he said: "Men, we have to build a kingdom here. This is no time to be afraid. I *must* go back; and you must stay here and plant and reap next summer so that we'll have food the next winter."

Suddenly a man broke under awful grief and fear and loneliness and left the group; and the other men stared at him, and then at Brigham.

"You know," said one, speaking more calmly than the others, "that we don't amount to much without your leadership. I guess we can try it; but don't be surprised when you come if you find us all dead."

"If you put your faith in God, you will all be alive when I return. I promise that."

"Has God told you that?"

"The spirit of God is in me this morning. I speak for Him when I say you will all live until I return."

Brigham had not gone far in his wagon when a white-faced man came running after him.

"What is it?"

"Brother Brigham, do you have all our letters?"

Brigham turned to Clayton. "Do we?"

"Yes, Brother Brigham."

The man turned away and went back to the camp where the other men were standing like children, eager to gaze at their leader as long as he was in sight. Brigham's eyes were misty when, dropping over a hill, he could no longer see those he was leaving. "I know," he said to Heber, "they will be all right. God has made me feel it." But he was deeply troubled and he was silent for a long while.

His journey was uneventful until he had covered several hundred miles. Then, unexpectedly one morning, he saw Porter riding back down the canyon at full speed, waving his hat and shouting. Brigham rose in alarm, knowing that Porter had unwelcome news.

"Hell and damnation!" roared Porter, galloping up to the wagon.

"What is it?"

"You won't believe it! Parley Pratt and John Taylor are up there! They set out with sixteen hundred saints and there they be!"

For a long moment Brigham was too amazed to speak. Then he said, "My God!" in a voice that choked. Heber whipped his team and drove at a trot up the canyon; and Brigham, jolting around in the wagon, felt rage and despair. He had left these apostles on the Missouri to watch over the thousands: if the blockheads had disobeyed orders—and they had: when Brigham came up, he found them with sixteen hundred men, women and children, headed for the Utah Basin.

So furious that he shook all over, Brigham climbed down from the wagon and went over to face Parley. "By the God of Israel," he thundered, "what does this mean?"

"Why?" asked Parley.

"You blockhead! You incredible feeble-minded fool! What in the name of God do you think you are going to do in a desert in winter-time with this multitude? Are you out of your mind?"

"Why——"

Brigham turned to Heber. "We'll hold council at once. Call Parley and John in."

Heber saw that Brigham's face was violently red with anger. It was still red when he faced the other apostles.

"I don't like what I see!" he roared, looking at Parley and John. "The affairs of this church are managed by the Twelve, with me at their head. We work out plans for the good of all of us and then some pig-headed person upsets the whole damned works. When one of this quorum interferes with the plans of this quorum, he does wrong and God will punish him.

"Brother Parley, what right had you to set out into a wilderness with all these people? By what common sense do you set out with sixteen hundred men, women and children into a huge unknown land with winter coming on?"

Parley's face was red too. His eyes flashed with anger.

"What under the heavens," Brigham demanded, "do you think all these saints will eat this coming winter? Where are the houses for women and children? What did you know of the land we'd find, or whether there would be wood to make fires, and flour and meat to fill hungry mouths? In Iowa you had fields, crops to harvest, houses to live in. Yet you set out on a long journey with women and children, not knowing where you're going or what you'll find when you get there! I will not tolerate such interference and such insubordination! If I am the leader of this church, then I am the leader, and I will not have my plans upset by men who refuse to act as God has commanded us. If I am not the leader—" He turned to other members of the Twelve. "Do you sustain me?"

"Yes," said Heber, speaking for them.

"If you sustain me, raise your hands." All of those present except Parley and John raised their hands. "All right, then. I will chastise Brother Parley or any other member of the Twelve as much as I please when they do wrong. I do it for your good and by the power of God invested in me."

"If," said Heber, "I or any of the brethren do wrong, tell us and we will repent."

"I chastise you," said Brigham, "that you might be saved and love me and stick to me. You are all exiles in a wilderness now. I am proud of the men who are helping me. There isn't a finer or braver set of men on earth. I love every one of you and I will stick by you and fight for you; but we have to stick together and fight as one man, not as individuals. It is us against the world now. We are going away into a desert to build our homes and our kingdom. We have been driven out of the Christian world. That's all right with me. To hell with the Christians. But I know we have a job on our hands, and if I am to be your leader, you will have to have faith in me and obey me. We left seventy men back there in a desert, not knowing if they will be dead when I return; and here you are with sixteen hundred saints, headed for a desert in wintertime. I tell you it is madness! It is damnable folly!"

Brigham turned and left the group. Taylor moved forward quickly and took his arm. "I have a terrible surprise for you," he said in a sepulchral voice. "I hope you can stand the shock."

"After the shock I've just had, nothing can surprise me."

"It is terrible. Don't be overcome by what you see."

"Is it mountain fever?"

"Much worse."

Brigham was surprised by what he saw. While he had been re-buking Parley and John, the women of the camp had prepared a great feast; and Brigham now gazed upon rows of improvised tables, laid with snowy white linens and burdened with fish and wild meats, fruits and jellies and relishes, white bread and cakes. John took him to the head of a long table and asked him to sit. Brigham sank weakly to a box, wondering if this was actually a banquet for him and his men, or a mirage of the kind he had seen when crossing the desert. He was unable to twinkle humorously as he usually did when outwitted; for he was thinking of this multitude headed for the Utah valley and perhaps starvation. This feast looked like the last irony in a foolhardy undertaking. Having eaten nothing for days except fish, he stared at the heaped food, the spotless napkin by his earthen plate, the silverware, the great roasts of venison and antelope. Still thinking of the desperate winter ahead of these sixteen hundred men, women and children, he found himself unable to eat.

This feast was for the men returning with him; and they now filed in, speechless with amazement, and took their places at the tables. As flushed and excited as schoolgirls, the younger women in Parley's caravan stood behind the men and served, urging them to try this roast, that boiled tongue, this stuffed heart; and the men, hungry for both food and women, so divided their attention between the girls and the tables that they upset their plates on the white linen, spilled broth in their laps, and swore by heaven and earth that not even the Romans ever tasted anything so good. The women had seen starved men, but never such zestful gluttons as these. The smacking and gurgling and loud laughter could be heard in the quiet evening for half a mile.

"You sure took the soles off of my shoes," said one, and accepted another huge helping of venison.

"I'll have a misery in my belly for a week," said Porter, and made such a racket gulping a bowl of broth that another man slapped his shoulder and knocked his face into the bowl clear to his eyes. Porter set the bowl down and tongued his lips. He had crumbs of flesh hanging to his eyebrows, and grease glistening on his black beard. A woman stepped forward and wiped his face with a napkin. "Thanks," he said, and looked at a plate heaped with antelope tenderloin. "I feel all set to tackle it again." Then he looked over and observed that Brigham was not eating. "Brother Brigham, what's the matter with your appetite?"

"I don't feel hungry," Brigham said.

"You better get a good fillun. This is our last one till we reach the Missouri."

"Look," said another, "at all them there delicacies on Brother Brigham's table. That's why he can't eat."

"I guess so," said Porter. But Heber looked over at his friend and knew what was on his mind.

"I don't feel very hungry either," he said.

Porter patted his belly and groaned. "There ain't no sense in my stoppun now. Sister, just load my dish with a pile of that elk heart. I intend to eat enough to last me clean to Headquarters."

"It's fish tomorrow," said another. "I aim to set here and stuff till daylight comes."

When the feast was done, the men walked around solemnly, bloated with food and pain. One of the men called for music and dancing, recitations and songs. A full moon was up now, and moonlight and firelight flooded the cove where the saints had gathered. The musicians struck up a quadrille, and the men scurried for partners, seeking the loveliest women and not caring whether they were married or not. One of them climbed to a wagon and shouted the turns; and a hundred men and women curtsied and whirled and pranced for all they were worth. A French four was next, and then a Scotch reel. Some of the dancers were barefooted, some were in rags.

Brigham sat in a wagon, still thinking of the winter ahead of these people, and frowning on the dancing. On the banks of the Missouri there had been shameful sins, and there had been adulteries among the converts on boats from England. The full moon, the music and laughter, and the strangeness of the country put wicked notions into the heads of the men here. He saw a girl slap a man's face. He saw another man try to seduce his partner into a thicket along the stream. So he rose and strolled through the brush and around the camp, his eyes and ears alert.

"Brother Brigham," said Parley, overtaking him, "I'm sorry for my disobedience. I have humbled myself before the Lord."

"It's high time."

"I want forgiveness."

"Parley, you may all starve to death this winter. There's no food in the valley, no crops to harvest. And if you all perish this winter, do you think God will forgive you for that?"

"I guess not," said Parley, humbled.

"It's the most damn fool thing I ever heard of. Another thing: I'm told you took two more wives while I been gone. Haven't I said that none of the leaders can take wives without my permission?"

"Yes."

"Then why did you? You waited until I got out of sight and then married two women."

"I converted them in England——"

"What if you did! Are you going to marry every woman you convert?"

"They love me, Brother Brigham."

"Parley, I'm the leader. I cannot allow the brethren to marry every time they take a notion."

"But you," said Parley with spunk, "usually do. And Heber has more wives than I have. I have only eight."

"Take no more wives without my permission. How is the Trail from here to Headquarters?"

"Bad."

"Any big emigrant trains on it?"

"None that I know of."

"Did you have any trouble with Indians?"

"Nothing serious."

"How is the grass through the buffalo country?"

"There isn't any."

"It is good from here to the valley." Brigham gazed at him, his eyes cold with displeasure. "God knows, Parley, what you'll live on this winter. If all these people starve to death, the sin will be on your head and God will never forgive you. Humble yourself after this."

"Yes," Parley said.

After the feast, a hush had fallen on the camp and the dancing and singing suddenly stopped. Word had gone from tongue to tongue that Brigham was very angry; and after much excited talk, the saints understood why. When the horrible realization came to them of what they had done, they were appalled and many were overcome by dread. They had set out on a gay adventure; and here they were, sixteen hundred of them, with little food and insufficient clothing and bedding, headed for a desolate valley and a hard winter. From tongue to tongue, too, went the rumor that Brigham had said they would all freeze and starve to death; and that when he returned, he would find only their bones in the nests of the wolves.

There was no more singing or dancing. Except in whispers, hardly a word was spoken. A terrified people went to their wagons and tents and sat in silent groups, thinking only of what lay ahead of them, of what indiscreet and shortsighted fools they had been. And when morning came, they loaded their wagons and hitched their teams, but they moved as if all life and hope had gone out of them. They looked at the stern face of Brigham, the anger and pain in his eyes, the tightness of his mouth, and could think of nothing to say, nothing to do except to move forward and accept their fate.

"You have to go on now," he said to Parley and the other leaders of the caravan. "There is nothing I can do to help you. You will need great courage and resourcefulness or you will all die. I urge you to put your faith in God and be faithful in your prayers, and perhaps He will watch and protect you; but even the Almighty can do nothing when His children disobey orders, upset plans, and act like fools. We'll all pray for you and hope for the best."

The faces of Parley and John and of the others were very pale when they turned away. They sought their wagons, going like old men; and the huge caravan moved westward down the canyon. A thousand pairs of anxious eyes looked backward to Brigham and Heber, who stood apart, in silence, as the last wagon disappeared.

Brigham drew a long breath. "Heber, I doubt we ever see them alive again."

Heber put an arm across Brigham's shoulders, and they turned to face the east.

He had much to do this winter. He had to appoint heads to missions in eastern states and in England where the church had twenty thousand converts; as well as in China and the East Indies, Australia and the South Seas—because Joseph had sent missionaries to those lands. The saints in England he commanded to emigrate as soon as they could and to bring with them choice seeds of grain, vegetables, fruits, shrubs and trees; the finest machinery they could buy for spinning and weaving; the best of their animals and fowls. He wrote them to bring corn shellers, grain threshers and cleaners, machines and mills—and every other implement and article that would promote health and prosperity.

Nearer home he had many problems. It was, he said again and again, the duty of the well-to-do to assist the poor, to give them employment, to watch over their happiness and health. It was the

duty of parents to be for their children examples of righteous living. When Heber observed slyly that Brigham had better stop
chewing tobacco, Brigham's eyes twinkled but his lips did not smile.

"It's a nasty habit. I hope the saints have too much sense to
imitate their leaders in all things."

He pointed out the need of printing presses and a museum in the
new Zion; of all kinds of scientific instruments and equipment; of
education in all fields. In the Utah Basin he expected to be, he
wanted to be, isolated from the world; and he wished to have there
everything necessary in the building of a model society. He did not
intend to import anything, or want or need anything from the
world which he was leaving.

"Not even tobacco," he said. "If the saints must use the vile stuff,
we'll grow it."

Such was the larger dream to which he gave his resourceful mind.
Here in the settlement were many things to be done before the
great migration could begin: wagons to be repaired, oxen to be
shod, crates and carrying racks and boxes to be made, clothing to
make or mend, herbs and roots to be gathered for medicine, and all
the companies to be organized. It was, he wryly admitted to himself,
the most preposterous assortment of people and goods ever to em-
bark on a long journey. Nothing was to be left behind; and in consequence they had seed and shovels and tongs, bureaus and secretaries, sideboards and sofas and pianos, chairs and carpets and
stoves. They had broken-down horses, some with fistula or ring-
bone or pole evil, some that were spavined or fallen-hipped. They
had cows with only one or two teats, oxen with three legs. They had
pigs and chickens, cats and dogs and goats and geese, ducks and
doves and beehives, and even pet squirrels.

And in May Brigham moved off in charge of the first train of
three hundred and ninety-seven wagons and twelve hundred and
twenty-nine persons. In his company were seventy-four horses,
nineteen mules, twelve hundred and seventy-five oxen, eight hundred and eighty-three head of cattle, four hundred and eleven sheep,
one hundred and forty-one pigs, six hundred and five chickens,
thirty-seven cats, eighty-four dogs, three goats, ten geese, two beehives and eight doves. Falling in behind was Heber's huge division;

and behind him came another ungainly caravan. Others were to come a little later.

They set out over the vast and lonely prairies, over the interminable distance to their new home, not knowing if they would find those in the Basin alive or dead, and with the bitterness of journeying in a country they had tried to leave. Under leadership less wise and energetic than Brigham's, the motley pilgrimage would have ended in disaster during the first weeks; but under his firm and watchful guidance it moved slowly ahead, day after day, with every person among the thousands knowing his task, with every captain at his post. Messengers traveled daily from division to division; and Brigham knew of every woe and disobedience, apprehension and dread in every camp. Some of those whose relatives had gone with Parley were convinced that only the bones would be found of those sixteen hundred; and they would be bones now in a United States graveyard. That was the galling ignominy which they found it hard to take.[1]

"To think we went twelve hundred miles to get away and now find ourselves governed by our enemies again! I can't understand why God allowed that to happen."

"Mebbe its to test our faith."

"Hasn't it been tested enough? And I guess He will test it again by showing us seventeen hundred skeletons!"

"You're too gloomy. Most of them will be alive."

"What did they have to eat last winter? Brother Brigham doesn't think they'll be alive. You 'n see it in his eyes."

"Brother Brigham has lots of worries we don't know about."

"Since he heard the Utah country is in the United States, don't you think he's aged faster?"

"Some. He looks awful full of trouble."

"But he never says much."

Another in the group spoke. "He says plenty to the complainers."

"We all complain too much," said a woman. "Let us pray and hope. Mebbe God has saved their lives."

---

[1] Since Brigham Young had returned, the Mexican War had ended and the Western area had been joined to the United States.

"It's nice to say mebbe," said a second woman. "But none of us really believes it in his heart."

"Well, let's not complain. Brother Brigham will be hearing about it."

When Brigham heard of the loafers, troublemakers and complainers, he rebuked them with thoroughness that made their heads swim.

"Brother Philo says he won't go no farther without he has a better team." It was Porter speaking.

"Tell Brother Willard to lay the law down. If he don't come to his senses, throw him out."

"And Sister Betsy won't walk. She's barefooted and she says she won't drive pigs."

"Tell Sister Betsy if she don't take her pigs, she'll never have any in Zion."

"In Brother Heber's company, there's a man Hesekiah says he's afraid."

"Afraid! Tell Heber to send him back to the Christians."

"And a man named Arnold," said Porter, grinning, "he hit Brother Albert."

"Tell Heber I said to put him in irons."

To these thousands of wayfarers, the journey came overwhelmingly through all five senses. In appearance there had never been anything like it, Brigham declared, since the Israelites fled from their enemies. The oxen yoked to the schooners were weary and rawboned: under fleshless hides, their ribs rose like washboards as they breathed; their bellies were raw from the traces; their dull tired eyes blinked solemnly in the dust. Team by team, wagon by wagon, the caravan stretched in an unbroken chain for miles, lying over the hills and down across the hollows, with the crawling progress of it so slow that it seemed hardly to move at all. Though superficially much alike, the hundreds of wagons were all different in their heaped cargo of persons and goods. One was loaded with flour and bacon and seed; visible on the next was only a teamster; the third was freighted with sofa and sideboard, tubs and kettles, axes and tongs and shovels; and the fourth was piled high with

chicken crates and cats and a beehive, above which a cage holding
two doves swung from a bow. In some the canvas framed a half-
dozen heads of women and children.

On either side were the loose cattle, the dogs and cows, sheep and
goats and pigs, herded together and driven by men, women and
children, some of them barefooted and most of them in rags. Farther
out were horsemen, the scouts who watched for Indians and wild
beasts, the hunters alert for game. Dust rolled in low lazy clouds
that sometimes completely hid the train, that filled the sky, that so
obscured the sun that it shone dimly like a disc of gold. Out of the
fog the riders appeared and into it they vanished.

The ungainly appearance was less vivid than the sounds; for there
was every jangle and discord known to the human ear. The great
and steady undertone came from the chugging and rumbling of the
wagons as the wheels dropped into ruts, shook over hummocks of
tough grass, or howled across streams bedded with cobbles. There
was a continuous squealing in the hubs, squeaking of dried beds,
flapping of schooner canvas in the wind. Above the maddening
rumbling was the bleating of sheep, the lowing of cows, the goaded
and persistent squealing of pigs, the barking of dogs, the dismal
wailing of sick babies, the profane yelping of the herdsmen, the
excited gabbling of geese and chickens, and the sudden and terrible
braying of mules. Scouts declared that on a quiet afternoon, they
could hear the confused thunder ten miles away. If they put ears
to the earth, it sounded like the mighty stampede of a buffalo herd,
except that above it, sharp and clear, came the squealings and cries.
At first the infernal din almost drove some of the people insane: they
could not sleep because the night was full of grunts and bleats and
barks and the blood-chilling racket of the mules; but after a while
they became used to the infernal uproar and would have felt lost
without it.

They became used to the odors too: the sweating stink of plodding beasts, the dank breath of oxen that had the smell of warm
intestines thrown in the sun, the strong stench of the hogs and the
sickening smell of the sheep. When a breeze was blowing, a sensitive
nose could, in the beginning of the journey, identify a score of different odors. It might be the smell of hot axle grease, the foul air from

a crate of chicken feathers and dung, the clean fragrance of salt
bacon, apples or flour. It might be the smell of bedding full of
human sweat or the dry heat of the vast prairies; the scent of wild
flowers trampled under the feet of the beasts or the stink of dogs
that had rolled in an old carcass and then swum a creek. It might
be the smell of diapers hanging from schooner bows. After journeying a few days, the pilgrims could not tell one odor from another;
everything was blended in one offensive and omnipresent smell and
they became as used to it as to their own breath.

On tongues also, the journey laid its earthy tang. In hot days,
when no breeze was blowing, the wheels, turning belly-deep in white-
loam or sand, rolled up clouds of dust that spilled like fountains of
flour or bellied upward in blinding density till sun and sky were
hidden. Dust lay in powdered depth on canvas top, on the goods
within, and like melting snow on the sweating beasts. It rimmed the
eyes and mouths of both beast and person and made them look red
and raw. The travelers breathed it and tasted it until the flavor of
hot prairie was more familiar than that of the food they ate. They
tasted also the strong wet smells of the teams and the milling herds;
as when, again and again, a teamster or a drover cracked his whip,
sheathed with dung, and filled the air with brown particles that
floated in the dust and settled and melted on human tongues. Hogs
cooled themselves in wallows and emerged looking like grotesque
monsters of mud; and in the hot sun the mud dried and scaled off
and mingled in floating particles with dried manure, with seared
vegetation powdered under the marching feet, with hair and wool.

They felt the journey in every aching muscle and bone. Women
and children, crowded into wagons among crates and boxes and
bedding, were hardly able to move a limb all day long. Cramped
and suffering, but complaining rarely, they fought off mosquitoes,
closed their eyes against the heat and dust, and rode the jolting and
squealing wagons over the endless miles. Other women and children
helped to drive the beasts, some barefooted, others in ragged shoes
that admitted the sand and grit; and the feet of all of them were
gouged and abraded into bleeding sores. For the sick and the very
old, the chugging of the wagons was almost unendurable; for the
shuddering drop of a wheel into a deep rut shot excruciating pains

through them; and the rumbling monotony so beat upon their senses that they were more dead than alive.

Some of them did die, and some babies were born dead or died soon after birth. These were buried in the vast loneliness of the prairies. Throughout the long journey, there were graves to the right or left of those who had died in former pilgrimages. Into most of the graves wolves had dug and scattered the bones; but if a woman turned faint at thought of leaving a loved one to be exhumed by wild beasts, Brigham scowled and declared that the dead were safe with God. If their bones were bleached by prairie wind, it mattered little: they would be gathered in the Resurrection and made whole again.

"It's the living who need us. The dead are at peace."

The women, nevertheless, gazed back across the miles, remembering the graves left one by one. Some of them almost lost their minds: nearly every day they saw desolate graves or now and then a tiny graveyard upon the prairie, with only Indians and wolves to keep watch. When, one evening, a woman threw herself on a mound and said she would never leave her child, Brigham called two men and had her forcibly borne away. This was no time for grief. This was a time for courage; and never once, no matter how terrible the scene he witnessed, did Brigham's stern face soften. His goal was the Utah Basin and he would get there with as many live persons as he could. If the sick or the old or the babies died, they would have to be wrapped in a blanket and left to their God.

He reflected, indeed, that the saints would be lucky if they were not attacked by Indians or some dread scourge and wiped out entirely. He kept the boldest scouts busy and every man close to his gun; he watched his camp like a hawk for signs of malaria or other fevers and for dysentery, tirelessly urging them to be calm and cheerful, to sleep soundly, to be careful of what they ate, and not to worry about the saints in the Basin. It was only to his unrelaxed and stern vigilance that the caravan owed its life.

Through it all, awake and asleep, Brigham was impelled by a great vision. He felt that this journey fed from the eager and searching millenniums in the remote background of human striving: it was more than a desperate flight from enemies: it was a pilgrimage toward freedom, toward a fuller and richer destiny for the entire human race. In all its suffering and patience and courage, it was a mighty symbol of that struggle for perfection and peace that had been the heritage of humanity for centuries. He was fighting for a society that would be charitable and righteous and free.

His problems now were many. Having been told of Shefmolan's stealthy warriors a year ago, the saints were fearful of Indians; but Brigham cried with an oath that they were only the Lamanites, a degenerate offshoot of one of the Lost Tribes, and cowardly rascals every one of them. Nor did Indians show their faces while the divisions moved through the Sioux and Pawnee land. Brigham had not expected them to. When, he said, their scouts saw several thousand men on the march, all armed and alert, the dastardly redskins would flee to the hills—and apparently they did.

Brigham thought little about them, so pressing was his search for feed. Expanses of prairie had again been swept clean by fire and buffalo; and after camp was pitched in late afternoon, it was necessary to scatter the animals far out. Herdsmen watched them until the beasts fed and lay down; and then the men drew a blanket or a coat over themselves, placed a gun within reach, and slept back to back against the oxen. The sheep and hogs foraged during the day, the former eating weeds and every stray blade of grass, the latter rooting in the earth and devouring anything they could find. Sometimes they came upon old carcasses and made a feast of withered hide and bleached bones; sometimes they tried to eat buffalo skulls. They were fed a little grain daily. The cats and dogs received the leftovers from meals; but all the other animals had to take what they could. As the prairies became more barren and desolate, the oxen and horses and mules looked like skeletons set upon legs. A few of the cows were milked night and morning, and the cream was put in jars and churned daily by the jolting wagons.

It was a busy camp each evening after the simple meals were done. Blacksmiths set up their forges and made music with hammer and tongs as they shod limping oxen, reset rattling wagon tires, repaired axletrees, crates and tongues. The women patched clothes or attended the sick; or now and then one withdrew to the shelter of a schooner to give birth to a child. There was not the music and song and dancing of the rain-drenched journey from Nauvoo to the Missouri: too many were ill, too many were dying, and too many, thinking of the pilgrims out in Utah, were overwhelmed by the desolation around them. These were not the reckless men who journeyed with Brigham a year ago. For the most part they were men with families, some of whom filled two or three wagons; and they were pressing into an unknown land and toward nobody knew what eventual doom. When they asked Brigham what the new home was like, he always gave the same answer: it would do well enough.

"But doesn't Frémont say it's a desert?"

"The soil is all right. There's water."

"But you say there ain't any timber."

"We'll build adobe houses."

"Will fruit and vegetables grow there?"

"Anything will grow there."

The men were not sure of that. In the faces of some was a fixed and anguished hopelessness; but others, with more faith in Brigham, strove to cheer their companions.

"At least we'll have freedom until the United States drives us out. Human beings can starve, they can suffer, but if they don't have freedom they are only beasts."

"But what about Indians?"

"Brother Brigham will scare them right out of their war paint."

"Porter says the valley is full of wolves, so why in hell are we taking sheep?"

"Well," said a man, grinning, "we're leaving one kind of a wolf for another. The wolves out there don't pretend to believe in God."

"I'll deacon a calf if we don't all starve to death!"

The journey was enough to bring fear to the boldest heart. When a man's spirit was lifting, he turned to behold graves that seemed fresh, or to see his own people carry a burden to a hillside. There were the abandoned articles of former migrations: broken wagons, yokes, cast-iron stoves, bones of horses and oxen that had been slain or had starved to death. There were the ruts of the Trail where wheels turned as if in six inches of dirty flour; dust in stifling clouds until children could barely see out of red and inflamed eyes; sheets of earth upon the wagons ahead, behind, until the plodding teams were lost in the dry blind pall of it. A day of this, or even a week or two, would have been tolerable; but to go endlessly, exhausted by thirst and heat, choked by dust, and to flay gaunt beasts that fell in the harness—to plod hour after hour westward, expecting to find seventeen hundred skeletons at journey's end: that was enough to break the spirit of any man.

When a wind came to drive the dust in gray mountains upward, then the landscape ahead, shimmering in hot air, was a vast garden of beautiful lakes, of forests, of soft blue hillsides, with the mirage lying upon distance as far as eyes could see. Often women wept to see such fresh loveliness and thought they were approaching their new home; and some did not learn for many days that they were gazing only at the tantalizing sorcery of desert heat.

There was much sickness in the divisions, but cholera was the scourge Brigham feared. The plague on the Missouri had taught him a lesson; and now in central Nebraska he had men dig wells when river and creek did not look good to him. Tirelessly, day after day, he moved through his own camp, watching for signs of scurvy and blackleg, rebuking the strong who behaved like weaklings, cheering the sick and old.

"Why do you set there on your hinder? You have a wagon tire about to fall off."

"I know it," said the man, and looked at the wheel, twisted by heat and dust. "I guess you'll have to leave me behind."

"Get busy. Repair that wagon before you go to bed."

"It's busted."

"Sister," said Brigham, turning to another wagon, "are you going to make it all right?"

"I don't guess so," said a woman whose face was gray with fatigue and age. "You'll have to bury me and go on."

"You ride in one of my wagons tomorrow and rest."

Porter came up, knocking dust out of his beard and clothes. "I see about twenty buffalo today."

"Then let's have fresh meat tomorrow."

New life possessed the camp when, next morning, the first shaggy beasts were seen coming over a western hill. Women gasped in amazement; children stared in solemn red-eyed wonder. Nearly every man in camp wanted to give chase, but Brigham chose a few hunters and ordered the others back to their posts. After the caravan entered the buffalo country, and herds raced like a low dark storm over the hills, there was terrible confusion. Hogs ran in circles, squealing and terrified, as if thunder and lightning were imminent; and one night the camp narrowly missed extermination under flying hooves.

When Brigham sat up, aroused suddenly from sleep, he heard a sound like that of approaching wind. Leaping to the earth, he saw at once that the camp was loud with terror: dogs were howling dismally, pigs were woofing and scurrying in the darkness, and mules were braying as if goaded with hot irons. Brigham listened to the ominous roar: it reminded him of a deep and distant storm upon an ocean.

Hundreds of persons were leaving their beds.

"Porter, what is it?"

"Sounds like a buffalo stampede. It's headed this way."

"Listen." The sound now reminded Brigham of the heavy muffled roar of a river down a gorge. "Quick, Heber, have the men bring the animals in—all the sheep and cattle and pigs right here in the inner circle." Soon, squads of men vanished into darkness. "Have a hundred fires built," he said, turning to captains. "Move quick, everyone!"

The excited cattle were now being driven in. They came hunched up, heads down, in terror, blowing from their nostrils.

"It's gettun closer," said Porter.

"Yes." Brigham ran from captain to captain to urge haste and then listened again. There could no longer be any doubt of it: the mighty journey of thousands of terrified beasts was bearing down upon them. A full moon was up; and in a few moments Brigham saw the vanguard come into view like a low dark wall. Then it was a moving tide of darkness that flowed over a hill and down, and breasted the next hill, with the black expanse of it pouring over hill and into hollow like a thundering sea.

"It's headed straight for us," said Porter. His voice was calm.

The tide had vanished now, but the thunder of it beat into the earth until the wagons trembled. Brigham knew that the vast herd was crossing a ravine; and while it was out of sight, he looked around at groups of women and children, clinging to one another and screaming; at the hundreds of men setting the fires; at the milling terror of cattle and hogs. He stared northward again; and after a moment, a wall of shaggy heads and shoulders came suddenly into view, and the tide poured up and spread in a flowing avalanche. It was a dense mass that seemed to unroll like an enormous blanket. Then heads appeared, obscured but certain, and the vanguard became visible as a thousand thundering beasts, with an unbroken depth of moving flesh behind.

The fires were burning brightly and made a reef of flame across the northern edge of the camp. In the next few minutes, Brigham realized, his people would be mangled and gutted, or the sight and smell of the fires would turn the hordes. He was unafraid but he was shaking all over. The women and children behind him sounded as if they had all gone mad; and the men around him were so appalled that they fell over one another in gathering dung for the fires, or ran in circles, not knowing what they did.

"Look!" a man cried. "They're turning!"

It was so. Swerving, as if turned by a huge rudder in the rear, the wild breast of the stampede swung in an arc to the northeast. The earth shook under the roaring feet. Such a stupendous spectacle these people were never to see again. Women still screamed and hid their faces, but all the men now gathered by the fires and shouted hideously, with fright ringing madly in their cries. When the vanguard swerved, it was no more than three hundred yards from the camp; and now every person who watched could clearly see the magnificent wild journey, the low heads and the flashing horns, the shaggy manes pouring backward in the wind, as the stampede like a dark and heaving landscape rolled by.

How many there were, nobody could guess; but several minutes passed after the first heads snorted and turned before the last of them came even with the camp. Some afterward said that for ten minutes, some for an hour, the seething ocean swept past them in rolling tide upon tide. When the last of it vanished, the thunder grew fainter and fainter; and except for the milling of the stock and the weeping of women and children, the night was silent again.

"By God," said Porter, biting off a quid of tobacco, "that's as close as I want to come to death."

"The fires done it! May God bless Brother Brigham."

"Go over," said Brigham to the captains, "and tell the sisters to stop their damned infernal yelling. They'll scare all our animals to death." Brigham looked down at his hands; they were still trembling.

After this horrible experience, the saints wanted to hasten through the buffalo country, but Brigham said they must kill and jerk all the flesh they could haul, as well as fatten all the meat-eating beasts, including the pigs. Tons of meat were jerked. After leaving the prairies and approaching the foothills, hunters fetched in deer and antelope, and sometimes sheep and goat and bear. Sight of the first brown bluffs of the Rocky Mountains made some of the men think they had almost arrived, and they wanted to push forward to learn the fate of the colony.

"Calm yourselves!" cried Brigham. "You've still got over six hundred miles."

They were now in the land of wolves and rattlesnakes. Almost daily the reptiles buried their fangs in stray cattle; and during the night, herdsmen had to keep watch against wolves. There were, nevertheless, a few amusing stories to cheer the heartsick wanderers. A man was hammering one evening when Brigham asked him if he had had poor luck.

"Dodgast it, yes. One of them varmints made a jump at my right ox yesterday and set his old tongs in my wagon tongue. It swole and swole until I had to unhitch."

"You mean the tongue or the snake?"

"The tongue. It swole up until I chopped six cords of wood out of it."

Brigham made a face. "I've heard that story before," he said.

That story and others went through the camps. Legends were also told of the sheep: the rattlers struck at them and got their fangs entangled in wool, whereupon they were yanked along like ropes, with their rattles fraying out and their hides peeling off. Herdsmen then seized the snakes by their throats and used them for whips. It was said, too, that the hogs, and especially a big savage boar, despised rattlesnakes and pursued them with snorting fury. This boar also

hated wolves; and when during the night he heard the skulking
creatures, he charged like a small buffalo and almost frightened the
other pigs to death. Every day some tale was told that brought a
smile to tired and dusty faces.

"You should a-seen President Martin Van Buren. That's our big
ram. He stumbled into a nest of rattlers and got so gad-danged mad
that he thought his own horns was snakes. He romped around all
afternoon a-tryun to shake them offen his head. He even thought the
tail of a mule was a snake, and durned if he didn't bust old Gudget
a blow that knocked his hinder right up even with his short ribs!"

The days were cooler now, the streams fresh; and day by day the
westward view became more beautiful. Brigham rode in the lead
wagon, with his division stretched out for two miles behind him, or
he advanced on horseback, seeking camping spots and food. Because so few of the pilgrims actually knew that polygamy was practiced by their leaders, he discreetly rode and slept with Mary Ann
Angel, and had little to do with the others who followed in wagons
behind. The time was coming when he would have to make public
announcement of plural marriage—and coming soon if gossiping
women did not keep their tongues still; but he was not ready yet.
He wished first to establish his people beyond the reach of persecution.

How he would do that, he did not know. It was a tremendous
irony that he should lead them beyond the United States and then
find himself returned to the nation he had left. But he would be far
from his enemies, and federal authorities would leave him alone for
a long while. He would build an army, as Joseph had done; but this
time it would be a fighting army, and snoops and fools and other
breeds of the ungodly would find their hides warmed if they came
to the Utah Valley. Of this, of a hundred other matters, he thought
as he rode along; but as he steadily approached the goal, he thought
chiefly of the colony which he would soon find. In spite of his belief
that God had watched over them during the past winter, he could
not deny or hide his apprehension, or quiet the growing fear of his
people.

Most of them were convinced that they would find only seventeen
hundred skeletons. Daily men begged Brigham for permission to

ride ahead of the caravan and learn the truth; but he said no. If they were all dead, then they were dead, and that was that.

"But if they are, Brother Brigham, we cannot stay there. We'd all go mad."

"Of course we'll stay there. If God has called them home, we'll bury the skeletons."

"We couldn't! We couldn't stand to look at them!"

"Be quiet," he said.

"But think," said a woman who had overheard, "think if they died and the wolves have gnawed all the flesh off— Oh, Brother Brigham, let's find out, and if they're dead, let's not go there!"

"That is our home," said Brigham. "And in the name of the God of Israel, calm yourself! We need courage, not whining."

He was calmer than his people; but his face became white and more drawn as he approached the Basin, and his nights were troubled. He did not believe that God would desert him now. He remembered, nevertheless, the severity of winters in the valley—for explorers and trappers had told of them; and he remembered that the huge colony had entered in the fall of the year, and almost without food. He was still ten days from journey's end when he called Porter to him.

"Porter, in the morning take the best and fastest horse and go at top speed to Zion. Find out what happened. Come back just as fast as you went."

"Yes, Brother Brigham."

"Don't let anyone know you're going. And if they're all dead, just tell me when you come back."

In spite of excited pleas, Brigham now held the caravan to a few miles a day. He wanted the truth before he entered the valley: if the colony was dead, he would have to go on, of course, even though his people became delirious with grief and terror. While Porter was gone, he prayed often and earnestly, but always alone; and he was lying awake in his wagon an hour before daylight when Porter returned. Brigham felt a hand on his arm. "Yes?" he said, raising the canvas to look out.

"It's me, Brother Brigham."

"Well?" said Brigham, trying to speak calmly.

In a voice shaken by deep feeling, Porter said: "They're all **right.**"
"Thank God!" said Brigham, and rose to kneel in prayer.

When, the next morning, he called his people into meeting, **he** could tell by their faces that they expected dread news. A part **of** the anxiety left their eyes when they saw their leader smile. "Brethren and sisters, I want to tell you something that will make **you** happy. The colony in Zion is alive and well." Without saying more, Brigham sank to his knees, and the multitude knelt with him; and for several minutes, not a head rose from prayer. Then, rising, Brigham said: "It's time you sang again!"

A deep voice started in song and hundreds followed:

"Let Zion in her beauty rise, her light begins to shine!
 Ere long the King will rend the skies, majestic and divine!
 Ye heralds sound the golden trump to earth's remotest bound!
 Go spread the news from pole to pole in all the nations round!"

Brigham stood apart and gazed at his people. There were tears in the eyes even of men.

By Bernard DeVoto

JONATHAN DYER: FRONTIERSMAN

I

ELDERS JACOB GATES and Martin Slack brought to Hertfordshire tidings of the wrath to come. Curates, deans, even bishops were disturbed by the number of converts the American missionaries made. They were dissenters of a new and particularly objectionable kind, but their appeal was strong. Sermons were preached against the "Mormonites"; riots began to occur at their meetings; here and there an elder was drummed out of town or set upon with eggs or thrown into a horse pond. Employers were consulted, and some of them acted. Mr. Young Crawley took action in the name of an Englishman's religion, and Jonathan Dyer found himself without a job.

We are concerned with Jonathan Dyer not because he was perse-cuted for his faith but because that faith merged him with the strongest current in the New World from which the missionaries came. Baptized a member of the Church of Jesus Christ of Latter Day Saints on the 27th of May, 1852, and discharged by Mr. Crawley almost at once, he did not at once yield to that current. He got work in a linseed-oil mill, where his skill with machinery brought him an advancement, and he began to advance also in the hierarchy of his church. Jonathan became a deacon, a teacher, and finally a full priest in the Order of Aaron. He converted his mother and two of his brothers but, as a proselyter in the villages of High Cross and Collier's End, found the opposition of the established church too vigorous for him. At Roydon, however, the Paxman family listened to him and were convinced. A daughter of the house was fair: during two years Jonathan found it desirable to visit Rhoda and instruct her in the Mormonite faith. Both twenty-two years old, they were married at Roydon on the 26th of April, 1856. They resolved to live their religion: to leave England and, joining the current, move westward to Zion.

Jonathan Dyer's emigration is not explained beyond that sentence. He was a mechanic; he had no trouble finding work; he was not interested in the cheap land that tempted millions to America. He was an industrious, methodical, unimaginative young man—no restlessness for the road's end and the far slope of the hill ever troubled him. But for Elders Slack and Gates he would have stayed in Hertford, joined a workingman's library, and ventured no farther from home than a ride on the railroad would have taken him. The voice of the Lord called him eight thousand miles. Of America he knew only what the elders told him and cared to know no more. In a place called Jackson County, Missouri, the Garden of Eden had been planted. The place was man's lost paradise and would be restored to him in the Last Days, tokens of whose swift coming were on every wind. Meanwhile the Saints were gathered in Desert, "the land of the honey bees," their present Zion, somewhere in a vastness known as the Rocky Mountains. This too was a paradise, a land like Canaan, fertile and beautiful and walled away from the Gentiles. God's will was that the Saints should build up the kingdom there and await the Last Days.

Passage to America cost from three pounds six shillings to four pounds, exclusive of food. Jonathan's savings were perhaps two pounds. He borrowed two sovereigns from his wife's parents and the rest from the church. The priesthood would lend money for emigration, the notes to be paid from the borrower's earnings in Zion. Jonathan and his wife and his brother Richard were to sail in the *Horizon*, Captain Reid, in May, 1856, but the ship was full when they reached Liverpool, and they had to await the forming of another company. On June first, with one hundred and forty-three other Saints and lay emigrants to the number of three hundred and fifty, mostly Irish, they sailed in the packet *Wellfleet*, Captain Westcott. Storms sickened most of the Saints; their provisions spoiled; there were quarrels with the ungodly about the cooking arrangements. The superstitious Irish resented the Mormonite hymns. The Irish too were lousy and within a week had infected the whole company. On the tenth of July, one day short of six weeks after she was towed down the Mersey, the *Wellfleet* anchored off Quarantine at Boston. At once a Negro sailor gave the pilgrims a symbol of the new civilization by stabbing the second mate.

The church thriftily kept on the eastern seaboard all immigrants for whom work could be found until they had saved enough to pay their way westward. The boom times of the early fifties slackened toward the prostration of the next year, but the country proved able to absorb the Dyers. Richard found work at Lexington, and the linseed-oil mill of Field, Fowler & Co., at Charlestown, took Jonathan in and made him foreman. The summer of 1857 brought distress to the Saints and to the nation. President Buchanan, a "mobocrat" and an enemy of God, rejected the counsel of Brigham Young, appointed a new governor of Utah Territory, and ordered an army west to escort his appointee. By the end of July the troops were marching, and soon afterward Col. Albert Sidney Johnston took command of them. The priesthood forbade women to cross the plains but welcomed men for the defense of Zion. Richard Dyer left his wife to the care of Jonathan and departed, writing back that it took him six weeks to cross Iowa, through sloughs sometimes so bad that they pulled the soles off his boots. God moved swiftly to punish a nation of mobocrats. On August 24th, the Ohio Life Insurance and Trust Company announced its insolvency. Its failure carried with it the financial structure of the United States. Banks failed everywhere, even in New England—it was believed that no bank was solvent. The stock exchanges followed the banks. By autumn unemployed men were rioting in the cities, farmers were abandoning their land, trade was prostrate, exchange was impossible. Windows were broken in Charlestown and mobs surrounded the closed mills or surged sporadically in the direction of bake shops. Field, Fowler & Co. shut down. Jonathan peddled crockery. The mill opened again, shut down, reopened. But Jonathan was able to pay off his loans, to assist the emigration of another brother, and to lend the Boston branch of his church fifty dollars.

Wages were very low in 1858, and the mill closed once more. Jonathan moved to South Boston, where he worked as a glass packer. The mill was running again by 1859, and Jonathan's first son was born. Jonathan now invented better valves and pistons for the mill's machinery. His employers promoted him and, the next year, sent him to Brooklyn to build and manage a new mill. The Brooklyn branch of the church received him as a man of substance.

Jonathan's first daughter was born in March, 1861, on the day before Abraham Lincoln became President of a nation careening toward certain destruction. Jonathan beheld passion, violence, and panic and he knew that prophecy was on the march. The nation which had spilled the prophet's blood must now meet its doom. On Christmas Day, twenty-nine years before, the blessed Joseph had foretold the rebellion of South Carolina, which Jonathan had now witnessed, and had said "the Southern States shall be divided from the Northern States"—which had come to pass. The world spun toward the Last Days. England too, Joseph had said, must join this apocalypse, and all Europe would follow till "war shall be poured out on all nations." Then famine and plague and earthquakes "and the fierce and vivid lightnings also," and at last the terrible day of the Lord.

Bishop Penrose had sung to the church, "Thy deliverance is nigh, thy oppressors shall die, and the Gentiles shall bow 'neath thy rod." Jonathan's residence in Brooklyn, his journal says, had been the happiest year in his life, but it was time to enter on the kingdom. He sold all that he had and by the first of July reached Florence, Nebraska, where the ox trains formed. With Brother Hudson he bought a wagon and two yoke of oxen. Ten weeks of bitter marching through the desert, up the nation's sternest trail, brought them to Great Salt Lake City. Jonathan lived with Richard during the winter, working as a teamster when he could, although "no money to be earned." (Life was not so hard for everyone in Salt Lake, that winter. "The Lady of Lyons" made a great success before crowded houses. Everybody was reading Mr. Collins's *Woman in White*. Tickets to the Territorial Ball sold for ten dollars, and the Governor presided at a dinner whose menu lists four soups, nine roasts, nine boiled meats, six stews, nine vegetables, and fourteen desserts.)

In the spring of 1862 the church rented him forty-odd acres in the valley of Easton, thirty miles north of Salt Lake City, where the Weber River breaks through the Wasatch. He had no voice in the selection of this land, but he wanted none—it was Zion and that was what counted. So a migration of eight thousand miles ended amid sagebrush on a southern slope above the Weber. The place possessed "a dugout or a little room dug out of the bank. Quite a contrast this to my style of former living in Boston and Brooklyn, where I lived in a large house, carpeted rooms, etc., and it has tried my faith very much." The words are the only complaint that Jonathan Dyer ever expressed.

He had entered on the kingdom. And . . . Jonathan Dyer, of Hertford, had begun the most typical, most fundamental of American experiences, life on the frontier.

II

It is to be observed that Jonathan was a mechanic. He had grown up in a town, he knew the qualities of woods and the tools that worked them, he was adroit with machinery and had invented valves and pumps, but he had never lived on a farm and was as unfitted as possible to exist by agriculture. Commentators too often forget that the frontier held many like him. We are familiar with the thesis—now favored because people who explain things feel that it has some bearing on these difficult times—that the free land of the frontier was a kind of economic safety valve or stabilizer. When previous depressions came, this theory says, the man who was thrown out of work when the factories closed was not desperate, since he could always go west and, starting over, be sure of a living. Just how he raised money for the emigration and just how city dwellers of mechanical training could expect to make their way in an alien trade remains unexplained. The theory also omits to explain why, if the frontier was a sponge that absorbed social unrest, so much of the social unrest in America originated on the frontier.

Well, social unrest did not affect Jonathan Dyer. Utah was not insulated from the nations, and many waves of resentment and discontent traveled across it during his lifetime, which covered the great revolution in our national life. They touched Jonathan not at all. Revolutions are always struggles between special groups; only propaganda tries to make them seem the will of the people in action. The people remain mostly unharried by them, neither willing nor acting, and in the end pay tribute to the old group, victorious, or to the new one which has cast it out. Even agrarian revolt has little to do with agrarians in the mass. American history exhibits the farmers in revolt from the beginning up to now, and the farmers mostly have worked their land voiceless and unstirred, a mere name invoked by speculators who are their self-consecrated champions. They have paid taxes, gone bankrupt for the profit of adventurers, and served as the stuff of financial and political exploitation. From Rome to the valley of Easton there has been no change.

Jonathan's dugout was in a hillside in the valley of the Weber, a valley which in two hamlets besides Easton held some two dozen families. The squalor of those first years is now difficult to appreciate. Life was possible only through the complete communism of the poor. After a year he had a house, a one-room cabin of pine logs brought down from the canyons of the Wasatch, since only soft poplars and cottonwoods grew in the valley. Its puncheon floor, built-in bunks, and rain-tight roof meant an advance over the dank clay of the dugout. Lean-tos were added in time, but a good many years were to pass before Jonathan could build a farmhouse. The cabin meanwhile filled with children: his generation all told was one son and seven daughters, of whom one died in childhood. It is the children who most readily reveal to us the conditions of the frontier.

Sarah, the girl who was born in Brooklyn, was nine when she first wore shoes; the earliest pair were kept for display at Sabbath school or on the clapboard sidewalks of Ogden, eight miles away; they were not put on till one got out of the wagon, and they were

passed on to the descending series of sisters. Her clothes during
that time, she remembered, consisted of apronlike garments cut
from remnants which Rhoda had brought west with her, from the
gunnysacking that also made containers for potatoes, and once
from a bolt of calico. She had no underwear, as a rule, but in the
winter Rhoda would manage to fashion for her, out of God knows
what, garments which failed to beautify her but helped against the
canyon gales. She anticipated the stockingless children and adoles-
cents of the 1930's—in that early time there were no sheep in Easton
and no pennies to buy knitting wool in Ogden. No shoes in winter,
eight miles from a town? Well, children have gone to school, gathered eggs and firewood, and played their games with their feet
bound in sacking or rabbit skins. Of those games Sarah remembered
most pleasantly coasting down the winter hills in a grain scoop.
Once, disastrously, they caught a skunk in a figger-4 which had
been set for rabbits. There was the river, the widening fields, the
cottonwood groves—springs, ditches, hay stacks—spelling bees,
quiltings, Sabbath schools. After a while rattlesnakes grew
uncommon.

How did Jonathan bring them up at all? At the end of 1863 he
writes, "I raised this year a good crop of corn, some wheat, and
some oats." The sentence carries no overtone of the labor so strange
to a mechanic. Jonathan would have had trouble forcing this harvest from the earth anywhere, even in Illinois bottom land, where
the soil is forty feet deep and is watered by generous summer rains.
But at Easton there were no rains and the thin soil was poisoned
by alkali. The sagebrush was the index. Where sage grew, there
other stuffs would grow also, after heart-breaking labor had cleared
it away. Jonathan hacked at that hellish growth. Spines and slivers
that no gloves can turn fill one's hands, the stench under the desert
sun is dreadful, and the roots, which have probed deep and wide
for moisture, must be chopped and grubbed and dragged out inch
by inch. Then, before anything will sprout in the drugged earth,
water must be brought. Through a dozen years of Jonathan's journal we observe the settlers of Easton combining to bring water to
their fields. On the bench lands above their valleys, where gulches
and canyons come down from the Wasatch, they made canals,

which they led along the hills. From the canals smaller ditches flowed down to each man's fields, and from these ditches he must dig veins and capillaries for himself. Where the water ran, cultivation was possible; where it didn't, the sagebrush of the desert showed unbroken. Such co-operation forbade quarrels; one would as soon quarrel about the bloodstream. A man was allotted certain hours of water. When they came, at midnight or dawn or noon, he raised the gates into his own ditches and with spade and shovel and an engineering sense coaxed the water to his planting.

During those first years there would be, besides the corn and wheat and oats of Jonathan's note, potatoes and a few other garden vegetables—carrots no doubt, for this was Utah, perhaps cabbages and surely squash. Brother Kendall, two miles down the valley, had been a farmer's man in England and could help Jonathan with the mysteries of cultivation. Brother Kendall or someone else had a cow to spare and chickens. There was thus milk for the children, and Rhoda churned cream for butter, learned to make cheese, gathered eggs and set hens, acquired the myriad skills of the frontier farm wife who as yet has had no celebrant in literature. There had been settlers at Easton since 1849, but they had not yet been able to harness the Weber to a mill. There was a small affair run by horse power (Jonathan improved the gears) and its crude stones ground the meal for the corn mush which Sarah remembered as the staple of her childhood. The oats, of course, were dedicated to the horses, the wheat to the chickens. Beef was out of the question—cows were too valuable to be slaughtered—but after a while there were hogs, which Jonathan killed and quartered. He had no crops, he could have none till all his land was cleared. Sometimes he would go into the high canyons for several days and fill his wagon with wood. This could be sold in Ogden for the only cash that came to him; but everyone cut wood, and so it could not be sold for very much.

Still these years showed some progress. He began to buy his land from the church on generous but sternly enforced terms. He cleared it. He gridded it with ditches. He put down larger crops, began to sell part of them, bought horses and some cows. He lamented the failure of the church to organize Easton—sometimes a month went by without a service and there was neither juvenile instruction nor priesthood meeting. In view of the Mormon care to organize even the smallest and remotest settlements, this failure is strange. But they made out.

The break came in 1868. The crops were about three inches out of the ground when grasshoppers settled on them, as they had done before the historic miracle which Mahonri Young was to relate in bronze and granite. Three-quarters of the green shoots were destroyed at once and ruin seemed inevitable. But at once surveyors followed the grasshoppers to Easton, and suddenly most of the settlers there, Jonathan among them, were working for the Union Pacific Railroad, hauling timber for ties and construction or, as the year closed, rock and rubble for the grade. For the first time there was money in the valley; Jonathan could now drive to Ogden on Saturday night and bring back milled flour, a few groceries, farm implements, cloth, buttons, a mirror. Sarah's first shoes date from this time. She remembered also a strange pleasure surpassing anything she had imagined, rock candy.

By midwinter the rails came through Weber Canyon and the violent town called Hell on Wheels erected itself at Easton. Jonathan says that there were "many bad men" in this company, who drank and gambled and whored to the disgust of the Saints, and says no more about them except that they burned his fences for firewood. The fences had already been pierced, for the roadbed ran straight across his land, and he worked among the bad men as a teamster and did not scruple to sell them produce. Sometimes he mounted guard with an enormous horse pistol to drive the boisterous Irish away. Hell on Wheels passed rapidly on, to Corinne, to Promontory Point, but it had raised the valley out of squalor. Also it had destroyed Easton by building a station two miles farther down the valley than the nucleus of houses that constituted "the settlement." The station was just a mile east of Jonathan's house. Its signboard wore a queer misspelled name which still remains, Uinta.

Sarah's first candles came now—tallow had been too precious for such use—and later there was the magnificent new "rock oil," much better than the rag floating in melted home-cured lard which she had known. This marvel came westward on the "U.P.," which also brought coal from Rock Springs, though Jonathan would not burn it

for some years yet. Stoves came too, and many marvelous new
things. All the children had shoes by 1870, and Rhoda could make
excellent clothes for them. But the railroad's power was best shown
by the impetus it gave religion. Jonathan had long since organized
a Sabbath school. Now he could get books for it. The valley's new
prosperity enabled him to raise, by dances and "entertainments," a
fund which, sent to Chicago, bought "between 130 and 140, which
proved a blessing for the children."

Now that all the children had shoes, Jonathan was clearly doing
well. To this time belongs a story which he remembered when he
was nearly eighty. The Bishop of Uinta (the church "ward" was now
organized) came to Brother Dyer and suggested that since the Lord
had rewarded his efforts, it was clearly his duty to take another wife
and raise up more seed for Israel. In the only rebellion against his
teachers he ever experienced, Jonathan got out the horse pistol and
ordered the Bishop off his land, and thereafter there was no mention
of polygamy. . . . A grandson has seen the horse pistol but does
not believe the story. These folks at Uinta were the humble of
Mormonry, and the humble had little to do with polygamy. There
seems never to have been a plural marriage in the valley. The story
merely means an old man's memory that he had not believed in
polygamy. He was one of many Saints who did not. But, be very
sure, if the Bishop, a lineal descendant of Aaron, had commanded
Jonathan to take another wife, then another wife would have come
to share Rhoda's labors and add children to Jonathan's glory.

III

What can be said about Jonathan Dyer? He was a first-class
private in the march of America—a unit in the process that made
and remade the nation. Yet History can make singularly little of
him. You could not write the history of Utah or of the Mormon
church without mentioning, for instance, the "New Movement"
which, from the point of view of historical forces, must have shaken
this commonwealth to its base. Its occurrence could be guessed from
nothing whatever in Jonathan's life and from only a single line in

his journal which says that it began in 1869. You could not write either of those histories without detailing the violent disturbance of the public peace which was called the "Morrisite war"—the appearance of a false prophet in Israel and his suppression by Brigham Young. The prophet Morris and his followers pitched their camp across the narrow Weber from Jonathan's lower field and there, a few rods from him, they were at last attacked by the army of the Lord. After three days of rifle and artillery practice the false prophet and some of his flock were killed and their camp was scattered. It may be that bullets kicked up dust in the field that Jonathan was plowing, it may be that he climbed a cottonwood to gaze at the riot, but the event was worth in his journal only one sentence and an aphorism about the stubbornness of evil. Of the rest of history during his lifetime, nothing whatever appears. Mormon and Gentile battled for supremacy, polygamists were hunted down, at least the whole church was proscribed and its property confiscated. And all this was less than a shadow to Jonathan, who notes the fall of rain, which counts in a desert, and the annual increase of his crop.

History, it may be, is not of the humble. Some millions of Jonathans were creating America. Over all the empty land such minute nuclei as his stood out. They grew by aggregation, while men made farms of what had been just wasteland, and then the land wasn't empty any more. The unit, the nucleus, the individual kept up his not spectacular warfare against anarchy, for self-preservation. What had he to do with the currents of national life? They weren't, for him, currents at all. They were waves perhaps, which flowed an unrecognized energy through or around him and on to his neighbor, lifting both and letting both fall back, their position in space unchanged, water still to be brought to the fields. Occupied enough with his own struggle for survival, incapable enough of feeling himself a part of a nation, Jonathan had a further unawareness in his faith. It was, the Mormon faith, a superb instrument for the reclamation of the desert, for the creation of the West. It rewarded the faithful for industry and offered rewards for further effort. It identified with heavenly grace the very qualities that were most needed in a new country: unquestioning labor, frugality, co-operation, obedience. So long as the faithful worked to redeem the earth so long were they building up Israel and strengthening God's kingdom.

So, though Jonathan was a religious emigrant, there was not even much religion as philosophers know it in his life. The Sabbath school which he established became the best in Weber County; it was commended in Quarterly and even Annual Conference, and was permitted to march in Pioneer Day parades. Jonathan was sometimes called upon to advise other educators of the young. He was made a high priest. Sometimes he met dignitaries of the church and listened to counsel. He was never promoted above his sergeantcy, for in Mormonism as elsewhere the humble do not become leaders. He accepted the hagiology of his church and its dogmas and its expectations, but they were merely a background. He did not think about them often or very deeply. He was advancing Israel, making sure his glory, but—and this was what counted—his fields came under the plow and he was setting out fruit trees. If religion was just smoke on the horizon, politics was even less. The grandson who has been mentioned remembers asking Jonathan whether he was going to vote for a son-in-law who had been nominated for some office now forgotten. Jonathan was not, he said. The son-in-law had been nominated by the Democrats, and the Bishop of Uinta had told Jonathan that it was best for the Republicans to be in power. Didn't the leading men in church and party know what was best? You will not write political history by consulting the ideas of the humble.

These were just smoke. It was real when Rhoda and all the children—five of them at that time—fell sick with smallpox. We have forgotten the terror of that plague. Neighbors whipped their horses to the gallop, passing by, averted their faces and held their breath against infection, burned smudges, wore amulets of vile-smelling stuff. No one dared to come to Jonathan's help or even to bring a doctor from Ogden. Somehow he nursed his family through till Rhoda was on her feet and then he too collapsed. The well got contaminated one summer and they all had typhoid fever; there was help this time and they all survived. One year Rhoda's breast "gathered" and she had to drag herself about the grinding labor of a farm wife; she failed slowly, nothing could be done for her, but that also passed and she could go on. One summer, chopping wood, Jonathan cut a gash in his leg. For the rest of the year he could not work; Rhoda and the children shortened their sleep, carried on the irrigation, and brought in the crop. The menace of such accidents was constant. One Sunday noon Jonathan came back from Sabbath school and found that a mule had kicked his son, young Jonathan, in the head and "broke his skull." Jonathan went to Ogden, and by ten o'clock that night had brought Dr. Woodward back. For five hours, by the light of a Rochester lamp in the kitchen, the doctor operated on the boy. The doctor came twice more to dress the wound. Jonathan paid him: "cash, $20; pig, $4; corn and corn meal, $2.70; wood, $6" and, a month later, some more wood. The boy had recovered four months later. And so on . . . "November 21st (1872), this morning about 4 o'clock my wife confined and gave birth to a daughter; also, I took a load of wood to Mrs. Savage."

All that was real and so was the earth. The desert yielded. There was never to be ease or luxury at Uinta—what would a farmer do with either? Education was impossible for the children. The little school at the "settlement" was like its equivalents throughout rural America, and when Sarah wanted to learn more she had to go to Ogden, where she paid her board by housework and walked three miles each way to Professor Moench's academy. The children had to strike out for themselves as soon as possible, Jonathan as a telegrapher down state, and Sarah as a waitress in a railroad lunchroom at Green River. But, if not ease, comfort came to Uinta and security and the rude plenty of the farm. The daughter whose birth is noticed came to a frame house painted green. There was an ell later. The dooryard had a small lawn—incredible in the desert—and mulberry and walnut trees and Rhoda's flower garden. The ditch that paralleled the railroad tracks in front of it flowed beside Lombardy poplars of Jonathan's planting. There were wells and springs of mountain water. Half a dozen cows and as many horses grazed in the west pasture; a few sheep were about, and annually Jonathan cured hams and bacon from his hogs. These hung beside home-butchered beef and mutton and the children tended sizable flocks of chickens, turkeys, ducks, and guinea fowl. Sheds multiplied, filling with cultivators, harrows, plows, and similar implements which the unseen America beyond the Wasatch was creating. There were hay sheds, chicken houses, a "warehouse" (for Jonathan was English and his wagons were "carts"), an embryonic machine shop, a cider press. The thrashers harvested Jonathan's wheat; it was stored in a granary with his corn and oats and barley. Rhoda made cheese and butter; she "put up" vegetables from the garden and her jams and jellies are nostalgically remembered. She baked every day. There were eggs all winter long.

Is it clear that all this sprang from desert land, that Jonathan created it out of nothing at all? That is the point. Sometimes noticed, it is seldom realized in discussions of the frontier. Some people are pleased by the frontier's pageantry, and the literary are frantically ashamed of what they feel must have been its ugliness; but somehow the plain fact of creation gets overlooked. . . . In 1862 a hillside in Utah, sloping down to cottonwoods along the Weber River, had been no more than sagebrush. The sage, *Artemisia tridentata*, is glamorous in folklore, where it is called heartsease, and it seems beautiful under distance to tourists of the tamed West, but it is the type-symbol of desolation. There was here—nothing whatever. A stinking drouth, coyotes and rattlesnakes and owls, the movement of violet and silver and olive-dun sage in white light—a dead land. But now there was a painted frame house under shade trees, fields leached of alkali, the blue flowers of alfalfa, flowing water, grain, gardens, orchards.

Especially orchards. Under the sagebrush roots the earth held the ashes of a volcanic age. When Jonathan brought water to it chemistry was set free. Something in that volcanic ash gave a superb flavor to fruit. All the Utah fruits are glorious, but especially the strawberries and apricots and apples, and most especially the peaches. One who has not tasted, fresh from the tree, a peach grown on the eastern slope of the long valley that holds the Great Salt Lake may not speak of peaches. All these fruits, together with cherries and plums and pears, came in time to Jonathan's hillside. How should this Hertford mechanic learn to divine the hidden necessities of trees? The thing is impossible but happened. He was a farmer by virtue of blind strength and the mistakes of years, but he was a fruit-grower by divination. He walked among his orchards and could read their needs. So that as the years passed Jonathan Dyer's orchards became the greater part of his farm, and they were known.

This in what had been a dead land. Water flowed in his ditches, stock grazed his pastures, instead of desolation there were fields and orchards. The children came in at nightfall to a house built from his lumber. They ate bread made of his wheat, cheese from his milk, preserved fruit from his orchards. There had been nothing at all, and here were peaches, and he had come eight thousand miles. That is the point of the frontier.

IV

Uinta was eight miles over the hills from Ogden—four hours when the road was in its April state the time Jonathan drove in for Dr. Woodward, seventy-five minutes in a buggy behind old Prince when the grandson's memory of it opens, about 903, and eleven minutes in 1933. Those figures speak also of the frontier. The 1903 memory preserves quiet and isolation—summer afternoons beside the beautifully sited canal in the shade of the poplars, a dusty road vacant of travel, sometimes a wagon climbing the immense hill which was named for Peg-leg Labaume, sometimes rails humming before a U.P. train emerged from Weber canyon, no other movement except that of clouds and wind, no other sound but cicadas and the whine of Jonathan's mower in the alfalfa. The crest of Jonathan's comfort and success. The fields were clean, the orchards combed and trim, the sheds plumb. Nondescript cows had given place to Jerseys; the hogs were now Poland Chinas. A greengage tree rose in the dooryard; it was followed by Japanese plums and other foreign fruits whose growth endlessly interested Jonathan. On Thanksgiving and Christmas when the children and grandchildren gathered, Rhoda would spend the day cooking great dinners, and every item of them had grown under her eyes. Home-butchered roast beef with Yorkshire pudding is remembered, suckling pigs with Jonathan's apples in their mouths, turkeys, butter and cheese from Rhoda's milk room, endless breads and biscuits and cakes from flour traded in grist a mile away. Winters were snug; spring plowing turned earth that was ignorant of alkali. This was Deseret, the land of the honey bee.

Yet even in 1903 its doom had been pronounced. A large wagon—

Jonathan called it a van—from the Kasius Grocery in Ogden began to make weekly visits to Uinta. Jonathan and Rhoda were sixty-nine; soon it seemed foolish to butcher their own meat, churn their own butter, set rennet for their own cheese. For the rest of his life Jonathan was more an orchardist, less a farmer. Then another corporation asked for an easement over the farm, and steel towers rose carrying transmission lines from power plants deep in the Wasatch. Jonathan and Rhoda were alone. The four hours to Ogden had been difficult but not difficult enough, for none of the seven children had stayed on the land. None had remained in the Mormon church. None, even, had married a native of Utah. Three of them had moved out of the state. The twenty grandchildren were to be dispersed from San Diego to Boston, and though they were to take up trades as wide apart as boilermaking and novel writing, not one of them was a farmer. They were products of the frontier—which had fallen.

The plenty of 1903 lingered on. But Jonathan and Rhoda grew old. A farm requires vigor and, though Jonathan's remained phenomenal, Rhoda's failed, and it was not always possible to find a granddaughter in her teens who would live with them and help. At last Jonathan began to show the strange mania that sometimes comes upon fruit-growers. He would suddenly notice something wrong about one of his fruit trees and decide that it must make way for a new, young shoot. He would get out his axe. The glorious orchards began to fall. So, a little dazed, uncomprehending, Jonathan made in 1917 the journey which during fifty-five years he had scorned to make—he and the rejoicing Rhoda moved the eight miles to Ogden to live with a daughter. The farm was sold. The buyer kept things as they were, but four years later some ass who had money to spare bought the place, leveled the orchards, let the fields perish, and began to raise silver foxes. He was a Goth plowing the land with salt.

Rhoda died in 1919. Jonathan lived four years more in a growing bewilderment. Sometimes he would disappear from the daughter's house. A grandson would know where to look for him, for the old man would start out unerringly for Uinta but would grow confused and wait wretchedly for a known face. When found he would explain that he was desperately needed at the farm. He had not seen it again when he died, and of the children and grandchildren only the novelist, a romantic, has traveled those eight miles.

What can be said in judgment of Jonathan Dyer's life? In terms of money, his estate, after the expense of six years away from the farm, was about six thousand dollars. He had come from Hertford and labored for fifty-five years to bequeath seven hundred and fifty dollars to each of his children. Or, in different terms, he had raised seven children who, with their children, had merged with the frontier into the republic. Not much else can be said: an item in the history of America had fulfilled itself. You must multiply Jonathan Dyer by several million, looking westward from the Missouri River to the Rocky Mountains, across a space which your oldest maps will call the Great American Desert.

After that multiplication you see Jonathan Dyer as something else, and a carelessly parenthetical sentence in a letter from Ogden lights up with sudden meaning. "They are farming your grandfather's land again." So the fox farm has collapsed, with so much other obscenity that belonged to the boom years. There will be crops again on that hillside which slopes downward to the Weber. Alfalfa flowers will be blue in the north field once more and the canal will divert shimmering water to the kitchen garden. Perhaps other orchards will rise in the places where Jonathan's were uprooted; the volcanic ash will once more work its chemistry.

The earth was poisoned, and Jonathan made it sweet. It was a dead land, and he gave it life. Permanently. Forever. Following the God of the Mormons, he came from Hertford to the Great American Desert and made it fertile. That is achievement.

By Brewster Ghiselin

NEW WORLD

THIS is the land our fathers came to find:
They found the old world only, they found the known
Measures of the moods of their own minds:
The blue mountains' dying, the plain's surmise,
The bones and bountiful nakedness and thought
Of barbarous rock, and the green peace of earth;
They found the hostile forests of the heart.
This is the earth that should have had our love,
The loam that deepens by the deepening streams,
The mould that feeds the forest and the flower,
The musk and metal of a stony dust:
Three centuries the foothold of our life,
Never the roothold. How could we love a path?
A place of passage or unwilling rest.
In our blood's need we came from the cold cliffs,
Up from the low shores and the smell of spray,
Westward from the duneland and the pines.
We crossed the silent rivers in the plains
And climbed the abrupt west, and fed our need
With dust and sun and the humming juniper,
And came to the broken coast, the barrier sea:
No earth, a pathless glimmering of waves.
No way behind us but the traveled lands,
No way before us but the lemmings' grave.

II

Now meanings bleed like dreams: the past is paling,
Asia, Europe, Africa, the islands.
Unmastered shadows over the known land
Come like the umbra to the mortal city.
Empty and naked, wading the languid grass
Of cactus kingdoms for the snake's possession,
We pace the measures of the heart's release,
We step the prelude of our blood's return.

III

But where is the new world? Only in time,
In moments of the individual mind:
Flashes and fragments: seen in the waste wall
And rock-ridge, heart-defining height and hawkfall
Isolations, and on Joshua slopes
Blacked with burnt blocks of rock whose drummings answer
Bourdon and hornvoice grooves and gold of hills,
Music to name our needs: too briefly seen
Between the many voices of the past:
Brief as the tinsel of the morning star;
Known as the swimmer knows the stumbling wave.
We turn in bed at dawn, we hear the sunrise,
We hear the silence of the mockingbird:
Over the earth the sudden future comes
Like beauty to the body of one loved.
Then day surrounds us like an empty room.

TEMPLE BUILDERS

AT 2 P.M. the Temple hands in their working clothes marched double file up the street to the courthouse to welcome Brigham Young and his retinue. The men carried two banners, one inscribed with "Holiness to the Lord," and the other with "Zion's Workmen" and an All-Seeing Eye. Behind these, stretching across both lines was a third banner, "Welcome to Brigham Young, Our Chief Builder."

The men's faces were creased with smiles, but they were orderly. They debouched on the south side of the new adobe courthouse, with its stone stairs and pillars and arched colonial doorway and hangman's trap in the spire. Far down the road they could see rising dust and the approaching company of carriages and scouts on horseback.

Struggling with suppressed elation, the men whispered among themselves. Uncanny how the woodwork inside the courthouse resembled bird's-eye maple, and those columns in the Tabernacle resembled marble. And now Brother Milne, the Scotch artist, had painted the Garden of Eden room in the Temple until you felt you were wrapped in the greenness of a tropical forest.

Looked like the weather would be perfect for the dedication tomorrow. Dixie Aprils were enchanting, with the oose and cactus in bloom on the hills and the roses climbing the poplar trees.

And now the President's party is turning the corner.

The Temple hands, stretched in a single line, are very still. The scouts, the coaches, and finally Brother Brigham himself pass slowly in review. The workmen take off their hats and bow low to the ground. Brother Brigham returns the salute. The coaches roll on by, and the Temple hands two abreast march back down to the shoveling, plowing, and scraping yet to do on the white-capped hill.

There was a thrill in the very air, Clory thought, as she stooped to let Tempie hook up the back of the emerald green moiré. Studying her bangs, to which Abijah had at last consented, the crisp ruching beneath her chin, the scalloped tops of her fine leather shoes, she knew that not even in her teens had she been so good-looking as she was now in her thirties. And the children were entrancing. Jimmie with his black curls and Kate Greenaway jacket and pleated skirt. Tempie in her Swiss bodice and pantalettes. Clory tilted the new pillbox toque over her eyes and went out to join 'Sheba and Abijah. Even if the Temple was only a block away, they were going to ride in the white-topped buggy with the matched mules.

The building arose from the barren ground like a great white wedding cake. It was eighty-four feet high to the top of the parapet, battlemented like an old castle, and there was a hundred-and-thirty-five-foot tower on top of that. There were twelve Gothic buttresses along each side and five along each end, and the three-tiered spire had panels to balance the line of the buttresses. Inside, there were two spiral staircases winding upward the entire height of the building, eleven rooms in the basement and one main room above, with eight smaller rooms around it.

Long before the ceremonies were to start, a vast throng of people wandered around the block, squinted upward from the roadway, felt of the solid rock walls with their hands as if to bolster the evidence of their eyes. A Temple that would cost a million dollars. The world would have said it couldn't be done, and so they did it.

"Do you remember the angels in the sky when we dedicated the Nauvoo Temple?"

Keturah Snow sat in her husband's coach and studied the chaste white walls through half-closed eyes.

"And the rushing sound," said Martha in an awed voice, "the 'spirit of God like a mighty rushing wind.'"

"I remember the tiled floors and the Bible scenes painted on the plastered walls, and the font that they said was a copy of the baptistry in King Solomon's Temple," said Hannah Merinda, "but it wasn't as grand as this."

"No," sighed Aunt Ket. "Nothing could be as grand as this!"

Around the immense upper hall the throng assembled. Silk ribbons, fringe, tassels, jet, bugles, and embroidery, but uncovered heads and stockinged feet, for this was the House of the Lord. Taffeta sound of many skirts. Lavender and bergamot and lye soap. Half-audible beating of many hearts. The twelve Apostles were there, the Presidents of Stakes, dignitaries from all of Zion. But the Lion of the Lord had to be carried from room to room in a chair.

"Redeemer of Israel," sang the choir, and Clory was conscious of a sheen, a mellowness in the air.

Awe deepened her voice as veils fluttered and Clory stood revealed.

Erastus bowed his head and called forth blessings upon the surroundings, the Garden of Eden, rooms celestial, terrestrial, telestial.

The Twelve, the Presidents of Stakes, the High Council, and Brother Brigham carried by Erastus and Bishop Gardner went into the sealing rooms.

When they returned, the meeting was Brother Brigham's, and a sigh of anticipation rustled the throng. As the President got painfully to his feet and began to speak hesitantly, his voice gathering strength and resonance, Erastus squeezed back the foolish tears and reflected that this moment was worth all that had gone before.

One morning the brethren had brought him word that Sister Miles had at last found a pond big enough. Another morning he had watched Lon Tuckett and Betsy rumble away. The first of them all to quit. Before he left, Lon had shamefacedly given him a scrawled sheet of foolscap. His last piece.

There's nothing here to cheer, except prophetic sermons. . . .

There had been still another morning when the good Catholic fathers of Silver Reef had offered their first mass in this new country in the St. George Tabernacle. As the mighty Te Deums rolled out over a Mormon congregation, the Tabernacle clock had struck ten, inexorable as Fate above the solemn chanting. Erastus on the stand had watched his people look at one another, a silent cheer spreading from face to face. But on that March day of 1877 as John D. Lee toppled into his coffin at Mountain Meadows, Erastus saluted him.

Of such, the price a people paid.

"This is the greatest time since Adam," preached Brother Brigham. "Solomon had a temple, but as far as I can learn little or no endowments were given. The Jews killed the priest between the altar and the door because he would not divulge the secrets of the holy priesthood."

A sudden gust of wind rattled the windows and Brigham pointed with his cane. "The Devil's mad right now! . . .

"I tell you we have no business here other than to build up and establish the Zion of our Lord, who holds the hearts of the living in His hands and turns them as the rivers are turned. But the negligence, the folly of the Saints! . . . Some, if they had the power, would build a railroad to the bottomless pit. People act like fools, and I will never cease to strive until Satan is overcome and driven from the earth. There are men here who are no more fit to be here than the Devil from hell!"

His eyes glinted beneath their brows, his white beard trembled, and in his earnestness he smote the pulpit with his cane until the room rang. He looked down at the marks on the polished wood.

"You can putty this up, smooth it over, paint it, or leave it here as a testimony."

The forefinger came up in its old gesture. . . .

The President reorganized Stakes, set the priesthood in order, defined the duties of the Apostles, Seventies, high priests, elders, and lesser priesthood, and set apart Abijah MacIntyre to be first president of the first Temple in the new Zion.

Even after the meeting was over the people would not let the leader go. They waited for him outside on the grounds, beyond the fence, in the road, and as he appeared in his chair in the doorway and Apostle Snow and Bishop Gardner carried him on out, a cheer burst forth that echoed from the Sugar Loaf to the pastel mountains.

Brigham held up his hand to the cheering, clapping multitude.

The skin of his cheeks stretched tightly over the bones, his stocky body appeared to have crumbled within and settled down upon itself as an ancient mound settles.

"There are those now living who will see this valley thickly populated from ridge to ridge and from the red hill to the river."

He spoke meditatively and yet with conviction. The crowd quieted, leaned closer to hear.

"I see spires pointing heavenward and the Temple standing in the center of the valley, Utah's Dixie at the head of the State instead of the foot. . . ."

His voice lagged as if he were very weary, sunk to almost a whisper.

"'What doth the Lord require of thee but to do justice and to love mercy and to walk humbly with thy God?

"'For behold, this is my work and my glory, to bring to pass the immortality and the eternal life of man.'"

The banked fires of his eyes swept these Saints he had nourished so long.

"I would say to you . . . 'Do not betray your heritage.' There are some here who will bring it glory . . . but to you all I would say, 'Love God and each other. Love laughter.'"

His puckish humor played upon them for a moment.

"I calculate to die in the harness!"

A strange stillness fell upon the sober old ones with their burdens of floods and governments and polygamy, upon the laughing young ones with their heads full of kisses and the ancient mystery of lying together. Wonder touched their faces as the hushed lines parted to let Brother Brigham's chair go through. More than a tired old man had passed. An epoch had passed.

By Wallace Stegner

ARCADIAN VILLAGE

ARCADIA is a hard place to find, but if you drive down Highway 89 between Bryce Canyon and Zion National Park you will pass the place where it used to be in the 1870's. It doesn't look like Arcadia now. It looks like a pleasant little Mormon town strung along the valley of the Virgin River, sleeping peacefully under its red cliffs, shaded by its maples and mulberries and smoke trees, surrounded by its gardens and orchards. It is a village of between four and five hundred people hardly distinguishable from dozens of other Mormon villages. It is a nice town to stop at for a coke on a hot day, and in summer it smells of ripe peaches. But Arcadia? Not quite.

As a matter of fact, it never did look like Arcadia from the outside. It looked like a rather flimsy fort made out of deal boards during most of the eleven years of its heyday. But it came closer to being the perfect village than any the Mormons ever founded; it wedded utopian economics to millennial theocracy and got a result which for a long time (as utopian societies go) looked like the realization of man's ancient dream. It eliminated completely the fear of poverty and want; it furnished to all its members the amplitude of food, shelter, and clothing whose possession, according to some ways of thinking, ought to remove every source of human quarrelsomeness. It managed to bring its several hundred members into a communism of good, labor, religion, and recreation such as the world has seen only in a few places and for very short times, and to do it without

84

loss of gaiety or good nature. The life was strenuous, but it was also wholesome; it brought content. The number of people from that town who lived past eighty is good statistical evidence that heaven-on-earth does not breed the will to die.

They called it Orderville, not because of the meticulous orderliness of its community life, but because Joseph Smith, in an early revelation, had dreamed of an ideal social and economic system which he called the United Order of Enoch. All property was to be consecrated to common use, each man holding a stewardship for as much as he needed to support his family, and each putting his surplus back in for the benefit of all. That first United Order was put into practice in Kirtland, Ohio, and in Missouri, but it had to be abandoned after a short trial, partly because the hostility of the surrounding Gentiles interfered with economic experimentation, partly because there were no leaders strong and capable enough to hold together the Missouri Order when Joseph Smith had headquarters far back in Ohio, partly because the rich hung back from consecrating their property, and the poor flocked in in the hope of getting an inheritance. Joseph reluctantly put the idea away, telling his people that they were not yet ready for the practice of that divine institution, but that the day would come when it would be practiced in its fullness.

Brigham Young never attempted to re-establish the United Order on Joseph Smith's terms. To support the priesthood, who work in the Mormon Church without pay, but whose families sometimes needed support when the head was away on a mission, Joseph had instituted the "lesser law" of tithing, and Brigham was content to leave the Church resting on those foundations until the influx of Gentiles, the seizing of much of the merchandising business by Gentiles and apostate Mormons, and the panic of 1873 forced him into economic tinkering. Then, to whip the Gentiles and to stir up the weakening solidarity of his people, he turned both to coöperatives and to Christian communism. He and other Church leaders organized vigorously, beginning in St. George, which was by then a kind of "winter capital" of the Mormon Country, and building up local Orders all the way up the valleys.

In most towns the second United Order succeeded no better than the first one had at Kirtland and Independence. Many Mormons, especially in the northern towns, had grown wealthy; they were reluctant to endanger their prosperity by pooling their property. And for some reason—perhaps because he himself was dubious about the reaction of the leaders, and meant the Order only for the rank and file—Brigham did not insist upon communist economics as a divine command, and he never abrogated the "lesser law" of tithing, which according to the Prophet Joseph would be given up when the Saints were ready for the real Saintly way. The United Order, for Brigham, was an economic expedient, and though many communities obediently tried it, some with great enthusiasm, there was not the zeal that theocratic compulsion might have brought. The Gentiles, moreover, fought both the United Order and the coöperative Church stores which immediately preceded it, because such a Mormon coalition meant the eventual strangling of all Gentile enterprise. Zion's Coöperative Mercantile Institution, formed in 1868 to break the hold of Gentiles on the trade of the territory, did fifteen million dollars' worth of business in its first five years. After 1873, also, it acted as a covering institution for local industry, promoting goods produced under the revived Mormon program of self-sufficiency. And the Z.C.M.I. sold shares of its stock to no one who was not in good standing in the Church, paid up in his tithing, and possessed of a good moral character. It was almost as hard to buy into the Z.C.M.I. as it is to get into the Temple. No wonder the Gentiles fought it. No wonder they fought the United Order, which was even more closed to outsiders and which rendered whole towns ineligible as buyers of Gentile goods.

It was not, however, the Gentile opposition and ridicule that broke up the second United Order in most towns. It was dissension from within, signs of a cracking in the insularity of the Mormon population. Both rank and file Mormons and Gentiles noticed that the Church leaders, for all their talking, did not come forward in any numbers to consecrate their property to the Lord, or even to Brother Brigham as trustee-in-trust for the Lord. Imperceptibly, year by year, their wealth had grown, and even though they had followed Brigham's advice and stayed away from the gold fields, they liked well enough the prosperity that a generation in the valley had given them. They stalled, and for once the small Mormon caught on and stalled too. In most towns the Order lasted only a year or two before bickering, recrimination, bad management, or anger over imperfectly kept accounts broke it up.

But in the remote settlements, especially in the southwestern part of Utah, in the corner of Nevada adjoining, and in the pioneer colonies founded a little later along the Little Colorado and the San Juan, the United Order had a fair trial. Almost invariably, in settlements where all were poor, it worked. In Orderville it lasted with conspicuous success for eleven years, and hung on in altered and diluted form for some time after that. It is only necessary to look at the history of the families who settled the town to see why it was likely that coöperation would be taken more seriously, practiced more diligently, and clung to more tenaciously among them than among other groups.

For one thing, they had been tried over and over again in the faith. Some of them had been involved in almost every hegira the Mormon Church ever made. They had lost their property and even some of their friends and relatives in the Missouri troubles, and had been driven back to Illinois. They had built in Nauvoo and been chased out again, across to Winter Quarters and on over the plains to Salt Lake Valley. They had built again in the valley, and at Brigham's orders many of them had uncomplainingly pulled their stakes to go and colonize other settlements along the west slope of the Wasatch. In 1865 they had been called again, this time to the Muddy Mission in what is now Nevada.

They were not pioneers of the itchy-footed and free-elbowed sort. They had no claustrophobia when population got to be ten to the square mile. After all their wanderings they wanted to settle down, but they did not complain. For the third or fourth time they sold their land, turned their little wealth into seed wheat and plows and covered wagons, packed up the flour and ammunition and machinery that Brigham instructed them to take, and started out. There was no gold field in their mind's eye, not even a land overflowing with milk and honey. They were headed for a desert outpost where the chances were fifty-fifty they would starve to death.

Still, they went, and they went singing. The towns they founded, the Moapa Valley towns of Overton and St. Thomas and St. Joseph, later become famous for the quality of the garden truck they produced, but the pioneers found them no Canaan. The Indians were inquisitive and bothersome and light-fingered, the insects and the drouth and the uncertainty of irrigation were trials. And almost as soon as they had established themselves on the Muddy and become a way station on the Mormon Road to California, they found themselves cut off from their roots. The Moapa Valley was in 1866 taken away from Utah and added to Nevada. Nevada levied taxes; the Saints protested that they were paying their taxes in Utah. It was four years before an official survey definitely established the line, and the taxes owed to Nevada were four years behind.

The colonists appealed to Brigham to be released from their mission. If the railroad had not come, if the possibility of holding the empire's corridor to the sea had still been open, if the Colorado River route for bringing in supplies and converts had not faded out, Brigham would probably have counseled them to stay. But Brigham's plans had changed. The direction of planned settlement had shifted toward the Bear Lake country and southern Idaho. So Brigham advised them to abandon their villages and come back.

Now for the fourth or fifth time they gave up what they had seized from the desert. Some of them, worn out, trailed back to their old homes in the valleys. But two hundred of them went, again on Brigham's suggestion, to Long Valley on the Virgin River, where they resettled the town of Mt. Carmel, abandoned in 1866 because of trouble with the Navajo.

They were not even yet through moving. They had been at Mt. Carmel four years when Brigham instituted the United Order. Most of them wanted the Order, welcomed it. A good many less-seasoned settlers in the town did not. In the end, to avoid a break-up before the program could get well started, the bulk of the Muddy settlers and others in agreement with them picked up and moved two miles and a half up the canyon to found an entirely new town on communist principles. They had suffered and sacrificed too much to be fiddling away their time in disputes with their neighbors. They were the shock-troops of Zion, and they had taken a beating in the Lord's name for a long time—thirty years, some of them. They had, without their own knowledge, done their archaeological duty on the Muddy, leaving their town of St. Thomas to be drowned under Lake Mead and preserved in the ultimate sandstone along with the lost pueblo of the Ho-ho-kim. They did their sociological duty at Orderville, carrying to its logical extreme the group psychology of Mormonism. They lived their doctrine in its fullness; by one means or another, the work of their hands was marked for immortality.

If anyone had been mad enough to ride down Long Valley in the late seventies or eighties before five o'clock in the morning he would have found, quite naturally, that Arcadia slept. The sun comes fairly late over the walls of the canyon, and before sunrise the valley lies in a clear gray light so transparent that every leaf on the river cottonwoods is distinct, the timbered hillsides are sharp-edged and shadowless. The wind has not yet begun to stir.

The bottom is lush with orchards and fields, green with that vivid and almost unbelievable green observable only in places where vegetation is a lucky local accident. But the town is a disappointment. A high board fence encloses a block of land thirty rods square. The only break in the wall is a gate on the south side. Inside the enclosure, the place improves, though it is still curiously like a barracks. Along east, north, and west is a solid row of shanties, their high blank ends forming the outside wall of the town, their inner ends fronting on a wide sidewalk shaded by maples, mulberries, poplars, box elders, tamarisks. In the center of the court a larger building, twenty-five by forty feet, lies down behind a high flagpole as if tethered to it. For all the regimented look of the place, it seems peaceful in the gray light. Let it sleep, this hollow square that resembles a tourist cottage camp before the earliest tourists are awake. It is only five o'clock after all.

But out of the door of one of the shanties comes a large man with a cornet in his hand. He glances at the floating scarves of cloud over the east rim, cocks his eye at the scarred hillside above the town, spits in the dust, and puts the horn to his lips. This is Thomas Robertson, the blacksmith, the official dawn rooster, and his cock-crow is a Mormon hymn, "O Ye Mountains High." He blows not only loudly but with a certain sedate enjoyment, and when he has

finished he blows air through his horn and wiggles the keys and
goes back inside.

Within a few minutes people are stirring. A handful of girls and
another handful of women hurry across the square and disappear
into the central building tethered to the flagpole. The building
stretches itself and wakes. Its breath goes straight up into the air.
All along the rows of shanties men, women, and children appear.
Men and boys in gray homespun and floppy straw hats and heavy
cowhide shoes cut though the gate and around to the north side,
where the corrals and chicken coops are. A woman emerges to hang
a half-dozen diaper cloths on the line between her shanty and the
next. Down in one corner a girl is singing, continuing the hymn with
which Thomas Robertson awoke the town:

> "Oh, Zion, dear Zion! Land of the free,
> Now my own mountain home
> Unto thee I have come. . . ."

There is a buzzing, a preparatory hum, throughout the village,
like the hum you hear when you put your ear to a beehive. There
are greetings, windy yawns, snatches of laughter. Out of one door
bursts a boy with another boy chasing him. Staggering with
laughter, he circles a smoke tree and tries to cut back, but his pursuer
catches him, and they wrestle. They lie on the ground pounding
each other perfunctorily, they roll aside and rest, they rise to hands
and knees and go after each other again like a couple of pups, rolling in the dust. A woman calls them sharply from inside.

By seven o'clock there are people who are already through with
their morning chores, and who hang around as if waiting for something. Promptly at seven it comes. Thomas Robertson steps to his
door again and blows another hymn, "Do What Is Right, Let the
Consequence Follow." Nobody worries much about the consequence. What is right, at that hour, is breakfast. They break in
hurrying queues toward the central dining hall. Robertson, without
waiting to blow air through his horn, hangs it up and ties into the
line.

Three rows of tables stretch the length of the dining room. It is

rather like an immense boarding house, the plates turned neatly over
the knives and forks and spoons. There are no tablecloths or nap-
kins, but the wood of the table is scoured soft and smooth and white.
The Bishop, Thomas Chamberlain, waits until the room is quiet and
then offers prayer. One more preliminary, the hymn "Lord, We
Come before Thee Now," and the last hurdle is cleared. The plates
are turned over, the five cooks in the kitchen begin ladling out the
food, the six girl waitresses carry it in.

The waitresses do their work quickly and with seriousness, especially the three younger ones, eleven or twelve years old, to whom it
is a sign of growing up to be admitted as junior waitresses. People
eat fast. Do what is right, let the consequence follow. There is work
to be done. They push back by couples and threes and clear out.
Eventually Auntie Harmon, who is childless and hence is put in
charge of the whole swarming multitude of children, gets the place
empty and calls the kids. They come in a rush, duck their noses
briefly toward their plates, and fall to. When they are done it is
their duty to go up and say, "Please, Auntie Harmon, I'm done," and
she will say, "Well, get along to your mother then." Sometimes a
boy, excited because today a bunch of them are to be admitted to
the garden for gooseberry picking, bolts out the door still chewing,
pokes his head back to choke out a strangled "Please, I'm done,"
and vanishes.

The waitresses lug the dishes back to the kitchen for the cooks to
wash, scrub up the tables and benches, dump clean white sand on
the floor and scour it around, sweep it up again. (Soap is too
precious to be wasted on floors.) An hour before lunch is ready,
they are through, and go out in a giggling, secretive group to pick
wild roses for lunch. If they put one rosebud under each place they
will need only about four hundred.

At twelve o'clock Thomas Robertson will stop work in his smithy
outside the stockade, reach down his cornet, and tootle a luncheon
hymn. The five women in the kitchen and their man helper, all of
them serving a week's kitchen police, will have three great boilers
on the brick furnaces, bubbling with food—three bushels of potatoes
in one, several bushels of hominy in another, gallons of water gravy
in another. The bread, baked every night by two male bakers in the

ovens built under the kitchen—three hundred pounds of flour a day mixed in a mighty wooden trencher—is stacked ready. And from everywhere, from fields and orchards and corrals and chicken coops and tannery and furniture shop and cooper shop and shoe factory and grist mill, the queues will come hurrying again.

At six Robertson will roll down his sleeves, take off his leather apron, close up his smithy and lift his cornet and blow, and at supper there will be another prayer and another hymn, probably "Come, Let Us Sing an Evening Hymn." The dining room will fill and empty for the sixth time, the last straggling child will snatch a crust and disappear. Then the dining hall will lie down behind its flagpole and sigh like a run dog and drop its head between its paws and sleep again until the five o'clock bugle, unless there is a dance that night, or an entertainment, or amateur theatricals.

Whatever he did in Arcadia, every member of the community had three times a day to sink himself in the common life of the village. The punctual and communal meals brought the town's life to a point; they enlarged and stabilized and tested and tempered the coöperative spirit of the Saints. No matter how much neighboring towns laughed at community dining, no matter how many stories they told of troughs which carried the refuse of the adults' meals down to the children, no matter how visitors raised their eyebrows and wondered how one could stand eating always in a boarding-house bedlam, the people of Orderville liked it, and they stuck to it until a flood ruined the bakery ovens in the basement, and even after that, in the dying years of the Order, many of them yearned for the good old days when private life was reduced to a minimum and public life expanded to fit the principles of Saints who were brothers in fact as well as in faith.

Orderville was more than a hundred miles from a railroad then. The terminal of the Denver and Rio Grande Western branch line— called the "Wooden Shoe Line" sometimes because of the Scandinavian peasants working their fields in sabots—was at Marysvale. But it was not mere isolation from the world that let the communal village thrive where so many similar experiments in towns only a few miles away failed miserably. For one thing, you couldn't hold anything back on the Orderville brethren, consecrate part of your property and save out a nest egg. If you went in, you went in whole hog. For the sum of one dollar and other good and valuable considerations you signed over your entire wealth, even to pots and pans, to the Board of Directors as Trustee-in-Trust, and you got back shares in the company plus a flat wage and credit at the Order store. You were expected not to overdraw your wages, but if you had to you could. You were also expected to produce a surplus, but if you didn't it was all right. At the end of the year all debts were canceled and all surpluses absorbed and everybody started fresh.

No one could say that another got more than himself, because skilled and unskilled labor were paid alike. There were no plutocrats and no charity cases, and for a long time no bad feelings of any consequence between members. When they founded their town they were earnest for coöperation—so earnest that most of them were *baptized* into it. A new member was carefully quizzed by the board. Did he believe that the Lord had advised him to join this coöperative life? Was his family in agreement with him? Did he train his family in the fear of the Lord? Did he practice kindness and piety in his family life? Did he have any debts? Did he swear or use profane language? Did he break the Word of Wisdom? Did he steal or fail to return things he borrowed? Did he tell dirty jokes? Did he abuse dumb animals? Could he keep his temper? Was he willing to work according to his strength and ability at whatever task the board should assign him? Would he promise to avoid all lying and backbiting and slandering of brothers and sisters?

If he did and was and avoided all those things, they welcomed him in, turned his property into the common pool, and gave him a job, for which he received credit of a dollar and a half a day. His wife was worth seventy-five cents, as were his boys from eleven to seventeen. Daughters were not much of an economic asset. Between ten and thirteen they drew twenty-five cents, and under ten half that much. No money, of course, ever changed hands. There was no money to change. Credits and debits went down in the company's books. Board for adults cost about fifty dollars a year, with children's meals at half or three-quarters of that amount. A man's clothing was debited at $17.50, a woman's at $16.50 annually. If at the end of the year a member's accumulated wages exceeded his spending, he signed a waiver and gave the surplus back to the common fund. And the oddest thing of all—for years not a single wife in Orderville, apparently, ever rose to say witty and acid words about the annual adornment budget!

A good many of the women of Orderville were plural wives (Bishop Chamberlain, for instance, had five), but there seems to have been hardly a trace of the female bitterness that marred the domestic arrangements of good Saints in other quarters. Sometimes, in order to obey counsel and marry a second wife, a man would have to build another house, or establish part-time residence in another town, because he didn't care to bring a second wife into the same house or the same village with the first. But in Orderville people lived higgledy-piggledy in the uniform frame shanties and the net result of polygamy at close quarters seemed to be merely a wider and more varied circle of acquaintance for each woman.

The structure of the town was even stricter than that of the City of Zion, just as the town life carried to such extremes the most idealistic Mormon perfectionism that the Orderville brethren were almost aliens in the midst of the surrounding Mormon society. In Orderville, and in some of the less successful United Order villages like Kingston, Allen's Camp, Sunset Crossing, and Bunkerville, the Mormons approached closest to the community life of the Pueblos. They were peaceable, domesticated, virtually self-sufficient.

It is difficult to find anything that the Orderville brethren were compelled to buy, aside from arms, ammunition, and a minimum of machinery. In the town itself, or on the farms and ranches the Order acquired in the canyons, out on the Arizona desert, and down in the semi-tropical lower valley of the Virgin, practically every necessity was grown or manufactured. The orchard and vegetable garden, just outside the square, produced peaches, apricots, grapes, currants, gooseberries, garden truck, watermelons. From the hillsides came timber and firewood, and up the valley a few miles was a coal mine. Down near Washington, on the "Cotton Farm," they grew cotton that was ultimately processed in their own mill. At Moccasin Springs, between the Vermilion Cliffs and the Grand Canyon, there were great fields of sugar cane and the simple machinery and vats for making molasses. Sugar they could not manage, but what they could not manage they did without. Molasses, poured over crumbed-up bread, satisfied the sweet tooth of the children. Candy could be made from the green skimmings of the cane. Peaches and other fruit could be boiled down in molasses for preserves.

At various farms the brethren raised wheat, corn, and oats for their needs. Up the side canyons from the town there was good grazing for the beef and dairy herds, and as the flocks grew they traded a rifle and ammunition to a Shivwits chief for perpetual grazing privileges on Buckskin Mountain (the Kaibab Plateau). By 1881 they were paying taxes—and tithes—on five thousand head of sheep. They were making their own clip, carding and spinning, weaving their own cloth in their own mill. Women in the tailor shop made clothes for the community; other women braided wheat straw for the characteristic floppy hats. Men stripped bark from the scrub oak and stacked it for the tannery where all the town's leather was made. The shoemaker's shop was busy the year around making rough un-lined cowhide shoes, harnesses, saddles. There were dyeing vats for the coloring of cotton and wool cloth with home-made dyes like madder, indigo, kinnikinnick, logwood powder, grease-wood. A crew of soapmakers burned cottonwood logs for ashes, leached the ashes with water, added grease or ooze plant to make the harsh soap that all washed with.

They were an ingenious and industrious crowd. The furniture shop made chairs, tables, bedsteads, bureaus, for all the shanties in the village. (Some of those pieces are hunted by antique collectors now.) They had gristmills and sawmills, and in Brother Carling, who possessed a lathe, they had a combination Santa Claus, lapidary, and resident artist. Just before Christmas Brother Carling devoted his days to turning toys, dolls' heads, gadgets, while women sat in his shop and stuffed bodies for the wooden or plaster-of-Paris heads he made. At odd times during the year Brother Carling could be induced to melt down the infrequent dimes that came into the clutches of girls, and make rings out of them. He ran a night school and taught the rudiments of drawing and painting. It is pleasant to speculate on what the work of Brother Carling might have developed into if Orderville had gone on for let us say a century, untouched and unhindered by the world outside. Like everything else in Arcadia, art and the love of beauty were rudimentary and simple, but they were present. Witness the rosebuds under the dinner plates.

Orderville never had a luxurious existence, and it never quite attained a whole-hearted peace with neighboring towns. It was too successful; the pressure from outside was growing; the isolation that surrounded it was not proof either against ideas or against federal officers looking for "cohabs." Self-sufficiency was an ideal which at first was almost realizable, but the fact remained that Orderville existed under the laws of the United States, and in the midst of a society increasingly imitative of the world outside.

Other Mormons did not cheer when the Orderville brethren picked off the best grazing land by locating springs and water-pockets. They did not cheer when they noticed that by pooling labor and capital the Orderville people produced more and produced it more cheaply than an individual could. They did not refrain from laughing a little contemptuously at the sternly simple regimen of Arcadia, at the straw hats and the homespun and the cowhide boots. Like the Amish, like the colonists at Amana or Homestead in Iowa, like the Dukhobors and the Mennonites, the Ordervillians were clannish, not only because they had cultivated the group spirit to a point where it had no place for outsiders, but because they felt the ridicule that the outsiders heaped upon them. To a certain extent, the United Order of Orderville, by creating a self-sufficient microcosmic society in the midst of the Mormon macrocosm, put itself in exactly the same position that the whole Mormon Church occupied with respect to the United States. There was no persecution, no violence, but there was some bad feeling and a good deal of ridicule.

What killed Orderville? Was it the pressure from outside or weakness within? Could it have survived if its isolation had been more complete, or would it have broken down of itself?

It is difficult to answer these questions. Certainly there was one weakness in the structure of Orderville, and one which in combination with outside difficulties helped to break the village up. The founders of the village had forgotten one thing; they had made no provision for young men growing up in the Order. They had no property to consecrate, and as a result they held no shares in the Order and could expect nothing but the opportunity of working for a dollar and a half a day payable in food and shelter. And while they went on working for a subsistence, the boys from St. George and Washington and Kanab and Leeds and Harmony worked as teamsters for the silver mines at Pioche or Silver Reef and got paid in solid shining money twice as much as the Orderville boys got in credit. Young men of Arcadia looked resentfully upon the swaggering youths from other towns, and in their hearts envied them. The smart alecs wore store clothes, Stetson hats, silk handkerchiefs, riding boots.

In addition to that complaint, which the board might possibly have been able to adjust without the loss of more than a few of the young men, there arose difficulty over those who consistently overdrew their credit. The industrious began jawing the slothful. Skilled workers, looking around the country which was then in the midst of a boom from the Pioche and Silver Reef mines, discovered that in most places skilled labor was worth twice as much as common labor. They proposed that the wages be adjusted; the board wrote to the Church authorities asking advice, and the authorities advised them to adjust the wages. Immediately there was a counter-complaint. Some were getting more than others. The fine equality of the original community was gone, and it would never come back.

Orderville might have weathered its difficulties but for three things, none of them blamable upon the board. One was the opening of the silver mines and the sudden flow of easy money in the surrounding towns. Another was the error of the hierarchy in advising the adjustment of wages for skilled labor, an error that admitted the growing profit-motive in all Church affairs. The third was the polygamy prosecutions under the Edmunds-Tucker Act, and the coming of deputy marshals snooping for "polygs" and "cohabs." The men with plural wives, who were in effect the natural leaders of the town, fled to the underground. Wives lived as widows; second, third, and fourth wives stripped off their wedding rings (the absence of a ring ceremony in the Mormon wedding service harks back to that period of the persecution) and stayed out of sight as much as possible. There was little chance for the leaders to work out any solution for the inheritances of young men or the knotty question of wages. Orderville was caught in the larger war that Mormonism was waging with the United States, was actually a martyr to it.

By 1885 it was clear that the old perfect society was gone. The farm lands were sold off to the members at auction, only the livestock, the tannery, and the factory being held back as capital stock in the company. As late as 1889 the company paid dividends, and it was financially independent to the very end.

But the bond that had held it together, the capacity for abnegation and social living, was gone from the time the outside world began to crowd the valley; from the time when Orderville youths first noticed consciously that the Kanab punks wore fancy cowpuncher clothes, and that the St. George smart alecs had money to jingle in their store pants; from the time when the first Orderville girl saw out of the corner of her eye the brilliance of the silk neckerchief around the outsider's throat, and let her eye stray to the clumping and sullen clumsiness of her Arcadian swain; from the time when the annual allowance of $16.50 for clothes began to rankle in the bosoms of Orderville's fair.

One of the most important things that Orderville forgot, one of the things it would have had to settle if it had hoped to survive after the polygamy persecutions died down, one of the things it might have known from the beginning, was that the perfect society may starve, may freeze, may be changed and outlawed, may do almost any number of things almost permanently; but only for a very short time, during the very height of its initial enthusiasm, may it dispense with ornament. Brigham Young should have known that, but he never learned. He was always grousing about the fancies of his harem and fulminating from the pulpit against giddy fashions. He kept up that tirade for more than thirty years, but the fact is there as recalcitrant as a stone in a shoe: Fashion, as much as anything else, killed Arcadia.

Mammon's round.

GUNSIGHT TRAIL: GLACIER PARK

More than I the winds that pass
Have brushed the bloom from grass,
Carrying the Bear Bloom, sorrel
Past bars of stars; the coral
Moon drives headily in blacks
Upon sky-fastness tracks
Not as steep as Gunsight Trail
That prickly pines impale.
Over roller-coaster boulders
I interrupt my shoulders,
With a taste of Bear Bloom, sorrel
Beneath a moon immoral
Light, the whitened sprays of Lake
St. Mary leap and break.
I—not as moonshine gale,
Or beams of starlight hail,
Arrogance of pungent scent
On Bear Bloom Battlement—
Run the course my bronco leads
Where moonmist silver bleeds;
But I know what they don't see:
A desert south of me,
And beyond these middle heights
I sense the Northern Lights.

By Walter Van Tilburg Clark

A WESTERN INCIDENT

WINDER and his outfit started off, working single file into the woods. In a moment you couldn't tell which was riders and which trees. The snow blurred everything, and blotted up sound too, into a thick, velvety quiet. Ma Grier and Bartlett led off at an angle toward the valley. They were heading for the shallows of the creek, where there weren't any banks but an easy incline, a cross gully worn by sheep and cattle going down to drink. I'd seen deer drinking there too, but only in the early spring, and then warily. It would take time to find that crossing in this kind of a night.

Gil came alongside me.

"How you feeling now, fellow?" he asked.

"Good," I said.

"Take care of yourself," he said. "This still don't have to be our picnic."

"It looks like it was," I said.

"Yeah," he agreed, "but it ain't."

He went away from me, stepping his pinto a little long to catch up with his gang.

The rest of us, in Tetley's outfit, didn't talk much. There was nothing to do but wait, and none of the arguing ones were left with us. Only Mapes tried a little of his cottoning-up, he-man talk on Tetley, but since Tetley didn't want to talk, that stopped too. We weren't a friendly gang anyway; no real friends in the lot. Tet-

100

ley, I thought, was short with Mapes because he was trying to count in his mind, or some such system, to keep track of the time. Through the trees we watched the fire out by the cabin. Once it began to die down, and then a shadow went across it, and back across, and the fire darkened and flattened completely. At first we thought they had wind of us, but the fire gradually grew up again, brighter than ever. It was just somebody throwing more wood on.

The snowing relaxed for a spell, then started again with a fresh wind that whirled it around us for a minute or two, even in the woods, and veiled the fire, probably with snow scudding up from the open meadow. Then the wind died off and the snow was steady and slanting again, but thinner. It didn't feel any longer as if it might be a real blizzard. The branches rattled around us when the wind blew. Being in the marshy end of the valley they weren't pines, but aspens, and willow grown up as big as trees. When the horses stirred, the ground squelched under them, and you could see the dark shadow of water soaking up around their hoofs through the snow. In places, though, the slush was already getting icy, and split when it was stepped on.

Several times we heard the steers sounding off again, hollow in the wind, and sounding more distant than they could have been.

After a time Tetley led us out to the edge of the aspens to where the wind was directly on us again. We waited there, peering into the snow blowing in the valley, and the dark gulf of the valley itself, but unable to see the other riders, of course, or anything but the fire. It felt to me as if it must be one o'clock at least, but I learned early that I couldn't tell within four hours on a cloudy night unless I was doing some work I did every night, like riding herd in the same valley.

Finally Tetley said, as if he had been holding a watch before him all the time, and had predetermined the exact moment to start, "All right, let's go."

As we started Mapes asked, "Want us to spread out now?"

"No, we'll ride in on them in a bunch, unless they get wind of us. If the fire goes out, or there's any shooting, then spread and work toward the fire. In that case, you on the wings, don't tangle with Mrs. Grier or Winder."

So we went out in a group, plowing a wide track through the half-frozen sponginess. Tetley and Farnley and Mapes rode abreast ahead. They didn't any of them want another to get there ahead of him. Young Tetley and I came behind them, and there were two other riders following us. We all watched toward the fire steadily.

But even when we came much closer there was nothing to see but the fire, beginning to die again, and the little its light revealed of the cabin wall and the trunks of the closest pines on the other side. I got to wondering if they had built the fire up as a blind and had already run out on us, or even were lying up somewhere ready to pick us off. My head came clear again and I didn't even notice my shoulder. Only the snow annoyed me, though it was falling light and far-spaced now. It made me feel that my eyes were no good. The four of us in back kept watching out to the sides, feeling that we didn't have our side of the square covered, but the three in front continued abreast, seeming to watch only the fire and the clearing right around it, though I could tell by the way they sat there they were as wide awake as we were.

When we began to climb the little rise the cabin was on, I could see the three silhouetted clearly against the fire. Mapes reached under his armpit and got a gun out into his hand. Farnley's carbine moved across his saddle, and I thought I heard the hammer click. Tetley, though, just rode right ahead.

I reached my gun out too. There was a twinge in the injured shoulder when I raised the right one, and I didn't want to have to make a fast draw and get sick and dizzy as I had riding down the pitch. My head was clear, all right; I thought of every little thing like that. And my senses were up keen too. Without even looking around I could tell how the men behind me were getting set. I was excited, and peculiarly happy. It seemed to me that if the rustlers were concealed I could pick the trees they'd gone behind. Only young Tetley was wrong. I risked a look, and we were so close to the fire I could see his face. He was staring ahead, but blindly, and he wasn't getting any gun out. Now I can see that he was perhaps still having a struggle with himself that he was here at all, but then it just angered me that one of us failed to be alert; then it just seemed to me that he was too scared to know what to do, and I got furious at him for a moment, the way you will when you think another man's carelessness is risking your neck. I pulled over and jogged him, though jogging him wrenched my shoulder so my breath whistled. He turned his head and looked at me, and I could see he wasn't blanked out. He was awake, all right, but he still didn't look any better.

We were really into the edge of the firelight before Tetley stopped us. I had my mind made up they were laying for us, so what I saw surprised me. Between Tetley and Mapes I could see a man asleep on the ground in a blanket with a big pattern on it. His head was on his saddle and toward the fire, so his face was in the shadow, but when we looked at him he drew an arm up out of his blanket and laid it across his eyes. He had on an orange shirt and the hand and wrist lifted into the light were as dark as an old saddle. Not Indian, either; at least not thick and stubby like the hands of Washoes and Piutes I'd seen, but long and narrow and with prominent knuckles. We were so close that I could see on his middle finger a heavy silver ring with an egg-shaped turquoise, a big one, in it; a Navajo ring. By the bulk of him he was a big man, and heavy.

There were two other men asleep also, one with his side to the fire and his head away from me, the other on the far side with his feet to the fire. I couldn't make out anything but their shapes and that they had dark bluish-gray blankets with a black stripe near each end, the kind of blankets the Union had used during the rebellion.

I guess Tetley figured as I did, that they were strangers, at least, if nothing else, because he only waited long enough to be sure they were not playing possum, and then rode into the light, and right up to the feet of the man with the ring. We followed him, spreading around the edge of the fire as he motioned us to. After looking down at the man for a moment he said sharply and loudly, "Get up."

The other two stirred in their blankets, and began to settle again, but the man with the ring woke immediately and completely, and when he saw us said something short to himself and twisted up out of his blanket in one continuous, smooth movement, trailing one hand into the blanket as he came up.

"Drop it," Farnley ordered. He was holding the carbine at his thigh, the muzzle pointing at the man. The man had heavy black hair and a small black mustache. He looked like a Mex, though his hair was done up in a club at his neck, like an Indian's, and his face was wide, with high flat cheeks. He looked to me like a Mex playing Navajo.

He looked quickly but not nervously around at all of us, sizing us up, but didn't move the hand which had come up behind him.

"I said drop it," Farnley told him again, and nudged the carbine out toward him, so he wouldn't make any mistake about what was meant.

The Mex suddenly smiled, as if he had just understood, and dropped a long-barreled, nickel-plated revolver behind him onto the blanket. He was an old hand, and still thinking.

"Now put 'em up," Farnley told him.

The smile died off the Mex's face, and he just stared at Farnley and shrugged his shoulders.

"Put 'em up; reach, you bastard."

The Mex shrugged his shoulders again. "No sabbey," he said.

Farnley grinned now. "No?" he asked. "I said reach," he repeated, and jerked the muzzle of the carbine upward two or three times. The Mex got that, and put his hands up slowly. He was studying Farnley's face all the time.

"That's better," Farnley said, still grinning, "though some ways I'd just as soon you hadn't, you son-of-a-bitch." He was talking as quietly as Tetley usually did, though not so easily. He seemed to be enjoying calling the man a name he couldn't understand, and doing it in a voice like he was making an ordinary remark.

"No sabbey," the Mex said again.

"That's all right, brother," Farnley told him, "you will."

The other two were coming out of their sleep. I was covering the one on the cabin side, and Mapes the other. Mapes' man just sat up, still in his blanket. He was still fumed with sleep; a thick, wide-faced old-timer with long, tangled gray hair and a long, droopy gray mustache. He had eyebrows so thick they made peaked shadows on his forehead. The way he was staring now he didn't appear to be all there.

My man rose quickly enough, though tangling a little with his blanket. He started to come toward us, and I saw he'd been sleeping with his gun on and his boots off.

"Take it easy, friend," I told him. "Stay where you are and put your hands up."

He didn't understand, but stared at me, and then at Tetley, and then back at me. He didn't reach for his gun, didn't even twitch for it, and his face looked scared.

"Put your hands up," I told him again. He did, looking as if he wanted to cry.

"And keep them there."

The old man was out of his blanket now too, and standing with his hands raised.

"Gerald, collect their guns," Tetley said.

"What are you trying to do? What do you want? We haven't got anything." It was my man babbling, half out of breath. He was a tall, thin, dark young fellow, with thick black hair, but no Indian or Mex.

"Shut up," Mapes instructed him. "We'll tell you when we want you to talk."

"This is no stickup, brother," I explained to him. "This is a posse, if that means anything to you."

"But we haven't done anything," he protested. "What have we done?" He wasn't over his first fright yet.

"Shut up," Mapes said, with more emphasis.

Young Tetley was sitting in his saddle, staring at the three men.

"Gerry," Tetley said, in that pistol-shot voice he'd used to wake the men.

The boy dismounted dreamily and picked up the Mex's gun from the blanket. Then, like a sleepwalker, he came over to my man.

"Behind him," said Tetley sharply.

The boy stopped and looked around. "What?" he asked.

"Wake up," Tetley ordered. "I said go behind him. Don't get between him and Croft."

"Yes," Gerald said, and did what he was told. He fumbled around a long time before he found the old man's gun, which was under his saddle.

"Give the guns to Mark," Tetley ordered, jerking his head at one of the two riders I didn't know. Gerald did that, handing them up in a bunch, belts, holsters and all.

It made me ashamed the way Tetley was bossing the kid's every move, like a mother making a three-year-old do something over that he'd messed up the first try.

"Now," he said, "go over them all, from the rear. Then shake out the blankets."

Gerald did as he was told, but he seemed to be waking a little now. His jaw was tight. He found another gun on the Mex, a little pistol like the gamblers carry. It was in an arm-sling under his vest. There was a carbine under the young fellow's blanket. He shrank from patting the men over, the way he was told to, and when he passed me to give Mark the carbine and pistol, I could hear him breathing hard.

Tetley watched Gerald, but spoke to my prisoner while he was working.

"Are there any more of you?"

The young fellow was steadier. He looked angry now, and started to let his arms down, asking, "May I inquire what business . . ."

"Shut up," Mapes said, "and keep them up."

"It's all right now, Mapes," Tetley said. "You can put your hands down now," he said to the young man. "I asked you, are there any others with you?"

"No," the kid said.

I didn't think the kid was lying. Tetley looked at him hard, but I guess he thought it was all right too. He turned his head toward Mark and the other rider I didn't know.

"Tie their hands," he ordered.

The young fellow started to come forward again.

"Stay where you are," Tetley told him quietly, and he stopped. He had a wide, thick-lipped mouth that was nonetheless as sensitive as young Tetley's thin one, and now it was tight down in the corners. Even so you would have said that mouth was beautiful on some women, Rose Mapen for instance, the fiery or promising kind. And his eyes were big and dark in his thin face, like a girl's too. His hands were long and bony and nervous, but hung on big, square wrists.

He spoke in a husky voice. "I trust that at least you'll condescend to tell us what we're being held for."

Mapes was still busy being an authority. "Save your talk till it's asked for," he advised.

Tetley, though, studied the young man all during the time the two punchers were tying the prisoners on one lasso rope and pushing them over to the side of the fire away from the cabin. He looked at them still when they were standing there shoulder to shoulder, the Mex in the middle, their faces to the fire and their backs to the woods and the little snow that was still falling. It was as if he believed he could solve the whole question of their guilt or innocence by just looking at them and thinking his own thoughts; the occupation pleased him. The Mex was stolid now, the old man remained blank, but the kid was humiliated and angry at being tied. He repeated his question in a manner that didn't go well with the spot he was in.

Then Tetley told him, "I'd rather you told us," and smiled that way.

After that he signaled to the parties in the dark in the woods and behind the cabin, dismounted, giving the bridle to his son, and walked over to the fire, where he stood with his legs apart and held out his hands to warm them, rubbing them together. He might have been in front of his own fireplace. Without looking around he ordered more wood put on the fire. All the time he continued to look across the fire at the three men in a row, and continued to smile.

We were all on foot now, walking stiff-legged from sitting the saddle so long in the cold. I got myself a place to sit near the fire, and watched the Mex. He had his chin down on his chest, like he was both guilty and licked, but he was watching everything from under his eyebrows. He looked smart and hard. I'd have guessed he was about thirty, though it was hard to tell, the way it is with an Indian. The lines around his mouth and at the corners of his eyes and across his forehead were deep and exact, as if they were cut in dark wood with a knife. His skin shone in the firelight. There was no expression on his face, but I knew he was still thinking how to get out. Then all at once his face changed, though you couldn't have said what the change was in any part of it. I guess in spite of his watchfulness he'd missed Tetley's signal, and now he saw Ma and her gang coming up behind us. He looked around quickly, and when he saw the other gangs coming in too he turned back and stared at the ground in front of him. He was changed all over then, the fire gone out of him; he was empty, all done.

The old man stood and stared, as he had from his first awakening. He didn't seem to have an idea, or even a distinct emotion, merely a vague dread. He'd look at one of us and then another with the same expression, pop-eyed and stupid, his mouth never quite closed, and the gray stubble sticking out all over his jaws.

When the young fellow saw the crowd he said to Tetley, "It appears we're either important personages or very dangerous. What is this, a vigilance committee?" He shivered before he spoke though. I thought the Mex elbowed him gently.

Tetley kept looking at him and smiling, but didn't reply. It was hard on their nerve. Ma Grier had ridden up right behind us, and said, before she got down, "No, it ain't that you're so difficult, son. It's just that most of the boys has never seen a real triple hangin'."

There wasn't much laughter.

Everybody was in now except the Bartlett boys. Some stayed on their horses, not expecting the business to take much time, and maybe just as glad there were others willing to be more active. Some dismounted and came over to the fire with coils of rope; there was enough rope to hang twenty men with a liberal allowance to each.

As if it had taken all that time for the idea to get through, the young fellow said, "Hanging?"

"That's right," Farnley said.

"But why?" asked the kid, beginning to chatter. "What have we done? We haven't done anything. I told you already we haven't done anything."

Then he got hold of himself and said to Tetley, more slowly, "Aren't you even going to tell us what we're accused of?"

"Of course," Tetley said. "This isn't a mob. We'll make sure first." He half turned his head toward Mapes. "Sheriff," he said, "tell him."

"Rustling," said Mapes.

"Rustling?" the kid echoed.

"Yup. Ever heard of it?"

"And murder," said Farnley, "maybe he'll have heard of that."

"Murder?" the kid repeated foolishly. I thought he was going to fold, but he didn't. He took a brace and just ran his tongue back and forth along his lips a couple of times, as if his throat and mouth were all dried out. He looked around, and it wasn't encouraging. There was a solid ring of faces, and they were serious.

The old man made a long, low moan like a dog that's going to howl but changes its mind. Then he said, his voice trembling badly, "You wouldn't kill us. No, no, you wouldn't do that, would you?"

Nobody replied. The old man's speech was thick, and he spoke very slowly, as if the words were heavy, and he was considering them with great concentration. They didn't mean anything, but you couldn't get them out of your head when he'd said them. He looked at us so I thought he was going to cry. "Mr. Martin," he said, "what do we do?" He was begging, and seemed to believe he would get a real answer.

The young man tried to make his voice cheerful, but it was hollow. "It's all right, Dad. There's some mistake."

"No mistake, I guess." It was old Bartlett speaking. He was standing beside Tetley, looking at the Mex and idly dusting the snow off his flat sombrero. The wind was blowing his wispy hair up like smoke. When he spoke the Mex looked up for a second. He looked down again quickly, but Bartlett grinned. He had a good many teeth out, and his grin wasn't pretty.

"Know me, eh?" he asked the Mex. The Mex didn't answer. Farnley stepped up to him and slapped him across the belly with the back of his hand.

"He's talking to you, Mister," he said.

The Mex looked wonderfully bewildered. "No sabbey," he repeated.

"He don't speak English," Mapes told Bartlett.

"I got a different notion," Bartlett said.

"I'll make him talk," Farnley offered. He was eager for it; he was so eager for it he disgusted me, and made me feel sorry for the Mex.

The young fellow appeared bewildered. He was looking at them and listening, but he didn't seem to make anything of it. He kept closing his eyes more tightly than was natural, and then opening them again quickly, as if he expected to find the whole scene changed. Even without being in the spot he was in, I could understand how he felt. It didn't look real to me either, the firelight on all the red faces watching in a leaning ring, and the big, long heads of horses peering from behind, and up in the air, detached from it, the quiet men still sitting in the saddles.

When Farnley started to prod the Mex again, Tetley said sharply, "That will do, Farnley."

"Listen, you," Farnley said turning on him, "I've had enough of your playing God Almighty. Who in hell picked you for this job anyway? Next thing you'll be kissing them, or taking them back for Tyler to reform them. We've got the bastards; well, what are we waiting for? Let them swing, I say."

Smith put in his bit too. "Are you going to freeze us to death, Tetley, waiting for these guys to admit they shot a man and stole a bunch of cattle? Maybe you know somebody who'd like to talk his head into a noose."

"There's the fire. Warm yourself," Tetley told him. "And you," he said, looking at Farnley, "control yourself, and we'll get along better."

Farnley's face blanched and stiffened, as it had in the saloon, when he'd heard the news about Kinkaid. I thought he was going to jump Tetley, but Tetley didn't even look at him again. He leaned the other way to listen to something Bartlett was saying privately. When he had heard it he nodded and looked at the young fellow across the fire.

"Who's boss of this outfit?" he asked.

"I am," the young fellow said.

"And your name's Martin?"

"Donald Martin."

"What outfit?"

"My own."

"Where from?"

"Pike's Hole."

The men didn't believe it. The man Tetley called Mark said, "He's not from Pike's, or any place in the Hole, I'll swear to that."

For the first time there was real antagonism instead of just doubt and waiting.

"Mark there lives in Pike's," Tetley told the kid, smiling. "Want to change your story?"

"I just moved in three days ago," the kid said.

"We're wasting time, Willard," Bartlett said.

"We'll get there," Tetley said. "I want this kept regular for the Judge."

Not many appreciated his joking. He was too slow and pleasurable for a job like this. Most of us would have had to do it in a hurry. If you have to hang a man, you have to, but it's not my kind of fun to stand around and watch him keep hoping he may get out of it.

Tetley may have noticed the silence, but he didn't show it. He went on asking Martin questions.

"Where did you come from before that?"

"Ohio," he said angrily, "Sinking Spring, Ohio. But not just before. I was in Los Angeles. I suppose that proves something."

"What way did you come up?"

"By Mono Lake. Look, Mister, this isn't getting us anywhere, is it? We're accused of murder and rustling, you say. Well, we haven't done any rustling, and we haven't killed anybody. You've got the wrong men."

"We'll decide as to that. And I'm asking the questions."

"God," the kid broke out. He stared around wildly at the whole bunch of us. "God, don't anybody here know I came into Pike's Hole? I drove right through the town; I drove a Conestoga wagon with six horses right through the middle of the town. I'm on Phil

Baker's place; what they call the Phil Baker place, up at the north end."

Tetley turned to Mark.

"Phil Baker moved out four years ago," Mark said. "The place is a wreck, barns down, sagebrush sticking up through the porch."

Tetley looked back at Martin.

"I met him in Los Angeles," Martin explained. "I bought the place from him there. I paid him four thousand dollars for it."

"Mister, you got robbed," Mark told him. "Even if Baker'd owned the place you'da been robbed, but he didn't. He didn't even stay on it long enough to have squatter's rights." We couldn't help grinning at that one. Mark said to Tetley, "Baker's place is part of Peter Wilde's ranch now."

Martin was nearly crying. "You can't hang me for being a sucker," he said.

"That depends on the kind of sucker you are."

"You haven't got any proof. Just because Baker robbed me, doesn't make me a murderer. You can't hang me without any proof."

"We're getting it," Tetley said.

"Is it so far to Pike's that you can't go over there and look?" Martin cried. "Maybe I don't even own the Baker place; maybe I've been sold out. But I'm living there now. My wife's there now; my wife and two kids."

"Now that's really too bad," Smith said, clucking his tongue in a sound of old-maid sympathy. "That's just too, too bad."

The kid didn't look at him, but his jaw tightened and his eyes were hot. "This is murder, as you're going at it," he told Tetley. "Even in this God-forsaken country I've got a right to be brought to trial, and you know it. I have, and these men have. We have a right to trial before a regular judge."

"You're getting the trial," Tetley said, "with twenty-eight of the only kind of judges a murderer and a rustler get in what you call this God-forsaken country."

"And so far," Winder put in, "the jury don't much like your story."

The kid looked around slowly at as many of us as he could see, the way he was tied. It was as if he hadn't noticed before that we were there, and wanted to see what we were like. He must have judged Winder was right.

"I won't talk further without a proper hearing," he said slowly.

"Suit yourself, son," Ma said. "This is all the hearing you're likely to get short of the last judgment."

"Have you any cattle up here with you?" Tetley asked.

The kid looked around at us again. He was breathing hard. One of the men from Bartlett's gang couldn't help grinning a little. The kid started to say something, then shut his mouth hard. We all waited, Tetley holding up a hand when the man who had grinned started to speak. Then he asked the question again in the same quiet way.

The kid looked down at the ground finally, but remained silent.

"I'm not going to ask you again," Tetley said. Smith stepped out with a rope in his hands. He was making a hangman's noose, with half a dozen turns to it. The place was so quiet the tiny crackling of the burned-down wood sounded loud. Martin looked at the rope, sucked in his breath, and looked down again.

After a moment he said, so low we could hardly hear him, "Yes, I have."

"How many?"

"Fifty head."

"You miscounted, Amigo," Tetley remarked. Amigo grinned and spread his hands, palms up, and shrugged his shoulders.

"Where did you get them, Mr. Martin?"

"From Harley Drew, in Bridger's Valley."

When he looked up, there were tears in his eyes. Most of the watchers looked down at their boots for a moment, some of them making wry faces.

"I'm no rustler, though. I didn't steal them, I bought them and paid for them." Then suddenly he wanted to talk a lot. "I bought them this morning; paid cash for them. My own were so bad I didn't dare try to risk bringing them up. I didn't know what the Mono Lake country was like. I sold them off in Salinas. I have to stock up again."

He could see nobody believed him.

"You can wait, can't you?" he pleaded. "I'm not likely to escape from an army like this, am I? You can wait till you see Drew, till you ask about me in Pike's. It's not too much to ask a wait like that, is it, before you hang men?"

Everybody was still just looking at him or at the ground.

"My God," he yelled out suddenly, "you aren't going to hang innocent men without a shred of proof, are you?"

Tetley shook his head very slightly.

"Then why don't you take us in, and stop this damned farce?"

"It would be a waste of time," Farnley said. "The law is almighty slow and careless around here."

The kid appeared to be trying to think fast now.

"Where do you come from?" he asked.

"Bridger's Valley," Farnley told him. There were grins again.

Martin said to Tetley, "You know Drew then?"

"I know him," Tetley said. You wouldn't have gathered it was a pleasure from the way he spoke.

"Well, didn't you even see him? Who sent you up here?"

"Drew," Tetley said.

"That's not true," Davies said. He came out from the ring and closer to the fire. He looked odd among the riders, little and hunched in an old, loose jacket and bareheaded.

"Don't let him get started again," Smith said in a disgusted voice. "It's one o'clock now."

Davies didn't pay any attention to him. "That statement is not true," he repeated. "Drew didn't send us up here. Drew didn't even know we were coming."

Tetley was watching him closely. There was only a remnant of his smile.

"As I've told you a hundred times," Davies told us all, "I'm not trying to obstruct justice. But I do want to see real justice. This is a farce; this is, as Mr. Martin has said, murder if you carry it through. He's perfectly within his rights when he demands trial. And that's all I've asked since we started, that's all I'm asking now, a trial." He sounded truculent, for him, and was breathing heavily as he spoke. "This young man," he said pointing to Martin and looking around at us, "has said repeatedly that he is innocent. I, for one, believe him."

"Then I guess you're the only one that does, Arthur," Ma told him quietly.

Tetley made a sign to Mapes with his hand. Mapes stepped out and took Davies by the arm and began to shove him back toward the ring of watchers. Davies did not struggle much; even the little he did looked silly in Mapes' big hands. But while he went he called out angrily, "If there's any justice in your proceedings, Tetley, it would be only with the greatest certainty, it would be only after a confession. And they haven't confessed, Tetley. They say they're innocent, and you haven't proved they aren't."

"Keep him there," Mapes told the men around Davies after he'd been pushed back.

"Indirectly, Drew," Tetley said, as if Davies had not spoken.

"Now, if you're done," he went on, "I'd like to ask another question or two." Martin seemed to have taken some hope from Davies' outburst. Now he was looking down again. It was clear enough what most of the men thought.

"First, perhaps you have a bill of sale for those cattle?"

Martin swallowed hard. "No," he said finally. "No, I haven't."

"No?"

"Drew said it was all right. I couldn't find him at the ranch house. He was out on the range when I found him. He didn't have a bill of sale with him. He just said it was all right, not to wait, that he'd mail it to me. He told me it would be all right."

"Moore," Tetley said, without looking away from Martin.

"Yes?" Moore said. He didn't want to talk.

"You ride for Drew, don't you?"

"Yes, what of it?"

"How long have you been riding for Drew?"

"Six years," Moore said.

"Did you ever know Drew to sell any cattle without a bill of sale?"

"No, I can't say as I ever did. But I can't remember every head he's sold in six years."

"It's customary for Drew to give a bill of sale, though?"

"Yes."

"And Moore, did you ever know Drew to sell any cattle after spring roundup, this year, or any other year?"

"No," Moore admitted, "I don't know that he's ever done that."

"Was there any reason why he should make a change in his regular practice this spring?"

Moore shook his head slowly. Young Greene shouted from over in front of Davies, "I heard him myself, say, just a couple of days ago, that he wouldn't sell a head to God himself this spring."

"Well?" Tetley asked Martin.

"I know it looks bad," the kid said, in a slow, tired voice. He didn't expect to be believed any more. "I can't tell you anything else, I guess, except to ask Drew. It was hard to get them from him, all right. We talked a long time, and I had to show him how I was stuck, and how nobody wanted to sell this spring because there were so few calves. He really let me have them just as a favor, I think. That's all I have to tell you; I can't say anything else, I guess, not that would make any difference to you."

"No," Tetley agreed, "I don't believe you can."

"You don't believe me?"

"Would you, in my place?"

"I'd ask," Martin said more boldly. "I'd do a lot of asking before I'd risk hanging three men who might be innocent."

"If it were only rustling," Tetley said, "maybe. With murder, no. I'd rather risk a lot of hanging before too much asking. Law, as the books have it, is slow and full of holes."

In the silence the fire crackled, and hissed when the snow fell into it. The light of it flagged up and down on the men's serious faces, and turned to observe Tetley. The mouths were hard and the eyes bright and nervous. Finally Ma said mildly, "I guess it would be enough, even for Tyler, wouldn't it, Willard?"

"For Martin, perhaps," Tetley said.

"The others are his men, ain't they?" Farnley inquired.

Others quietly said it had been enough for them. Even Moore said, "It's no kindness to keep them waiting."

Still Tetley didn't say anything, and Ma burst out, "What you tryin' to do, play cat and mouse with them, Tetley? You act like you liked it."

"I would prefer a confession," Tetley said. He was talking to Martin, not to us.

Martin swallowed and wet his lips with his tongue, but couldn't speak. Besides Smith, Farnley and Winder were knotting ropes now. Finally Martin groaned something we couldn't understand, and abandoned his struggle with himself. The sweat broke out on his face and began to trickle down; his jaw was shaking. The old man was talking to himself, now and then shaking his head, as if pursuing an earnest and weighty debate. The Mex was standing firmly, with his feet a little apart, like a boxer anticipating his opponent's lunge or jab, saying nothing and showing nothing.

"We've had enough questions," Winder said. "They aren't talking."

Tetley said to Martin, "You called the old man Dad. Is he your father?"

"No," Martin said, and again added something too low to hear.

"Speak up, man," Tetley said sharply. "You're taking it like a woman."

"Everybody's gotta die once, son. Keep your chin up," Ma said. That was bare comfort for him, but I knew Ma wasn't thinking of him so much as of us. His weakness was making us feel as if we were mistreating a dog instead of trying a man.

The kid brought his head up and faced us, but that was worse. The tears were running down his cheeks and his mouth was working harder than ever.

"God Almighty, he's bawlin'," said Winder, and spit as if it made him sick.

"No," said Martin, thick and blubbery, but loudly. "He works for me."

"What's your name?" Tetley asked, turning to the old man. The old man didn't hear him; he continued to talk to himself. Mapes went and stood in front of him and said loudly in his face, "What's your name?"

"I didn't do it," argued the old man. "No, how could I have done it? You can see I didn't do it, can't you?" He paused, thinking how to make it clear. "I didn't have anything in my gun," he explained. "Mr. Martin won't let me have any bullets for my gun, so how could I do it? I wasn't afraid to, but I didn't have any bullets."

"You didn't do what?" Tetley asked him gently.

"No, I didn't, I tell you. I didn't." Then his wet wreck of a face seemed to light up with an idea. "He done it," he asserted. "He done it."

"Who did it?" said Tetley, still quietly, but slowly and distinctly.

"He did," burbled the old man, "Juan did. He told me so. No, he didn't; I saw him do it. If I saw him do it," he inquired cutely, "I know, don't I? I couldn't have done it if I saw him do it, could I?"

The Mex didn't stir. Farnley was watching the Mex, and even his hard grin was gone. He was holding his breath, and then breathing by snorts.

Martin spoke. "Juan couldn't have done anything. I was with him all the time."

"Yes, he did too do it, Mr. Martin. He was asleep; he didn't mean to tell me, but I was awake and I heard him talking about it. He told me when he was asleep."

"The old man is feeble-minded," Martin said, slowly and quietly, trying to speak so the old man wouldn't hear him. "He doesn't know what he's talking about. He's dreamt something." He looked down; either it hurt him to say this or he was doing a better job of acting than his condition made probable. "You can't trust anything he says. He dreams constantly; when he's awake he invents things. After a little while he really believes they have happened. He's a good old man; you've scared him and he's inventing things he thinks will save him."

Then he flared, "If you've got to go on with your filthy comedy you can let him alone, can't you?"

"You keep out of this," Mapes shouted, stepping quickly past the Mexican and standing in front of Martin. "You've had your say. Now shut up."

Martin stared down at him. "Then let the old man alone," he said.

Mapes suddenly struck him across the face so hard it would have knocked him over if he hadn't been tied to the others. As it was, one knee buckled under him, and he ducked his head down to shake off the sting or block another slap if it was coming.

"Lay off, Mapes," somebody shouted, and Moore said, "You've got no call for that sort of thing, Mapes."

"First he wouldn't talk, and now he talks too damned much," Mapes said, but let Martin alone.

We had closed the circle as much as the fire would let us. Tetley moved closer to Martin, and Mapes made room for him, though strutting because of the yelling at him.

"You mean actually feeble-minded?" Tetley asked.

"Yes."

"What's his name?"

"Alva Hardwick."

"And the other speaks no English?"

Martin didn't reply.

"What's his name?"

"Juan Martinez."

"No, it isn't," old Bartlett said.

Tetley turned and looked at old Bartlett. "You seem to know something about this man?" he asked.

"I've been trying to tell you ever since this fool questioning started," Bartlett told him, "but you've got to be so damned regular."

"All right, all right," Tetley said impatiently, "What is it?"

Bartlett suddenly became cautious. "I don't want to say until I'm sure," he said. He went up to the Mex.

"Remember me?" he asked. "At Driver's, last September?"

The Mex wouldn't know he was being talked to. Bartlett got angry; when he got angry his loose jowls trembled.

"I'm talking to you, greaser," he said.

The Mex looked at him, too quick and narrow for not understanding, but then all he did was shake his head and say, "No sabbey," again.

"The devil you don't," Bartlett told him. "Your name's Francisco Morez, and the vigilantes would still like to get hold of you."

The Mex wouldn't understand.

"He talks better English than I do," Bartlett told Tetley. "He was a gambler, and claimed to be a rancher from down Sonora way somewhere. They wanted him for murder."

"What about that?" Tetley asked Martin.

"I don't know," the kid said hopelessly.

"Does he speak English?"

The kid looked at the Mex and said, "Yes." The Mex didn't bat an eye.

"How long's he been with you?"

"He joined us in Carson." Martin looked up at Tetley again. "I don't know anything about him," he said. "He told me that he was a rider, and that he knew this country, and that he'd like to tie up with me. That's all I know."

"They stick together nice, don't they?" Smith said.

"You picked him up on nothing more than that?" Tetley asked Martin.

"Why don't you come to the point?" Martin asked. "Why ask me all these questions if you don't believe anything I tell you?"

"There's as much truth to be sifted out of lies as anything else," Tetley said, "if you get enough lies. Is his name Morez?" he went on.

"I tell you I don't know. He told me his name was Martinez. That's all I know."

Tetley sent two riders to help the Bartlett boys shag in the cattle they'd been holding. At the edge of the clearing, seeing the fire, and the men and horses, and being wild with this unusual night hazing anyway, they milled. But they didn't have to come any closer. As they turned, with the firelight on them enough, we could see Drew's brand and his notches.

"Anything you haven't said that you want to say?" Tetley asked Martin.

Martin drew a deep breath to steady himself. He could feel the set against him that one look at those cattle had brought on if all the talk hadn't.

"I've told you how I got them," he said.

"We heard that," Tetley agreed.

"You have the steers, haven't you?" Martin asked. He was short of breath. "Well, you haven't lost anything then, have you? You could wait to hang us until you talk to Drew, couldn't you?"

"It's not the first time," Tetley said. "We waited before."

He studied Martin for a moment.

"I'll make you a deal, though," he offered. "Tell us which of you shot Kinkaid, and the other two can wait."

Martin half-way glanced at the Mex, but if he was going to say anything he changed his mind. He shook his head before he spoke, as if at some thought of his own. "None of us killed anybody," he said in that tired voice again. "We were all three together all the time."

"That's all, I guess," Tetley said regretfully. He motioned toward the biggest tree on the edge of the clearing.

"My God," Martin said huskily, "you aren't going to, really! You wouldn't, really! You can't do it," he wailed, and started fighting his bond, jerking the other two prisoners about. The old man stumbled and fell to his knees and got up again as if it were a desperate necessity to be on his feet, but as clumsily as a cow because of his bound wrists.

"Tie them separately, Mapes," Tetley ordered.

Many ropes were offered. Smith and Winder helped Mapes. Only Martin was hard to tie. He'd lost his head, and it took two men to hold him while he was bound. Then the three were standing there separately, each with his arms held flat to his sides by a half-dozen turns of rope. Their feet were left free to walk them into position. Each of them had a noose around his neck too, and a man holding it.

In spite of Mapes trying to hold him up, Martin clumped down to his knees. We couldn't understand what he was babbling. When Mapes pulled him up again he managed to stand, but waving like a tree in a shifting wind. Then we could understand part of what he was saying. "One of them's just a baby," he was saying, "just a baby. They haven't got anything to go on, not a thing. They're alone; they haven't got anything to go on, and they're alone."

"Take them over," Tetley ordered, indicating the tree again. It was a big pine with its top shot away by lightning. It had a long branch that stuck out straight on the clearing side, about fifteen feet from the ground. We'd all spotted that branch.

"The Mex is mine," Farnley said. Tetley nodded and told some others to get the rustlers' horses.

Martin kept hanging back, and when he was shoved along kept begging, "Give us some time, it's not even decent; give us some time."

Old Hardwick stumbled and buckled, but didn't fall. He was silent, but his mouth hung open, and his eyes were protruding enormously. The Mex, however, walked steadily, showing only a wry grin, as if he had expected nothing else from the first.

When the three of them were lined up in a row under the limb, waiting for their horses, Martin said, "I've got to write a letter. If you're even human you'll give me time for that, anyway." His breath whistled when he talked, but he seemed to know what he was saying again.

"We can't wait all night," Mapes told him, getting ready to throw up the end of the rope, which had a heavy knot tied in it to carry it over.

"He's not asking much, Tetley," Davies said.

Old Hardwick seemed to have caught the idea. He burbled about being afraid of the dark, that he didn't want to die in the dark, that in the dark he saw things.

"He's really afraid of the dark," Martin said. "Can't this wait till sunrise? It's customary anyway, isn't it?"

Men were holding the three horses just off to the side now. Farnley was holding the hang rope on the Mex. He spoke to Tetley angrily.

"Now what are you dreaming about, Tetley? They're trying to put it off, that's all; they're scared, and they're trying to put it off. Do you want Tyler and the sheriff to get us here, and the job not done?" As if he had settled it himself, he threw the end of the Mex's rope over the limb.

"They won't come in this snow," Davies said.

"I believe you're right," Tetley told Davies. "Though I doubt if you want to be." He asked Bartlett, "What time is it?" Bartlett drew a thick silver watch from his waistcoat pocket and looked at it.

"Five minutes after two," he said.

"All right," Tetley said after a moment, "we'll wait till daylight."

Farnley stood holding the end of the rope and glaring at Tetley. Then slowly he grinned up one side of his face and tossed down the rope, like he was all done. "Why not?" he said. "It will give the bastard time to think about it." Then he walked down to the fire and stood there by himself. He was wild inside; you could tell that just by looking at his back.

In a way none of us liked the wait, when we'd have to go through the whole thing over again anyway. But you couldn't refuse men in a spot like that three or four hours if they thought they wanted them.

It was already getting light; the cabin and the trees could be seen clearly. There was no sunrise, but a slow leaking in of light from all quarters. The firelight no longer colored objects or faces near it. The faces were gray and tired and stern. We knew it was going to happen now, and yet, I believe, most of us still had a feeling it couldn't. It had been delayed so long; we had argued so much. Only Tetley seemed entirely self-possessed; his face showed no signs of weariness or excitement.

He asked Martin if there was any other message he wished to leave. Martin shook his head. In this light his face looked hollow, pale, and without individuality. His mouth was trembling constantly, and he was careful not to talk. I hoped, for our sake as much as his, that he'd make the decent end he now had his will set on.

Sparks was talking to the old fool again, but he, seeing the actual preparations begin, was frightened sick once more, and babbled constantly in a hoarse, worn-out voice, about his innocence, his age and his not wanting to die. Again and again he begged Martin to do something. This, more than anything else, seemed to shake Martin. He wouldn't look at old Hardwick, and pretended not to hear him.

We were surprised that the Mex wanted to make a confession, but he did. There wasn't any priest, so Amigo was to hear the confession, and carry it to a priest the first time he could go himself. There couldn't be any forgiveness, but it was the best they could do. They went down to the place where the sheds had stood, the

Mex limping badly, and Amigo half carrying him along. Bartlett
was stationed at a respectul distance as sentinel. We saw the Mex
try to kneel, but he couldn't, so he stood there confessing with his
back to us. Occasionally his hands moved in gestures of apology,
which seemed strange from him. Amigo was facing us; but, when
he wants, Amigo has a face like a wooden Indian. If the Mex was
saying anything we ought to know now, which was what we were
all thinking, we couldn't tell it from watching Amigo. He appeared
merely to be intent upon remembering, in order that all the Mex's
sins might be reported and forgiven.

In his field-officer manner Tetley was directing. Farnley knotted
and threw up three ropes, so they hung over the long branch with
the three nooses in a row. Then others staked down the ends of the
ropes. The three horses were brought up again, and held under the
ropes.

Tetley appointed Farnley, Gabe Hart and Gerald to whip the
horses out. It was all right with Farnley, but Gabe refused. He gave
no excuse, but stood there immovable, shaking his head. I was surprised Tetley had picked him.

"Gabe's not agin us, Mr. Tetley," Winder apologized, "he can't
stand to hurt anything. It would work on his mind."

Tetley asked for a volunteer, and when no one else came forward
Ma took the job. She was furious about it, though. Moore looked
at Smith, and so did Tetley, but Smith pretended to be drunker
than he really was. Really he was scared sober now.

When it seemed all settled, young Tetley, nearly choking, refused
also.

"You'll do it," was all Tetley told him.

"I can't, I tell you."

"We'll see to it you can."

The boy stood there, very white, still shaking his head.

"It's a necessary task," Tetley told him, evenly. "Someone else
must perform it if you fail. I think you owe it to the others, and to
yourself, on several scores."

The boy still shook his head stubbornly.

Moore, although he had refused on his own account, came over to Tetley and offered to relieve Gerald. "The boy's seen too much already. You shouldn't press him, man."

Tetley's face abruptly became bloodless; his mouth stretched downward, long and thin and hard, and his eyes glimmered with the fury he restrained. It was the first time I'd ever seen him let that nature show through, though I had felt always that it was there. He still spoke quietly though, and evenly.

"This is not your affair, Moore. Thank you just the same."

Moore shrugged and turned his back on him. He was angry himself.

Tetley said to Gerald, "I'll have no female boys bearing my name. You'll do your part, and say nothing more." He turned away, giving the boy no opportunity to reply.

"That must have been a very busy life," he remarked, looking down where the Mex was still confessing to Amigo.

When at last the Mex was done and they came back up, and the three prisoners were stood in a row with their hands tied down, Martin said,

"I suppose it's no use telling you again that we're innocent?"

"No good," Tetley assured him.

"It's not for myself I'm asking," Martin said.

"Other men have had families and have had to go for this sort of thing," Tetley told him. "It's too bad, but it's not our fault."

"You don't care for justice," Martin flared. "You don't even care whether you've got the right men or not. You want your way, that's all. You've lost something and somebody's got to be punished; that's all you know."

When Tetley just smiled, Martin's control broke again. "There's nobody to take care of them; they're in a strange place, they have nothing, and there's nobody to take care of them. Can't you understand that, you butcher? You've got to let me go; if there's a spot of humanity in you, you've got to let me go. Send men with me if you want to; I'm not asking you to trust me; you wouldn't trust anybody; your kind never will. Send men with me, then, but let me see them, let me arrange for them to go somewhere, for somebody to help them."

Old Hardwick began to whimper and jabber aloud again, and finally buckled in the knees and fell forward on his face. The Mex looked straight ahead of him and spit with contempt. "This is fine company for a man to die with," he said.

Martin started to yell something at the Mex, who was right beside him, but Mapes walked up to him and slapped him in the face. He slapped him hard, four times, so you could hear it like the crack of a lash. He paid no attention to protests or to Davies trying to hold his arm. After the fourth blow he waited to see if Martin would say anything more. He didn't, but stood there, crying weakly and freely, great sobs heaving his chest up and making him lift his chin to catch his breath because of the bonds.

Others put the old man back on his feet, and a couple of shots of whisky were given to each of the three. Then they walked them over to the horses. The old man went flabby on them, and they had nearly to carry him.

I saw Davies keeping Amigo behind, holding him by the arm and talking. Amigo's face was angry and stubborn, and he kept shaking his head. Tetley saw it too, and guessed what I had. Smiling, he told Davies that a confession was a confession, and not evidence, even in a court.

"He doesn't have to tell us," Davies said. "All he has to do is say whether we'd better wait; then we could find out."

Amigo looked worried.

Tetley said, "Men have been known to lie, even in confession, under pressure less than this." Amigo looked at him as if for the first time he questioned his divinity, but then he said, "It wasn't a priest; I don't know."

"Even if it had been," Tetley said, eying the Mex. "I'll give you two minutes to pray," he told the three. They were standing by the horses now, under the branch with the ropes hanging down from it.

Martin was chewing his mouth to stop crying. He looked around at us quickly. We were in a fairly close circle; nobody would face him, man after man looked down. Finally, like he was choking, he ducked his head, then, awkwardly because of the rope, got to his knees. The Mex was still standing, but had his head bent and was moving his lips rapidly. The old man was down in a groveling heap with Sparks beside him; Sparks was doing the praying for him. Moore took off his hat, and then the rest of us did the same. After a moment Davies and some of the others knelt also. Most of us couldn't bring ourselves to do that, but we all bowed and kept quiet. In the silence, in the gray light slowly increasing, the moaning of the old man, Sparks' praying and the Mex going again and again through his rapid patter sounded very loud. Still you could hear every movement of the horses, leather creaking, the little clinks of metal.

"Time's up," Tetley said, and the old man wailed once, as if he'd been hit. His face had a new expression, the first we'd seen of it in him. Martin rose slowly to his feet, and looked around slowly. The moments of silence and the crisis had had the reverse effect on him. He no longer appeared desperate or incoherent, but neither did he look peaceful or resigned. I have never seen another face so bitter as his was then, or one that showed its hatred more clearly. He spoke to Davies, but even his voice proved the effort against his pride and detestation.

"Will you find someone you can trust to look out for my wife and children?" he asked. "In time she will repay anything it puts you out."

Davies' eyes were full of tears. "I'll find someone," he promised.

"You'd better take some older woman along," Martin said. "It's not going to be easy."

"Don't worry," Davies said, "your family will be all right."

"Thanks," Martin said. Then he said, "My people are dead, but Miriam's are living. They live in Ohio. And Drew didn't want to sell his cattle; he'll buy them back for enough to cover their travel."

Davies nodded.

"Better not give her my things," Martin said, "just this ring, if you'll get it."

Davies fumbled at the task. He had trouble with the rope, and his hands were shaking, but he got the ring, and held it up to Martin to see. Martin nodded. "Just give her that and my letter first. Don't talk to her until she's read my letter." He didn't seem to want to say any more.

"That all?" Tetley asked.

"That's all, thanks," Martin said.

They asked the Mex, and he suddenly started speaking very rapidly. He was staring around as if he couldn't quite see us. It had
got to him finally, all right. Then he stopped speaking just as suddenly and kept shaking his head in little short shakes. He'd been
talking in Spanish. They didn't ask the old man.

The three of them were lifted onto the horses and made to stand
on them. Two men had to support old Hardwick.

"Tie their ankles," Mapes ordered.

"God," Gil whispered, "I was afraid they weren't going to." He
felt it a great relief that their ankles were going to be tied.

Farnley got up on a horse and fixed the noose around each man's
neck. Then he and Ma got behind two of the horses with quirts in
their hands. Young Tetley had to be told twice to get behind his.
Then he moved into place like a sleepwalker, and didn't even know
he had taken the quirt somebody put in his hand.

The old man, on the inside, was silent, staring like a fish, and already hanging on the rope a little in spite of the men holding him
up. The Mex had gone to pieces too, buckling nearly as badly as
Hardwick, and jabbering rapid and panicky in Spanish. When the
horses sidled under him once, tightening the rope, he screamed. In
the pinch Martin was taking it best of the three. He kept his head
up, not looking at any of us, and even the bitterness was gone from
his face. He had a melancholy expression, such as goes with thinking of an old sorrow.

Tetley moved around behind the horses, and directed Mapes to
give the signal. We all moved out of the circle to give the horses
room. In the last second even the Mex was quiet. There was no
sound save the shifting of the three horses, restless at having been
held so long. A feathery, wide-apart snow was beginning to sift
down again; the end of the storm, not the beginning of another,
though. The sky was becoming transparent, and soon it was full
daylight.

Mapes fired the shot, and we heard it echo in the mountain as
Ma and Farnley cut their horses sharply across the haunches and
the holders let go and jumped away. The horses jumped away too,
and the branch creaked under the jerk. The old man and the Mex

were dead at the fall, and just swung and spun slowly. But young Tetley didn't cut. His horse just walked out from under, letting Martin slide off and dangle, choking to death, squirming up and down like an impaled worm, his face bursting with compressed blood. Gerald didn't move even then, but stood there shaking all over and looking up at Martin fighting the rope.

After a second Tetley struck the boy with the butt of his pistol, a back-handed blow that dropped him where he stood.

"Shoot him," he ordered Farnley, pointing at Martin. Farnley shot. Martin's body gave a little leap in the air, then hung slack, spinning slowly around and back, and finally settling into the slowing pendulum swing of the others.

Gil went with Davies to help young Tetley up. Nobody talked much, or looked at anybody else, but scattered and mounted. Winder and Moore caught up the rustlers' ponies. The Bartlett boys and Amigo remained to drive the cattle, and to do the burying before they started. All except Mapes and Smith shied clear of Tetley, but he didn't seem to notice. He untied his big palomino, mounted, swung him about and led off toward the road. His face was set and white; he didn't look back.

Most of the rest of us did, though, turn once or twice to look. I was glad when the last real fall of the snow started, soft and straight and thick. It lasted only a few minutes, but it shut things out.

Gil caught up and rode with me after he and Davies had helped Gerald. I'd thought, seeing him drop, that the kid had been killed, but Gil said no, it had been a glancing blow, that snow on his face and a drink had fixed him up enough to ride.

We rode slowly, letting the others disappear ahead of us, and Gerald and Davies came up behind us. It was difficult to turn in my saddle, but I did, to get a look at Gerald. His face had a knife-edge, marble-white look, and the circles under his eyes were big and dark, so that he appeared to have enormous eyes, or none at all, but empty sockets, like a skull. He wasn't looking where he was going, but the trouble wasn't his injury. I don't think he knew now that he had it. He was gnawing himself inside again. Passionate and womanish, but with a man's conscience and pride, that boy kept himself thin and bleached just thinking and feeling.

Davies, riding beside him, kept passing his hand over his face in a nerveless way unusual to him, rubbing his nose or fingering his mouth or drawing the hand slowly across his eyes and forehead, as if there were cobwebs on his skin.

We were all tired, even Gil half asleep in his saddle, and we nearly rode into the horses standing in the clearing before we saw them. They were quietly bunched under the falling snow.

"It's the sheriff," Gil said. "It's Risley."

Then he said, "Jesus, it's Kinkaid."

It was, too, with a bandage on his head, and a bit peaked, but otherwise as usual, quiet, friendly and ashamed to be there. The other three men, besides the sheriff, were Tyler, Drew and Davies' pimply clerk Joyce. The Judge was red in the face and talking violently, but through the snow his voice came short and flat.

"It's murder, murder and nothing less. I warned you, Tetley, I warned you repeatedly, and Davies warned you, and Osgood. You all heard us; you were all warned. You wanted justice, did you? Well, by God, you shall have it now, real justice. Every man of you is under arrest for murder. We'll give you a chance to see how slow regular justice is when you're in the other chair."

Nobody replied to him, that I could hear.

"My God," Gil said, "I knew it didn't feel right. I knew we should wait. That bastard Tetley," he finished.

Everybody would hang it on Tetley now. I didn't say anything.

The sheriff was stern, but he wasn't the kind to gabble easily, like Tyler. He was a small, stocky man with a gray, walrus mustache and black bushy eyebrows. He had a heavy sheepskin on, with the collar turned up around his ears. His deep-set, hard, blue eyes looked at each of us in turn. Nobody but Tetley tried to hold up against his look, and even Tetley failed.

When he'd made us all look down, he said something we couldn't hear to the Judge. The Judge began to sputter, but when Risley looked level at him too the sputter died, and the Judge just stared around at us belligerently again, thrusting his lower lip out and sucking it in and making a hoarse, blowing noise.

Risley sat silent for a moment, as if considering carefully, looking us over all the time. Finally he stared into the snow over us and the milky blue shadows of the trees through it and said, "I haven't recognized anybody here. We passed in a snowstorm, and I was in a hurry."

"That's collusion, Risley," the Judge began loudly, getting redder than ever. "I'll have you understand I won't . . ."

"What do you want to do?" Risley cut in, looking at him.

The Judge tried to say something impressive about the good name of the valley and the state, and the black mark against his jurisdiction and Risley's, but it was no use. Everybody just waited for him to stop; he couldn't hold out against all of us without Risley.

When he was just blowing again, Risley said, "I'm not even looking for the leaders. Nobody had to go if he didn't want to."

He went on in a changed tone, as if he had finished unimportant preliminaries and was getting down to business.

"I'll want ten men for my posse."

We all volunteered. We were tired, and we'd had plenty of man hunting and judging to hold us for a long time, but we felt he was giving us a chance to square ourselves. Even Tetley volunteered, but Risley didn't notice him; he passed up Mapes also. But he took Winder, which added Gabe Hart, and he took Moore, and after looking at him for a long time he took Farnley. Kinkaid looked up at that, smiled a little and raised one hand off the horn just enough so Farnley could see it. Farnley straightened as if he'd had half a life given back to him. Farnley was mean with a grudge, but honest. If he didn't like Risley right then, he liked himself a lot less.

When Risley had selected his ten men, he ordered the rest of us to go home. "Go on about your own business," he told us. "Don't hang around in bunches. If you have to tell anybody anything, just tell them I'm taking care of this with a picked posse. You can't stop the talk, but there'll be a lot less fuss if you keep out of it. Nobody knew these men."

He turned to the Judge. "It'll have to be that way," he apologized.

"Perhaps, perhaps," the Judge muttered. "All the same—" and he subsided. Actually, though, he was relieved. We didn't have to worry about him.

By Jonreed Lauritzen

INDIAN BOY

As THE COOL shadow of the west wall crept across the canyon floor the sheep began to get up, one by one, from the shades of the little junipers and nibble at the short grass. Sigor lifted his face from his sweaty, red-brown arm and rested on his elbows to rub the sleep and sand from his eyes.

He looked to see how many hours the sun was high above the west rim. He forgot the sun as his eyes followed the slow soaring of an eagle with the light shining through its wings like colored glass. Then he looked at the west wall over which it disappeared, and saw the thing that put a mist over yesterday and all the days before it, and made it seem that the long years of his growing up were over. The corner of his eye caught motion against the shell-white of the clouds lifting rounded edges above the canyon rim. It was the tiny, moving shadows of men.

His body was not now hot and glistening under the slanting rays of the sun. It had become cold, solid shaft of muscles drawn tense, alert with a strange dread. The silence that hung between the canyon walls was not a natural thing, but seemed to cover mutterings and whisperings and threats. It was like the blanket drawn across the door of the hogan where the war-council is going on. It held in the forces that might break out any time in savage ferocity.

Sigor forgot the sheep. With fast running he could reach the hogan of his mother before the sun sank in the teeth of the highest

132

rims. She would be home now from the trading-post at Fort
Defiance, but there would be no time to look at the things she had
brought, things that all day he had been thinking over—the bridle
she had promised, the bacon with its smoke odor, the salt, the flour,
the sweet lump perhaps.

Maybe she had been warned already. As he ran down the canyon
he saw women running up, staying close by the canyon wall. First
a few, then many came, singly and in groups. No need to warn
them. The red-brown faces wore a mask of fear. Their mouths were
panting and from some of them came low moans, like sounds carried in a far wind.

"Nijoni!" his hoarse murmur carried his mother's name up against
the smooth walls and back. He did not dare call her in the loud
tones he used when there was no danger. Sometimes no sound at all
would come, but he would shape the word "Nijoni" with his lips
and it would flow out with his breathing.

Soon he began to feel no more fear, but an opposite thing. Was
he not going to protect his mother, fight for her if the chance came,
if the enemy—Utes and Spaniards who slunk their cowardly way
along the rim—would come down and fight? They would find him
not a herder, not a boy, but a warrior. He would show them he
could use his bow against something besides rabbits and fat
wethers. Now he was glad the Diné men had not let him go with
them on the raiding. Now he, with the old men and boys, would
be the only defenders of the women. He could cover himself with
glory, be known as a warrior, and no one would ever speak of the
three quarters of his blood that was not Diné—or Navajo, as their
enemies called them. From now on he would be all Diné and the
people would forget that his mother was half Spanish, and his
father a white man who wandered among the canyons of the north
country. They would call him the Diné warrior, Killer-of-Utes-and-
Spaniards.

At the women whose shadows passed him as he ran he only
glanced. The old and fat who seemed to stand still and sway like
junipers in the wind he did not notice. But the slender and young
he gave a second glance. Nijoni would be one of them, for the
white blood in her had not let her go wide and flabby. He looked

closely at the tall ones' faces, for he could not tell by the clothes. She would have brought herself new skirts from the trading-post.

"Nijoni—Beautiful Mother!" He knew as he drew back the blanket in the door of the hogan that she was not there. She had been there since her trading, for out of the dimness came the smells of bacon, new leather, new cloth. Then his eyes caught glimpses of beauty— the bridle with the silver trimmings, the red velvet spread out to be admired. Perhaps her eyes had been looking on it, her golden fingers running over its smoothness, when the warning of danger came. For a moment he stood thinking they might have come and got her and taken her out to sell for a slave. That would be worse than their bullets, for she had been a slave when his father had bought her from the Spaniards. She had told him of the evil days, told him a little, enough so that he knew it was better to die.

He went outside and saw the tracks of her moccasins and she had been alone, walking toward the canyon. He followed her tracks at a trot till they mingled with the tracks of the other women going that way. Then he ran swiftly, for he knew she would be in the Canyon del Muerto, which comes into the Canyon de Chelly this side of where he had been with the sheep, and this is why he would have missed her.

"All the spirits of evil come on the Spaniard and Ute cowards!" He said the Diné words in his mind, his teeth too tight together to let the sounds through. They would kill all the Diné women for the lust of killing, and to rid themselves of those who bred Diné. They had reason to hate the Diné, who were the bravest of men and were feared by whites and Indians throughout all the canyon country. It was a good time for these coyote men on the rims to do their killing, for the warriors were away and it could be done without danger.

He ran faster, quickened with anger, his feet lightened by the rush of blood to his head. Some of the older, fatter women were still limping on and they sent their little wails and moans after him. Some had given up trying to reach better shelter and were huddled at the base of the canyon wall. Others sat silent under the junipers, likes ewes shaded up, their big black eyes wide with suffering. Here and there forms were stretched out in the sand as though resting, and he pulled his eyes quickly from them, for death was in them. There were stains of dark red spreading out from them in the light-red sands. Something he had not felt when a sick child had been chanted over and buried, something he had not felt when they brought warriors home to die from their wounds, came on him now. Always before, death had seemed far away, a thing that happened to other people. Now it was near; he was running in the cup of its palm.

Women and children were huddled in the great cave of the Canyon del Muerto. It was as if they had gathered there to get out of the rain and a sudden change of wind had brought it pouring in upon them. It was a shallow cave, facing the opposite wall, and a good target for the killer shapes hovering on the canyon rim. Light from the slanting sun streamed in over the strained, motionless figures, and for a space before the shower of arrows and bullets began to fall they were like figures molded in bronze. Even after death began to sing down upon them there was little motion among them except the general writhing; little sound but a general wail; a slumping and a sudden moaning here, a scream there.

His glance went from face to face swiftly until a hand reached out and caught his arm and a voice that belonged in the world of spirits said: "Nijoni—down by the forks, by the large juniper."

He went out of the cave, looking at the figures on the rim and cursing them and calling on them to come down and fight. As he walked down toward the canyon forks he did not hurry. He knew that Nijoni would wait. He strode with body straight as his bow-string, showing all the hate and defiance a body could show. He wished for one of their bullets to hit him, as a thirsting man in the desert would welcome the feel of a cold raindrop on his back. He watched the bullets strike the sand and throw up little puffs of dust, like the puffs of steam that come out of boiling mush.

Through the long night he lay by Nijoni's body, and through the morning, while the sunlight seeped down the west wall and came pressing its heat upon his back. Flies, too, big black blowflies, came crawling over her face in spite of his angry wavings, determined to show that death was where they took over, and they would not be cheated.

If his father had not come he might have crouched there until the sun shriveled him as it shrivels the corpses of dead sheep after the first bloating. There was no reason to live. Without Nijoni there was nothing. Without her all the days of herding sheep, of digging his bare toes in the sand, of shooting arrows at sparrow-hawks, of staring at the smooth faces of maidens and thinking of them afterwards, the dreaming of the day when he would be a warrior and have much glory and many maidens, the killing of Utes and Spaniards in his thoughts—none of it would mean anything now. He could not even feel shame for not wanting to live and kill as many of them as he could to avenge her.

"It would be shooting arrows into the sun," Lean Wolf had answered when Sigor had said once that they should kill all the white men. It was better to die than to live in a world of white men and Utes. It was no use living where it was no use to fight.

It was into such a world for Sigor that his father came with a tinkling and sparkling of bridle and spurs.

In the hours since yesterday Sigor had thought of Dennis, his father. Thought of him with hate. A grown man should be raiding or fighting. Dennis Julian did neither. No one knew what he did, except that he had been seen in many far places where the Navajo went—but he did not go to plunder as the Navajo went. If he had gone among the Utes and Mexicans to kill off their men, carry away their maidens and horses and cattle, he would have been a father to be proud of. Rather, he went, they said, like a man whose mind is over the next rim. He seemed to want nothing, and spent all his life finding it.

As Dennis came riding over the sand, there was that in his face that quieted Sigor's hate. In this place of death and murder it was good to see a face with friendliness in it. But the friendliness went from the face as the sound went from the spurs and bridle when he stopped. He pulled a long leg over the saddle and stepped down softly, knowing a thing had happened which he could not go away from. But he could not hurry toward it. Sigor could hear the creaking of his leather jacket as he knelt down to touch the face of Nijoni with his hands. Sigor looked once at the face of his father, then turned away, remembering the lean strong look of it, the smiling calm that was sadder than weeping, the look of round openness about the eyes, which were deep blue and fenced with wrinkles. Sigor remembered how those eyes had used to shine like the ornaments on a bridle when Dennis came and lived with them in the hogan of Nijoni. It had not been an eagle-fierce thing, as in the eyes of Sigor's Navajo uncles, but a tenderness such as was in Nijoni's fingertips.

He felt the hand of his father resting on his shoulder and he bowed his head and struggled with the tightness in his throat and chest, trying to keep the tears from coming.

Dennis had led a black-and-white pinto pony, and Sigor remembered the promise that had been given by his father in those days of the past that were in his memory like dim stars in a pool on a night of mists.

As Dennis got up and walked toward the horses, Sigor did not look at him, nor at the pony. Then Dennis stopped and turned and in a moment said: "There are many cowards yet on the rims. We must bury Nijoni and go."

He did not turn his head toward his father, nor answer. There was no fear that could put its poison on his spirit like the thought of burying Nijoni. One of the cowards' bullets through him would be a pleasant thing beside the thought of burying Nijoni. She did not belong in the earth. It was something that could not be done, this putting her away where her face could never be seen again, where she would never sing, nor walk, nor weave the woolen blankets. There must be some way to make her breathe again, before that burying could happen.

After a long time he lifted his head and saw that Dennis had ridden to the edge of the canyon where a small talus slope came down between the bottom of the cliff and the flood channel. Here, using a sharp stick to loosen the earth, Dennis scooped out a grave with his hands. When Sigor saw this he came and helped him. Each double handful of soil was a cruel act against Nijoni, throwing sticks of pain on the fire in his throat and chest.

Finally the burying was over, like something done in the midst of dying.

They rode out of the Chinlee country and west into the Deserta Pintura and north from there.

This journey through the Painted Desert was not something that happens; it was a thing that flows through the mind after a night of the Fire dance. It was a thing between waking and sleeping, this jog through a cloud of red-purple dust rising over a dead land of cliffs swinging down between wide sweeps of valley sewn in great curves by the torrents from sudden thunderstorms. All the while they rode, Sigor kept thinking that any time he would wake to smell the mutton frying and the juniper smoke and hear Nijoni humming an old Mexican song. The stillness about them was heavy with dust and heat; and the monotonous shrilling of the sage locusts and the dry-ratching sound of the brown-winged grasshoppers were as much a part of the silence as the shadow of his pony that glided over brush, crossed the patches of burned earth, and leaped the small gullies. Dennis, too, was part of the loneliness. Riding tall and alert, he gave no sound but the unnoticed tinkling of his spurs. Going out of a land of death they seemed to enter a land with no sign of living.

They came to a ridge where dead junipers threw gray, twisted arms against the red wind clouds in the western sky. Here Dennis dismounted, took hobbles from the saddlebags and put them on the legs of the horses. Then while the ponies stood sniffing the air for the direction of the water, Dennis took a kettle from the saddlebags and went down into a gully near by and scooped up water from a small seep which, shiny and smooth with alkali, trickled over the red rocks and made pools in the crevices. He kindled a fire on the knoll where they had put their saddles, and Sigor gathered dry limbs from the junipers and stacked them close by for the night. Dennis set the kettle to boil on the coals, and as it boiled he dropped pieces of jerky beef into it.

As night drained the red from the wind clouds over the far rims of canyons in the west, mountains in the north towered into black-bellied storm clouds from which quick knives of lightning drew the pale viscera of rain. The wind came down from there, cool like a dash of water into a furnace. Sigor began to shiver and stay close to the fire. His blood, thinned by the Chinlee heat, could not warm

him, and his flesh was taut and numbed from the many hours of
grief that had been piling up.

Dennis began to sing. Softly at first, then gathering strength, his
somber, resonant tones like a rising wind in the dead branches.
Slowly it caught Sigor's spirit up and carried it along until it seemed
to be tearing him apart inside. In that singing he could hear Nijoni's
voice, fading and indistinct, sweet, sad, mellow, in the tuneless
wail that had been her way in the Diné songs. Singing her own
Death Chant.

Tears came from his eyes like water through a broken dam. He
fell on his knees, forgetting he was Diné and almost a warrior, and
sobbed in his arms. Then his father came and put an arm around
his shoulders.

"Tears are good. Let them come, boy. They let out the poison.
When a rattlesnake has bitten, one must let out blood or die. It is
so with grief. The Diné saves it up and kills with it. The white man
lets it out in tears."

After he had sipped of the jerky-broth Dennis poured for him,
Sigor rolled up in his blanket and slept. It was the sleep of one
who has wandered many nights and days lost and hungry.

As they rode next morning down the long draw that leads to the
Ute Ford on the Colorado, Sigor thought on the words of his father.
The difference between Navajo and white man; was it that one put
his feelings into arrows, the other into words and tears? It was a
shameful thing, then, that he should be following Dennis, when it
was a warrior he wanted to be. He should be killing Utes and
Spaniards for what they had done to Nijoni and all the other women
and children. He was running away from a fight that called for
everything a brave could do with ferocity. A coward son of a
coward father, he would let the Utes and Spaniards finish their
purpose, which was to wipe out the Diné so that they would no
longer have anything to fear in their cowardly hearts.

He looked at Dennis' back. One could see no shame in him. He
rode with body erect, shoulders squared, his chin leveled against
the horizon, his head turning constantly as his eyes scanned every
visible object for any sign of motion. Sigor could not think of him
as running from man or beast that might cross their trail. The worst

that could be said of him was that he did not live by fighting, as a warrior should. But that was shame enough, to the Diné way of thinking.

Had he, Sigor, too much white blood to feel that shame—at least to turn him back, away from the ways of his father? He who wanted to be above everything else a brave fighter was following a man who would lead him into another kind of life, make of him a no-good whose mind would always be over the next rim. But Dennis had not said: "Come with me." Sigor could have stayed in the Chinlee. Even now he could go back and Dennis would perhaps say nothing. Then why had he come? Why did he not go back now, before his father made of him something he did not wish to be? He could not tell. Maybe there was something over the next rim he would want to see. One could not tell why one did things, any more than one could read the footprints of the gods in the sky-trails.

They crossed the tawny river and rode under the cliffs of many colors and went southward to the Kaibab and followed its gradual slope through endless marching pines till on the third day they came to the brink of the Canyon of Canyons.

After one look Sigor fell back a few steps from the rim, but Dennis bared his head and stood gazing while a breeze came up from below and stirred the golden-graying hair that framed the bronzed face. In this moment Sigor began to know something of the Dennis who had never been to their hogan, who had wandered among the canyons alone. There was a strength in the long, arched nose, the wide brow; a strength that was not like the strength of the Diné, which is of raping and killing and stealing, the herding of sheep, the growing of corn, the hunting of antelope. There was something in the blue eyes of Dennis as strange and terrible and lonely as the canyon which lay smoldering in the lights and shadows of sundown. It seemed to Sigor, looking at his father, that there was a spell upon him, that he, the son, was being drawn into it, being made a part of a great madness, or an unholy bond that was between Dennis and this awful and unholy scene.

Now he knew why all the Indian tribes kept back from this

canyon and left its secrets reverently to the gods. It was no place for a man of flesh and blood.

They laid their blankets on the pine needles some distance back from the rim so that the depth would not be pulling at them in their sleep.

It was evening of the next day before they came to the end of the tall pines, where the forest petered out in piñon, juniper, buck-brush, and chaparral. The yellow summer sun, resting on the jagged edges of mountains, poured a flood of mellow light on a scene of Kaibab falling away to a wide gray plateau above which, on the north, arose terraces, beginning with calico slopes in vari-colored stripes, then the Vermilion Cliffs in bright red amber, then white cliffs, and, capping it all, the pink palisades that broke out of the blue slopes of the highest rims. It was beyond thinking or speaking, and they went quietly to make a campfire and cut the boughs of the little junipers to put under their blankets for the night.

After the wind of the night had blown away whatever mist might have lingered on the Great Terraces, the morning air was like crystal and the walls and crevices of the palisades were clear to see through all the hundred miles from the lower Kaibab to the high Markagunt.

When they had eaten, Dennis beckoned to Sigor. "I will tell you of this country which has been for so long my own," he said, lead-ing the boy to a high point of rock. He told Sigor of the towers, the high mesas, the deep canyons, the many colors of these terraces —things too distant to be seen from here—and of the spirit people and the gods that were there and could not be seen at all, with the senses.

"We do not go there now," Dennis said, letting his hand drop to his belt. "We are heading for the Mormon villages which are north of the Tumurru, in the deep canyon valleys of the Virgin River."

For a little while Dennis did not speak; then he looked into the face of his son, and his tone was even more gentle and vibrant than before. "I said 'we,' son. Maybe I've brought you too far. Maybe I should have left you back there with Nijoni's people. It is not too late to go back. You could find your way alone. I do not want you to go into my country and live my kind of life because you are my son. I want you to choose which way to go. Mine is a lonely way—" He was looking at that horizon now, a hundred miles northward. "Mine is a way of being alone, even among people. I try to find love and friendliness in a land of hatreds. I try to find peace in the midst of a battleground between the Mormons and Navajo. But I find something which none of them seem to have, which I cannot tell you until you have found it for yourself. It is something like walking with your hand in the hand of the Great Spirit—" Dennis' voice was like the sound of the largest string on the guitar he had given Nijoni. Sigor could not look at his father. Yet while Dennis spoke he had felt as though he had been set free, as though he had left off flesh and blood and had become a part of the bigness and strangeness. Canyons, forests, cliffs rising up to the high mountains. Like Dennis he had become a god, and it was all within him and he was within it, and they were like parts in a beautiful blanket; but now that his father spoke of the future he became a small boy yearning for his mother, lost and not daring to ask the way. Again the tears came and he let them come, for he knew that the Diné could never claim him. He was white man—something of Dennis and Nijoni, ready to be molded by the gods of tomorrow.

"I go with you," he said, struggling with the words.

BREAKERS OF BRONCOS

So! breakers of broncos! With miles of jagged wire,
You seek to break the spirit of this range;
With lariat of barbed-wire fence, you hope
To tame its heart, and with your iron heel,
Hot from the desert, to sear upon its hip
Your molten brand—as wranglers at a round up,
With bit and spur and lasso, strive to curb
And brand an outlaw fresh from winter range.

O breaker of broncos, listen! Can't you hear
The northwind snickering at you? The coyote
Upon the mesa, jeering? The waterfall
Chuckling among the rocks? The croaking magpie,
The hooting owl, the crane, the curlew? Look!
The chokecherry blossom, the sage, the bitterroot,
Bending with mirth, wag their heads, and laugh
At you! Why, even the broomtail cayuse kicks
His heels against the mountain sky, and snorts!

O breakers of broncos, we fling you on the wind
This handful of dust, this bitter alkali!—
As well attempt to rope the bucking stars,
Or burn your bars upon the flank of the moon!
When will you whirl your lasso at the sun?
Or bridle it? Or straddle the lightning-flash?

BOISTEROUS BUTTE

You ROUND a corner on a highway clinging to the Continental Divide and there, suddenly, is Butte. It is sprawling and slovenly, a bully of a city, stridently male, profane and blustering and boastful: "The biggest mining camp in the world!" "A mile high and a mile deep!" "The richest hill on earth!"

Butte is no longer any of these; certainly it is no longer what its policechief once called it, "an island of easy money entirely surrounded by whisky"—though it still behaves like that. There was a time when the mine pay rolls of Butte averaged $50 monthly for every man, woman, and child, when miners made $10 to $20 a day on contract. Now money is not so easily come by, but it is still easily spent: the habit persists.

This city remains what Joseph Pennell called it in his *Wonders of Work*—"the most pictorial place in America." It could be one of those selected centers of sin which columnist Heywood Broun once facetiously suggested America might establish as places in which the ordinarily virtuous citizen might occasionally blow off steam, for Butte is notorious the nation over as a "good time" town. Indeed, its chamber of commerce has hinted delicately but nonetheless frankly in its literature: "Here they [visitors] may relax in the tradition handed down from the days of wayfaring prospectors, mining and cattle men, laugh and play in the red-blooded manner that is peculiarly Butte's. . . . Doors are wide open, nothing is hidden."

144

Butte is the black heart of Montana, feared and distrusted. From the sixth floor of one of its office buildings go forth the corporate commands to politicians, preachers, and press, all the pensioners and servile penny-a-liners of corporate capitalism. Butte is a sooty memorial to personal heroism, to courage and vigor even in rascality; and it is a monument to a wasted land.

It is a mile high, even a little more; but it is not a mile deep—the deepest mine is still a thousand feet short of that. If it is no longer "the richest hill on earth," probably it was: above the city, denuded of grass or tree, gray-tan and dirty, squats the mountain of copper which has yielded up metal worth $2,500,000,000 in half a century. Black triangles crowned with circles, like children's classroom compasses slightly askew, thrust up through the crust of this hill to stamp fantastic abstractions on the limitless Montana sky. Under the city twist 2,700 miles of tunnels, and in their dim hot depths thousands of men have worked and fought and died; thousands of feet in the earth, at the bidding of their masters, they have thrown up barricades, fashioned crude grenades of mine powder, and prepared to blow each other up—while their masters, securely above-ground, fought in corrupted courts for possession of a disputed vein.

Bullets have raked the tired streets hung awkwardly on this mountainside as these men have fought one another or have been fought by their bosses; and the battles have helped build vast fortunes—for other men. The miners have risen in wrath and smitten the Lords of the Hill, and struck, and fought again; and they have been betrayed and defeated and driven back into their holes. But sometimes they have won and wrested away a little more of their Hill's riches for themselves. Then the surface has rocked with Rabelaisian mirth, the drinks have been on the house, the girls on "the line" have bought new dresses, the effigies of the scab have been cut down from telephone poles, and everyone has gone cheerily back to work.

Butte was born in violence, bred in it, and lives it. Back in the boom days the mines killed or injured a man a day; there were sales on crutches in drug stores. Even today there are many cripples, frequent deaths, despite vast improvement in methods and efforts

by employer and union to elevate safety standards. Rock dust fills
the miners' lungs and sulphuric acid dripping from the walls of a
drift (the copper is in a sulphur formation) burns their clothing
and their flesh. The city's file of death certificates provides the
tragic coda for the dramatic song of Butte: "Occupation, miner;
cause of death, silicosis; was deceased's occupation responsible?
Yes." About twenty years ago federal Bureau of Mines experts
asked Butte workers to appear for silicosis tests; of the 1,018 who
came voluntarily for examination 42 per cent had silicosis—"miner's
con." The intervening years have brought the "wet drill" and vastly
improved ventilation; employers claim—for public consumption—
that silicosis is now virtually nonexistent. Yet men continue to die
of this and other pulmonary disorders. Butte's county, with one
tenth of the state's population, contributes about one fourth of
Montana's tuberculosis deaths.

Butte's dead are speedily carted to one of its six cemeteries and
added to their 40,000-odd census; for this city, only seventy-five
years old, has about as many dead as alive; its present population,
including all the "metropolitan area," is about 50,000, a drop of 11
per cent in one decade, 16 per cent in two.

In the carriage days there were races back from the cemeteries
to the saloons, and there the miners downed "boilermakers"—whisky
with beer or ale chaser—in memory of the departed comrade; frequently this funereal treat was paid for out of the deceased's estate,
by his command. Some still observe the traditional ceremony.

Butte has fascinated countless thousands of visitors, won their
affection and finally their citizenship. It has repelled and shocked
others, who have spoken and written savagely about it. Even this
writer, fond of Butte, finds the temptation to exaggerate its distinctive character almost irresistible. But the temptation must be resisted; travelers like Glenn Chesney Quiett, author of *Pay Dirt*,
should stop over for a day or so. Butte is not as ugly as he would
have it in his rather terrifying impressionist portrait, nor does his
impatient dismissal of it do justice to its notable history:

"So today the mining of Montana . . . has come to be symbolized
by the city of Butte on its grim and naked hills surrounded by
gaunt mountains gnawed out by an iron tooth. Over the vast honey-

combed hill is spread a nightmare network of trestles, railroad
tracks, scaffolds, wooden buttresses, crazy stairs, bunkers, fences,
houses, rusty iron pipes, electric transmission lines, hoists, buildings
black and red—a cosmic junk heap created by some ingenious and
saturnine Joe Cook of the gods. In this appalling Dantesque waste
land, where no flower blossoms, no seed grows, there are acres of
burnt slag, mountains of black boulders, mazes of chemical-in-
crusted iron. It is burnt-out, ravaged, raped and discarded, and as
the train slowly creeps through it on a hot summer day, the traveler
can only wearily pull down the curtain and say, 'Take me away
from Butte.' "

For half a century American writers have been discovering de-
lightedly that Butte's lusty history, its social and economic habits,
provide as rich a lode for their prospecting as the famous hill provided for the mining entrepreneurs, but none has captured the im-
pious and indomitable spirit of the brawling big town.

Nor has any skilled historian tried to do justice to the city's violent past—the story, for instance, of a now-vacant lot, once occupied
by a hardware store. At 10 o'clock one night in 1895 that store
caught fire, and Butte's fire department responded to the call.
Ladders were against the building, firemen on the ladders, the chief
and one other on the roof. Blasting powder illegally stored inside
exploded, annihilated the Butte fire department save for one or two
men busy with hose some distance away. Paralyzed for an instant
with horror as fragments of the firemen's bodies hurtled about
them, the watching miners then surged heroically into the blaze
in the hope of saving a few of the victims. There was another blast,
and a third. . . . Fifty-seven men were blown to pieces that night.
Butte men today tell how with hundreds of other boys they stood
around the morgues, watched gunny sacks filled with human
particles—heads, hands, bones, or just seared flesh—brought in for
the task of assembly and identification. The task was finally admitted to be hopeless.

Down another street was the miners' union hall. (Now the miners
own the once-luxurious Silver Bow Club, where the Lords of the
Hill entertained at least one President of the United States, scores
of famous actors and actresses, and other notables, where thousands

of dollars changed hands in epic poker games.) The union hall was blown up by dynamite June 13, 1914, in the midst of a bitter internal dispute which the miners still believe was inspired by the bosses. Butte was Local No. 1 of the Western Federation of Miners, toughest union in America in the '90's, the union of Big Bill Haywood. (It is still Local No. 1 of the WFM's successor, International Union of Mine, Mill & Smelter Workers, CIO.) In 1914, the IWW sought control of the WFM, and in the process it destroyed the Butte union's hall. Martial law followed (there was a strike in progress, too, and big war profits were endangered) and Butte's Socialist antiwar mayor, elected by the miners, was driven from office. The strike was broken and the miners' union did not come back until the days of NRA.

On top of the "richest hill," almost in the center, is the Granite Mountain mine. On the night of June 8, 1917, the flames of a miner's carbide lamp ignited the uncovered and frayed insulation of a temporary power cable near the 2,400-foot level. The timbers caught, the roaring draft down the shaft pushed smoke and gas throughout the workings. Within an hour 163 men had perished, all but two of them from suffocation. The unhappy miner whose cap-lamp had started the fire survived it; he had a German name and so far had the pendulum swung in once antiwar Butte that there was lynch talk, but investigators proved him to be guiltless.

As you drive out of Butte onto the highway leading to the smelter city of Anaconda, you come to a concrete underpass which replaces an old wooden trestle. The night of August 17, 1917, a gang of masked men seized Frank W. Little, an IWW organizer, as he lay in bed in a Butte rooming house, dragged him into the street without permitting him to dress, took him to the trestle and there hanged him. The victim, said the company press, "made no outcry." Such courage must have been difficult unless Little had fainted. At the time of the lynching he had a broken leg. None of his attackers was ever publicly named or tried, but there are those in Butte who will name them, and who will tell of the amazing retributive fate which has caught up with most of the murderers—violent or horrible death in one form or another. As for Frank Little, he gained the measure of immortality available for men of his hazardous calling—a commemorative ode in the IWW song book.

A narrow little street winding up the hill is Anaconda Road, traversing Dublin Gulch. One day in 1924 a close-packed mass of striking miners started up that road to picket a mine at the top. They were met by murderous fire from the guns of deputies and company guards. Several men were killed; oddly enough they were leaders who had been cold-bloodedly warned before the march that they would be killed if they did not get out of Butte. A reporter squatted behind a post and wrote an eyewitness account of the "battle."

Butte's exciting past is important only because few American communities are so enslaved by their own tradition—a tradition, in this case, which has helped to make Butte the outstanding example of exploitation by the American imperialist capitalism which has stripped the resources of the nation's own frontiers in half a century. Butte is not "the biggest mining camp on earth." It is not a mining camp at all; it is a northwestern metropolis, center of state and regional industry, metropolitan in aspect and influence. Nevertheless Butte thinks like a mining camp, acts like one, and was built like one. This must continue, inevitably as long as every man, woman, and child in this city is dependent in greater or less degree upon its only industry of importance, the absentee-owned mines.

Pierce Williams, writing in *Survey Graphic* on permanently depressed areas, called Butte "the outstanding example of community vulnerability to economic forces in the mining industry." It is that and more: it affords unequaled opportunity for scrutiny of the major economic trend of our era, the reversal of the frontier and monopolist concentration of the means of production. The men came west, but more and more of the products of their toil and the resources of their earth have gone east; and due to recurring market crises, war, technological advancement, and curtailment in real wages, less and less has come back.

The ideals of laissez-faire capitalism have been committing suicide in Butte. Individualism has made a last stand, and the compulsions of an industry caught in the disorganization of capitalist markets have been destroying in Butte that individual initiative which capitalism has always said it lived to defend.

Copper miners have always been individualists; as such they have contributed innumerable heroic or comic episodes to the saga of Butte. They may be, and usually are, loyal and militant unionists; but they would rather work "on their own" by contracting with the company on a piecework basis than work for the union minimum scale. These men are no slaves of the assembly line. Despite the great advance of metal mines technology since World War I, their job is still personal and integrated: the contract miner still "breaks" (blasts), shovels the ore into cars, and timbers the drift; it is a unified task and complete. His is still a man's work, a man's contest with Nature jealous of her riches, a fight against dust and heat and fire and gas.

But the contract system is the bane of the miners' union. Some 80 per cent of the men, according to union leaders, work under that system: they agree to a certain price per cubic foot of ore produced. This is an individual contract between miner and employer and the union has no control over the price except that, on contract or not, the miner must receive at least the union minimum. The contract price can be, and has been, cut at will by the Company; and as the men strive to maintain their wage standards, the union charges, a speedup results which is similar in effect to the speeded assembly lines of a motor plant.

The union strives constantly to increase the daily minimum wage in the hope that it may thus destroy this contract system. In time, the leaders argue, the contract miner may decide that the profits of his "free enterprise" bargain with his boss are not sufficiently greater than the minimum to be worth the extra effort. Then he would become a good deal more interested in union standards than he has been hitherto. Individual initiative, so dear to the heart of the industrialist, would be dead; but so would the speed-up be dead. The Company, on the other hand, insists that the contract system rewards the best worker, and it usually does. The miner, however, cannot choose his own drift and may be assigned to an unproductive working; this, says the union, encourages favoritism by foremen and impairs the independence of the men.

Technological unemployment is an old story by now, and Butte cannot claim that its distress as a result of it is unique. Nevertheless it is a grave problem for Butte. Copper production in this war exceeded that of World War I, but far fewer men were needed to get it out. Production in 1938, in fact, was equal to that of the best years of the first World War, but peak employment was 7,800 and that was 5,000 less than in the war period. Such was Montana's manpower crisis in World War II, however, that even this reduced number could not be found to man adequately the mines of Butte; and although many were released from the army to dig copper there, most of them found they preferred military life to Butte's hot workings, and went back to it.

Net production in pounds per man year when Butte started as a copper camp (1882) was 10,000; in 1930 it was 45,000. When Butte began producing, imported copper was only 8 per cent of American exported copper; in 1930 imports were 108 per cent of exports. Increasing imports in peacetime are bound up with technological change because it is cheap labor abroad which forces installation of machinery to supplant costlier labor in Butte. Because mining is still a man's job and no machine has been devised which can handle the three essential operations listed above, the changes have been few. But they have been remarkably effective in reducing employment. Principal mechanical aids have been the high-speed hoist, and the machine loader, or "mechanical mucker." This latter device, somewhat resembling a baby scoop shovel mounted on a truck, lifts the ore after blasting into a mine tram car. Two sizes of these machines have been introduced in Butte; the union estimates that the smaller one will displace two men and the larger, three.

The specter of the machine which does the work of the man first rose over Butte Hill in 1927, when the Anaconda Copper Mining Company installed high-speed hoists in the Belmont, Badger State, and Mountain Con mines. By means of these hoists it was possible to bring the ore from several mines to the surface through a single shaft in less time than it had taken before to lift the output of one. Many of Butte's mines are connected; thus the Badger and Belmont each works parts of several other mines. The effect of this consolidation of operations was immediate, particularly upon surface employment, and miners believe the hoists, rather than the mechanical loaders, are primarily responsible for the decrease in jobs.

Montana mines employment decreased 10 per cent between 1919 and 1929; in the same period there was an increase of 40 per cent in the rated horsepower of electrical or other power equipment.

Of all the cities which claim the unique and unhappy distinction of being the first to feel the effects of industrial recession and the last to recover, Butte's claim is better than most. The metal mines industry usually follows, seldom leads others into large-scale production, and Butte is forever down or up, never level.

Thus in the winter and spring of 1937–38 Butte mine employment plunged from 7,800 to 800. Virtually all the city's 50,000 people depended upon those 7,000 jobless miners, directly or indirectly. WPA and direct relief certifications skyrocketed and business collapsed; retail trade dropped 50 per cent. This crash came on the heels of a brief upturn which had followed an earlier long period of shutdowns, and the miners, if they could ever accumulate reserves, had not had time to do so. Few could, anyway, for Butte living costs are high, its spending temptations almost innumerable. And life is hard in the mines; when a miner can afford it, he likes to lay off. That is one reason, the miners claim, that the Company permits Butte's notorious "openness." The miner who is always broke cannot lay off and he cannot—when he tires of his dangerous and unhealthy job—quit and "drift" as he did in other, plushier times. The Company likes to have big "rustling lines" before the mines' employment offices; federal relief, keeping large numbers of workers rooted in a community many of whom otherwise would have left, has helped.

Butte businessmen accept as a matter of course their dependence on mines in which virtually half of the city's wage earners are employed. The more cynical among them will say that "the Company's loudest critics are usually on the Company's pay roll"; they have had considerable experience in Butte with agents provocateurs. This, however, does not lead to business confidence and businessmen do not make any save the most essential commitments. Loans and discounts of Butte banks plunged from $18,000,000 in 1929 to less than $3,000,000 in 1939 while the banks' cash reserves more than doubled.

Business has been tolerant, too, of the big gambling establishments which, though closed in intermittent reform waves, have given the city a nationwide reputation. They resent bitterly much of the sensational publicity, insisting "other towns are just the same, but not so honest about it." There is a measure of truth in this, but Butte's gambling has certainly been on a scale one would be unlikely to find in other cities of 50,000. An indication of its magnitude as an industry might be seen in the fact that the Arcade, one of the largest establishments prior to a statewide shutdown in 1940, was located on Butte's busiest, highest-rent corner. Curley Darragh, its operator, was hostile when questioned: "Get wise to yourself; if we weren't wanted in Butte we wouldn't be here!"

Operators of the games and bars in Butte and in its good-time suburb of Meaderville have always insisted that a very large share of their business comes from visitors, and a police officer once bitterly confirmed this. "We have to police not only Butte but the five adjoining counties too," he complained. "There's many a man who will live like a respectable gopher all week in Deer Lodge so he can get drunk and raise hell in Butte come Saturday night!"

Only about a third of the city's people are American born of American parentage. This has much to do with Butte politics, industrial practice, and social life. It is responsible for much of its color and some of its bad reputation. It has restrained any tendency to become "stuffed shirt"; a dance hall proprietor boasts, "All our patrons have to dress; see, they all have coats on." Though this proportion of foreign born and foreign or mixed parentage is much higher than in the average American city, it does not indicate a lower literacy standard. Butte, in fact, has less than half the national urban percentage of illiteracy—1.2 against 3.2.

Another Butte statistic perhaps sheds some light on the city's famous restricted district. It's still a man's town: it has more men in proportion to women than any other American city its size and far more than the average. In 1930, 54.3 per cent of its population was male; the national average was 49.5. Mining is more attractive as a career to unmarried than to family men, and Butte's dependence on that single industry also limits the field of employment for single women.

That is one reason "they treat sporting people very well in Butte," which is the way one of the "sporting people"—a girl in Butte's "Venus Alley"—put it. "After we go out of the alley we're just like anybody else. We work for our money; in good times the take'll run to $100 a week for some of the younger and prettier ones . . . Butte figures we give value for the money and we're just as good as anybody so we can live in nice places and it doesn't matter where we eat, even if they know we're sporting people. They don't kick us out of restaurants or make it tough for us, like some places I've been. . . ."

The restricted district is in a narrow alley-courtyard just two blocks from Butte's new modern high school and on the same street. When the school was built there was some reckless talk of closing the line, but it had been there for many years, it was accepted, and Butte decided it was necessary. So a compromise was reached: the three entrances were closed off with fences built somewhat like a maze, painted green and bearing the words "Men under 21 Keep Out." Youths mature rapidly in Butte and may be skilled miners before they are twenty-one, so the phrase is not as foolish as it looks. Further to protect Butte's knowing youth, the girls were ordered to abandon their "day shift" and not to appear in the alley before five o'clock.

The girls are protected from racketeers and cranks and disturbances are rare. However, the "line" is a cold-blooded business proposition. Its "cribs" are dingy, crude offices for a revolting "business," which even in tolerant Butte is a little furtive, a little afraid.

Under the leadership of an enlightened and progressive mayor who, unfortunately for Butte, died in office, the city began a few years ago with federal help to tackle its unique problem—to break with paralyzing tradition and the powerful forces which maintain that tradition: in the words of that mayor, Charles A. Hauswirth, "to refrain absolutely from boosting Butte as a mining camp, but advertise it in every conceivable way as an up-and-coming city."

Butte has behind it three quarters of a century of haphazard mining-camp development, decades of municipal mismanagement, and a community psychology born of miners' tradition—generous but heedless. Here are people oddly different from their nearest neighbors, even in other Montana cities. A spontaneous gesture of good-fellowship, perhaps a benefit dance to provide a "seeing eye" dog for a blind musician, can find wholehearted, immediate support; but Butte's patience is short and its vision dim, so a long-term program of community planning is more apt to run up against the phrase, "Oh, the hell with it!"

The handicaps under which such planning will have to proceed are worth special consideration. This "most pictorial city" of Joseph Pennell earned the artist's attention, he wrote, because

"Its mountain is crowned not with trees, but with chimneys. Low black villages of miners' houses straggle toward the foot of the mountain. The barren plain is covered with gray, slimy masses of refuse which crawl down to it—glaciers of work—from the hills. The plain is seared and scorched and cracked with tiny canyons, all their lines leading to the mountain. . . ."

That, accompanying Pennell's sketch of Butte, was published in 1916. His incisive, if superficial, judgment could have stood until the last decade; but the Butte which he saw is gone. It was an overgrown mining camp sprawling over some five square miles, completely without benefit of planning, cursed with offset streets and blind streets, even streets higher on one side than on the other. Some of its sewers—since replaced—were fifty years old and ran diagonally across the city; one had been laid by a mining magnate to connect two points for which he wanted sewer service, with complete disregard to the needs or convenience of the intervening sections. Much of the city had no sewer service until "new deal" public works projects were inaugurated, and relied on cesspools; the soil formation of Butte is unsuitable for these so scores of families were kept continually digging up their back yards in an exhausting struggle to dispose of their own waste.

But Butte's most incredible feature—it has struck casual visitors as very funny indeed, though it isn't—is its boundary. The city limits defy every rule of logic or draftsmanship because they dodge nearly all the mines; the boundary will run straight as a die to a mine fence, then swerve neatly around it, leaving the mine property happily exempt from city taxation.

Montana Street is one of Butte's busiest thoroughfares. In one section, one side of this street is in the city limits; the other side though occupied by several large warehouses and the passenger depot of a major railroad, is not—and the blissful tenants of that side of the street benefit by city sewers, fire protection, and other services but pay no city taxes. You can round a corner in Butte and leave the city, turn the next corner and be back in. This condition does not seem particularly strange to the citizens of Butte and planners despair of remedying it since Montana law provides that before a city may annex a district, 51 per cent of the district's property owners must consent. The property owners in these "islands" are unlikely to consent to added taxation.

The prospectors, and later the industrialists, who ruled Butte stripped the Rocky Mountains of their forests within a radius of fifty miles of the city. After copper was discovered came the horror of open-hearth smelting—the reduction of copper on giant wood and charcoal fires around the city, an operation which blanketed Butte with a perpetual pall of filthy yellow sulphurous smoke, hastening the demise of citizens with influenza or pulmonary disorders and denuding the hills of vegetation. Open-hearth smelting ended when the plant was built at near-by Anaconda ("beautiful," said Pennell, "with the beauty of death!") but the damage had been done. In recent years, however, Nature and relief workers have been bringing grass and trees back to Butte. It's a long job.

Federal help has enabled Butte to clean up the old mine dumps, bring some green back to its residential sections, and improve its recreational and cultural resources. Butte has never gone in much for culture, on a community scale, though in hundreds of mean homes and obscure and dingy bars there live the music and color and legend of a dozen peoples. In Meaderville swing blares from the "Rocky Mountain," and one of the city's masters, feeling his costly liquor, tosses $20 to the orchestra conductor in trade for his baton and leads the band, weaving drunkenly. Out on the "flats" hundreds squeeze into a hot little room, drink their cheap beers, and clamber onto a splintered floor to push each other around to the music of a juke box. Sunday, a miner and his wife and children may picnic at Columbia Gardens, the park given to Butte by William A. Clark. In it are free "rides" for the youngsters and brick stoves where the mother, who has cooked in a miner's hut all week, can cook again after her husband has built the fire. Here are trees and grass, not as dirty and worn as they used to be.

Such cultural efforts as have been made recently appear to have come from the upper levels of Butte society—for Butte has an élite; it even had, forty years ago, a *Blue Book*. That impressive volume, compiled by one John Boyle O'Reilly, set out as do all *Blue Books* to advise hostesses as to which fellow citizens might be bidden to their functions without fear of embarrassment; the ladies and gentlemen whose names were inscribed in his chaste scroll could be depended upon to refrain from the heartier expression of good-fellowship then popular in Butte social life—such as fights. But, warned O'Reilly very wisely, "the lines have not been too closely drawn." Despite this liberal interpretation of its scope, the *Blue Book* was not a success: it appeared but once.

Butte's only recent cultural development of importance was sponsored by its Junior League, whose eager maidens, aware of the city's artistic possibilities and ashamed of its cultural lag, established a municipal art center and later turned it over to a non-profit community organization and the Federal Art Project. Butte also has a concert association, similar to that in many cities of the hinterland. Though it is only fifty miles from the scene of operations of the Vigilantes, it has no historical museum nor any other kind save for the outstanding mineral and gem display in the State School of Mines.

Housing is poor and expensive. About 53 per cent of the residential units are substandard; nearly half of all dwellings lack private toilet and bath. The preponderance of single men encouraged construction of multiple-unit dwellings and discouraged family homes with yards. A United States Housing Authority project, completed within the last few years, has alleviated some of the worst conditions but could aid only a comparatively few families.

Wage scales of Butte building-craft unions are 20 per cent

higher than in seventy other selected American cities. Living costs
are slightly higher than average, lumping them all together; some
goods and services, such as clothing maintenance, personal care,
and household operation, are much higher than average. All of
Butte's utilities, even water, are privately owned and service is
costly compared with other cities. A Miles City, Mont., newspaper
man once essayed to describe Butte's economy in a sentence: "In
Butte everybody goes around happily 'sticking up' everybody else;
and they think they have prosperity!"

About fifteen years ago, a Bureau of Mines review of conditions
in Butte commented: "It is usual in American mining districts for
towns to begin as camps and progress into cities. Butte has reached
the latter stage, and if there remain reminders of the old days . . .
it is a matter which local public pride may be expected to correct
year by year." But public pride in Butte is an unpredictable and
ungovernable force, occasionally virile and well directed, occasionally going off on a tangent quite understandable to Butte but mys-
tifying to more staid communities. Butte was proud of and admired,
for instance, one Jerre Clifford, of whom the mayor's own newspaper said in eulogy: "He was one of the really big men Butte has
produced; many are the men in all walks of life whose burdens
have been made lighter by his benevolence and kindliness." Clifford
was Butte's biggest gambling operator and owner of a statewide
lottery, but according to Montana standards he was an upright and
a generous man. He made money, spent it, and gave it; and more
than that, plus rudimentary honesty and affability, Montana asks
of no man.

The city is shamefacedly proud of its periodic outbursts of maniacal exuberance, as when students defy police bans on pre-game
demonstrations, mass in little groups on obscure streets, and con-
verge on the business district in a rioting mob of three thousand,
routing the police with rotten eggs and looting a few candy stands.
City officials are angry but secretly appreciative of the students' ingenuity; for the vandalism they blame older rowdies, graduates of
Butte's once-notorious "overall gang," long since broken up.

But it is not mass movements which stick in one's memory as
most closely associated with Butte: it is rather the stories of the

heroic, foolhardy or pathetic individuals whose exploits have built the biggest mining camp's legend and still are building it.

Thus—hero: "American George" Chubb. . . . During a circus parade an elephant was maddened by stepping upon a fallen live wire, and charged the crowd. Miner Chubb, who never had seen an elephant before, leaped upon the berserk beast's trunk, was swung dizzily from side to side of the street; finally, clinging to the trunk, helped to beat the animal into submission with a club handed to him from the crowd. A few years later "American George" placed twelve dynamite shots in a drift while his partner started up a chain ladder. Before Chubb could get up the ladder the shots began to explode prematurely and he tumbled back into the winze. The ladder was beyond his reach and Chubb screamed to his partner to toss it down to him; but the partner, afraid to venture near the shaft, cowered in safety while blast after blast flung Chubb's body from wall to wall until it had been pounded to dust. The partner, shunned by all of Butte, crept nightly into a dark corner of a grimy bar and drank himself to death in a year.

Clown: "Colonel Buckets," race-track tout. . . . Illiterate, he was nevertheless persuaded by practical jokers to file in the primaries for lieutenant governor of Montana. Most of his campaigning was done in Butte's most disreputable sections; it was said that his was the first political campaign in history to be conducted entirely at night. He was induced to hand out on the street cards advertising a cure for waning manly vigor, under the impression that they were campaign cards for himself. "That's my platform," he told each shocked or incredulous recipient. Overcome by his labors getting out the vote, the "Colonel" was lost for three days after election. Butte was not particularly surprised to find that he received 12,632 votes—not, fortunately, enough to win.

Fool: an unnamed boy. . . . In strike time, cold spotlights pierced the night sky and grim gunners beside them watched pickets in the street below, playing horseshoes by the light of an ancient arc. Deep in the earth water rose and the scabs pumped frantically—for in the big 1934 strike the miners "pulled" the engineers and maintenance crews too. Suddenly a youngster slipped away from the horseshoe game's audience, seized a chain and risked his life by tossing it over a power line, releasing his hold an instant before it settled down on the wires. A flash crackled along the line, sparks from the chain bombarded the pickets, the pumps stopped. Desperate bosses called electricians; when they came, women and children pelted them gaily with rocks while the miner pickets, peaceably inclined, remonstrated.

Hero, clown, and fool; these are the men who have made Butte, these and that ordinary miner whom we left, several pages back, picnicking with his family at Columbia Gardens. After the picnic supper they will herd aboard a bus and ride through the clamorous night of their city up some precipitous street to their dreary, crowded, dingy home. The girls on the "line" will have drawn their painted rockers to the windows, the bars and streets will have begun to fill up: for the mines are working again and it's an all-night city in good times. But if the mines were closed by a strike, uneasy peace would settle over the avenues, picket lines would begin forming at the mine gates and the company's guards would inspect their weapons.

Busses roar noisily through the streets and planes roar overhead, and a drunken driver may hurtle into Broadway from the Meaderville Road, maiming a pedestrian. The police will get him, but it will be hard to convince a Butte jury: life is cheap here.

Then it is nearly dawn, and the darkness lifts from the edges of the encircling peaks. In strike time the pickets leave in relays for coffee and the guards loosen their grip on their guns; the searchlights go out. But now the mines are running. . . . A few men sidle out of the green gateway to the line, turn up their coat collars, clump off to cheerless rooms; a few drunks are ejected from bars; if the town is "open," janitors are cleaning up in Curley Darragh's Arcade. ("If he isn't at the Arcade, he isn't in Butte.")

At last, Butte sleeps.

By Clyde F. Murphy

HOGAN OF DUBLIN GULCH

Tom Gary and Denny O'Shea sat in the rear seat of a black surrey which had a resplendent patent leather dashboard and red wheel spokes. Cassidy, on the right-hand side of the front seat, held, in one hand, the reins of a pair of unevenly matched bays which stood fully harnessed at the door of the stable, champing their bits. In the other hand he held a long whip. Hogan had backed Feeney, the short and muscular liveryman, into a corner. Tom and Denny could not distinguish Hogan's words but his voice was high-pitched and strident and his attitude menacing as he drummed on Feeney's chest with a stiff forefinger. Feeney belonged to that class of businessmen who are dedicated to the principle that a customer is never wrong. But though Feeney, in matters of business, practiced self-restraint, he could stand only so much personal abuse. Hogan's remarks were making his face very red. Denny O'Shea was suffering from a hang-over and the delay made him grumble.

"What in hell's holdin' us up?"

Cassidy turned around slowly and when he faced Tom and Denny he raised his brows and grimaced sourly.

"That son of a bitch is the wise one all right."

"Who's wise?"

"That Feeney," grunted Cassidy. "There's a money-hungry lout if I ever seen one."

As Denny O'Shea looked at Tom, Tom shrugged. Denny turned back to Cassidy and stared.

161

"Who's Feeney?"

"That's Feeney that Hogan's talkin' to."

As a matter of fact Hogan, at that moment, was doing no talking. Feeney had discarded his mask of commercial patience, and had quit nodding his head. He was sputtering at Hogan and Hogan was backing up.

"What in hell's wrong?" Denny asked.

With his broad left hand, Cassidy deflected his voice to the rear. "The bastard rented out Minnie," he said hoarsely.

Denny's jaw dropped and his brow burrowed. He shook his head slowly from side to side. Then he exploded.

"Fur the love of God, Cassidy, who's Minnie and what in hell are ye tryin' to say?"

"Minnie's a damn fine mare," Cassidy explained, with precise patience, "and Minnie oughta be hitched up here to this buggy instead o' that. . . ." He used the whip to indicate the right-hand horse.

Tom and Denny noticed that Hogan had turned, in lofty contempt, from Feeney and had started for the surrey. He pivoted at the halfway point, not yet satisfied with his job of doing Feeney up. Grandly, he yelled:

"I oughta leave yur goddamned team and wagon here; and that's just what I'd be doin' if this wasn't the day of poor Toss O'Hara's funeral."

"Tssah!" snorted Feeney. He waved his open hand at Hogan in the manner of shooing flies.

Hogan lumbered to the surrey, climbed to the driver's seat and seized the reins. Cassidy slyly retained the whip.

"You do the drivin', Hogan," said Cassidy, "and I'll just keep this to touch 'em up a little. . . ."

Hogan lunged for the whip.

"Gimme that!" he thundered. His joust with Feeney had been, at best, indecisive. His self-respect demanded that he ride over Cassidy roughshod.

Hogan's whip sang vengefully in the air and cracked like a shot on the rump of the right-hand horse. The team vaulted madly from the stable with Tom and Denny clutching the robe rail. In the street the horses wheeled abruptly, whipped the surrey in a skidding half-circle and set off at a wild gallop.

"Whoa, goddammit, whoa!" yelled Hogan, sawing with the reins.

Feeney stood gaping at the door as his team plunged and reeled toward the open country to the east of Butte. He watched until a gray bank of dust came between; then he listened, in frenzied suspense, for the smash-up that would shatter the finest equipment of his stable. When the crash did not come, his heart at first leaped with hope that there was to be a miracle. It subsided shortly when Hogan's "Whoa, goddammit, whoa!" carried back to him over the commotion of the runaway and he caught a fleeting glimpse of Hogan through a rent in the dust cloud, half-standing for leverage, and jerking savagely on the reins.

But a miracle did occur. At the end of a half-mile breather, the horses slowed to a trot, became tractable, and yielded to Hogan's pulling them around. The experience had made Hogan's nerves raw and had put him in an ugly humor. He was muttering wrathfully to himself when at last he drew up his team in the next block down from the O'Hara home at the end of a long funeral procession.

Tom breathed a sigh of relief. He looked ahead of him and saw the tall, box-like hearse next to the sidewalk in front of the O'Hara home. There were four or five carriages standing in the street parallel with the hearse and about twenty others strung in a single line one full block and across the intersection into the next block. All horses were standing patiently. Some men and women had climbed out of their carriages and were gathered in clusters at various points along the narrow plank sidewalk. Tom leaned back in his seat and relaxed. He contemplated, with some pleasure, the trip to the graveyard. The morning was bright and warm. The air was clean and fresh and the rim of high hills around Butte was purple against a light haze. Denny apparently took no pleasure in the brightness of the morning. He had been unusually quiet. Tom saw that his face was white and his eyes bloodshot. Beads of sweat were sprinkled over his forehead and lined in a small column along his upper lip. He stared glumly ahead. Hogan and Cassidy, in the front seat, were huddled together speaking softly. Tom heard Hogan say,

"See if you can spot the son of a bitch."

Cassidy rose, steadying himself against the dashboard, and craned his neck, as he looked intently forward. Hogan remained hunched over in the front seat like a great black bear.

"Humph!" snorted Cassidy, his eyes narrowing.

"See him?" asked Hogan.

"Up near the head end he is," reported Cassidy, "as proud as you please." Hogan sat thinking for a time and at last he muttered,

"Pretty foxy he is. Pretty foxy all right. But we'll just see about Mr. Donner Gribbin. We'll just see."

Hogan's tone was one of frustration. But there was a ring of bitter defiance as if he had not yet given up even though the odds against him were heavy.

When Cassidy sat down he jarred the surrey. The team shifted their feet and tossed their heads.

"Whoa, whoa," growled Hogan as he gave the reins a sharp, unnecessary jerk. He sat up in the seat and faced Cassidy.

"He's got Minnie, eh?"

"He has," responded Cassidy grimly.

Though Tom was curious, he considered all of this to be none of his business and he did not intrude. Denny O'Shea, however, roused himself suddenly and leaned forward.

"What's up, boys?"

Hogan cleared his throat, shifted his immense bottom along the front seat and turned around. His face was red and his eyes were gleaming. When he spoke it was with a subdued voice as if, despite the rancor in his heart, he had not forgotten that this, after all, was the funeral of poor Toss O'Hara.

"I hired Feeney's best team fur this," Hogan said measuredly.

He paused for the sake of dramatic effect and used the interval to spit expertly over the opposite side of the buggy. The spittle skidded through the dry white dust and rolled into a ball.

"Well, sir," Hogan resumed, his voice rising in spite of the occasion, "when I comes to the stable this mornin' to get Prince and Minnie, what d'ya think happened? There was Prince all right but where was Minnie? 'She's out,' says Feeney. 'Out?' says I. 'Out,' says Feeney. And by the livin' Jesus, she was out. Instead o' gettin' Minnie, I got that goddamned leather-covered oat box."

Hogan pointed the whip to indicate the rangy right-hand horse. It was not a horse to be classed with Prince on the left. A loose, awkward animal, it stood listlessly and its bones pressed outward to form rough lumps on its skin that resembled the scuffed corners of a suitcase. Prince was glossy and he held his head up.

Denny nodded his agreement while Tom asked,

"Who's got Minnie?"

Hogan swung around.

"Donner Gribbin," he gasped. The bare mention of Gribbin's name was painful. "He gives Feeney a dollar extra so's to get Minnie and that goddamned money-grubber Feeney, fur a measly dollar, busts up the team of Prince and Minnie. Now what d'ya think of such unprincipled sonsabitches?"

A stir in the line distracted their attention. Tom saw the pall-bearers carrying the casket from the O'Hara home to the hearse. The groups on the sidewalk dissolved and sought their separate carriages. The drivers took up their reins and the procession moved slowly out of Dublin Gulch and south over Anaconda Road toward Butte.

As Hogan drove he clucked and slapped his reins on the rumps of the team. There was but one carriage behind them in the procession and Hogan turned frequently to study its driver. At last he said,

"Cassidy, take a look behind us. Who might that poor old soul be?"

Cassidy squinted briefly through the morning sunlight.

" 'Tis the widow McHugh," he answered.

"Hm-mm," mused Hogan, "a little old widow woman all by herself. Cassidy, we'll have to give her a hand tyin' up that horse when we get to the cimitery."

Tom looked to the rear and saw a woman, very old and withered, driving a big fuzzy horse, gaunt and weary-looking. It moved slowly, bobbing its head in rhythm with its gait. One of its bridle blinkers had been torn loose and it dangled and flapped as the horse plodded onward, its eyes riveted to the ground. Tom was puzzled by Hogan's concern over the old woman tying the horse at the cemetery. Once the horse stopped it would take a charge of dynamite to get it moving again. Oh well, Tom thought, Hogan doesn't know a hell of a lot about horses.

When the head of the funeral procession reached the graveyard and the hearse stopped at a freshly dug grave, some of the carriages were still out on the county road which was narrow and bounded on either side by barbed-wire fences. The gate stood open and there was no one left to tend it. Many carriages at the forward end drew out of line and bunched in a wide clear space near the grave; those behind closed up and the line shortened until Hogan's and Mrs. McHugh's carriages were inside the gate.

"Mind now, Cassidy," said Hogan, "we'll go back and help the little lady."

The two big Irishmen climbed out of the front seat and started back. Denny O'Shea, uninterested, stared ahead in silence. He had not said a word since the funeral procession first got under way. A hang-over always affected Denny that way—it made him quiet and sullen and irritable. Tom's curiosity, by this time, had been quickened and he watched Hogan, hat in hand, approach the old lady in the carriage behind them, with Cassidy about two paces to his rear.

"As I live and breathe," Hogan shouted heartily, "if it ain't Mrs. McHugh."

The little old woman eyed him sharply, but said nothing.

"Come now, let me help you outa that buggy, Mrs. McHugh," Hogan roared.

Mrs. McHugh shook her head emphatically and drew back to a corner of the seat.

"Didn't aim to be gittin' out," she said in a high shrill voice. "I'm cramped in my joints. I'm gonna stay right here."

"Oh now, now, is that so?" Hogan's smooth, soft voice prompted Cassidy to gaze at him in amazement. Hogan's smile was broad as he swept his arm in the general direction of the crowd.

"Sure now, Mrs. McHugh," he went on, with just a tinge of reproof, "you'd like to help with the prayin' at the grave."

"Well . . ." said Mrs. McHugh. Her conscience had been pricked.

Suddenly she nodded her head to indicate a change of mind. Moving from the corner of the seat cost her both effort and pain but she persisted. After winding the reins on the whipsocket, she backed from the buggy, with Hogan supporting her, fumbled one foot until she got it on a small iron step between the wheels. Then she clung tightly to Hogan and stretched her off leg slowly to the ground. Hogan was all solicitude.

"There now," he said to her, "Mr. Cassidy will take your arm and escort you right up there where them people are. I'll personally see to tyin' up this here horse."

"You don't need to," snapped Mrs. McHugh with a breathless chuckle, "he'll stand there all night in that one spot."

Hogan smiled down indulgently. Patting Mrs. McHugh on the shoulder, he said with careless ease:

"Pshaw now, this is no trouble at all. And of course . . ." His manner tightened; he stooped toward her, his face quite solemn. In a lowered voice he said, "We sure don't want no mishaps at poor Toss O'Hara's funeral."

"Well, no . . ." said the old lady uncertainly.

"I'll just tie him back here," Hogan said as he waved toward the gate.

Cassidy, all this time, had stood gaping, trout-fashion. Hogan nodded sternly at Cassidy but Cassidy did not move. Hogan glared at Cassidy, his face red and glistening, his eyebrows pinching together. Still Cassidy did not get his cue.

"Well, Cassidy . . ." Hogan thundered.

Cassidy jumped for Mrs. McHugh's arm and led her in the direction of the grave. Hogan seized the bridle reins of Mrs. McHugh's horse and led it around in a circle until he came to the graveyard fence. Then he swung along the fence until Mrs. McHugh's carriage stood squarely across the gate. Tom, in the back seat of the surrey, watched Hogan's every move. When Hogan had spotted the carriage so that not even a pedestrian could get through the gate without moving the horse and carriage, he pulled one of the reins free of the whipsocket and wrapped it around a fence post. Then he walked briskly toward the surrey from which Tom and Denny had not stirred. Hogan was whistling softly as he rubbed his hands together to rid them of dust. He climbed into the front seat of his rented surrey and turned his team so that they were headed

for the gate. Denny O'Shea frowned irritably at all these deploy-
ments but he waited, before speaking, until Hogan had set the
brake.

"What in hell are you up to, Hogan?"

When Hogan turned around he wore an expression of grim satisfaction.

"This'll fix Mr. Donner Gribbin, all right."

Without saying more, Hogan took, from the floor of the surrey,
a flat cast-iron weight to which was attached one end of a leather
thong whose other end was fitted with a metal snap. He fastened
the snap in one of Prince's bridle rings and dropped the weight in
the road at Prince's feet. His manner was very assured now.

"Well boys," he said jovially, "let's go up there and do the last
fur poor old Toss."

He led the way along the sandy footpath which bordered the
road. The three men, Hogan, Denny and Tom, walked past the
long line of waiting teams and carriages and took places in the circle of mourners about the grave. Tom was between Hogan and
Denny O'Shea, with Cassidy, just beyond, supporting old Mrs.
McHugh. Father Reardon sprinkled the coffin and the grave with
holy water and in his deep bass voice he said:

*Ego sum Resurrectio et vita: qui credit in me, etiam si mortuus
fuerit, vivet; et omnis qui vivet, et credit in me non morietur in
aeternum.*

As the priest began the *Canticle of Zachary,* Tom lifted his gaze
to a circle of a hundred or more people about the grave. Some
women were already dabbing their eyes; the men were tight in the
lips and verging on tears. Tom knew that these Irish people
mourned at the death of Toss O'Hara with a child-like intensity.
These Irish were not widely different from the Irish in Minnesota.
I wonder, he mused, if there are "different" Irish anywhere or if
Irish anywhere will change. He almost chuckled when he recalled
what Terry Flynn, back home, had said: "The changeability of the
Irish is their one unchangeable quality." Still, Tom thought—more
somberly now—the Irish must change if they are ever to climb from
the foot of the social and economic ladder. Maybe this rich new
Montana country will offer enough work, enough opportunity to

bring about a real change in the Irish. Maybe, he went on thinking gloomily, maybe, but I have many doubts.

The Irish nature itself cannot be trusted. If these Irish, around this grave, should adopt the same reverent attitude toward life they now show toward death, they would sweep the world before them. They've got brains enough and they work very hard. What could keep them down? This side of the Irish that I now see—their sincerity and simpleness of heart—is the best side of the Irish.

"*Requiem aeternam dona ei Domine,*" intoned Father Reardon. Tom joined in the swelling response,

"And let perpetual light shine upon him."

The priest sprinkled the casket with holy water and then the casket began to lower into the grave. Above the Latin intonations of the priest Tom heard choking sobs of women. He saw many men in the circle biting their lips as the tears ran down their cheeks. In a sudden melting of the heart, he almost cried himself. He loved these Irishmen for their tears; these Butte Irish were his kind of people. He felt as if he had known them always. Tom's eyes followed the casket downward.

> "*Requiescat in pace.*"
> "Amen."
> "*Anima ejus, et animae
> omnium fidelium defunctorum per
> misericordiam Dei requiescat in pace, Amen.*"

A quick stir and the scuffling sound of running caused Tom to take his eyes from the black wall of earth which was the far side of the grave. The solid circle of people about the grave had suddenly grown thin, as if by magic, and had broken entirely in several places. Straightening up, he saw that at least two dozen men had bolted the circle. They were making for their carriages as fast as they could run. Donner Gribbin was already in his and was hauling up a friend rather roughly into the front seat beside him. Donner's quick jerky movements and a certain resolute set of his chin showed that though he was tense and highly excited, he had a definite program in mind.

Derg Finley's team, frightened by the charging men, shied backward up a green slope, knocking over two headstones, with little Stubby Cavanaugh, Derg's pal, hanging to one bridle and reaching frantically for the other. Meanwhile Derg vaulted into the rear of the carriage and seized the reins. The hard-packed graveyard earth resounded like a monstrous drum to the stamping of many horses and above all a great banner of gray dust drifted with a light wind. While Tom and Denny stood bewildered, Hogan calmly took the arm of Mrs. McHugh.

"What in hell's wrong, Hogan?" shouted Denny.

Tom might have asked this question himself had he not been halted in his tracks by the spectacle of Donner Gribbin urging his little mare up a dangerous embankment, quite heedless of the tilt of his carriage and the groveling fear of his fellow passenger, an elderly stranger on his knees clinging desperately to the rail on the dashboard. Derg Finley had seen the march Donner was stealing and he began to force his team over Donner's course. Obviously Donner and Derg planned to skirt the long line of standing carriages to the graveyard gate. When Derg's team had negotiated the embankment, Derg released a yell that made the few mourners about the grave flinch and cross themselves.

Behind him Tom heard a rushing sound and he turned just in time to see Weeshy O'Toole, rather far down on the lower side of the road, alone in a single-seated buckboard, racing a great roan horse and buggy in a little hollow and now he pressed his advantage by lashing his animal across a sandy flat in a beeline for the gate. It would be nip and tuck between Donner and Derg and Weeshy.

Many other men, whom Tom had never seen, were now sprinting for their carriages. The graveyard was alive and loud with men running, horses rearing and the air was heavy with dust which settled into everyone's nostrils and sifted like white powder on the dark clothes of the men and women. There were shouts and some cursing now and, occasionally, the scream of a frightened woman.

Hogan looked over Mrs. McHugh at Cassidy, shook his head and sighed elaborately. Then he turned to answer the question that Denny had put to him some moments before.

"You see, Denny, my boy," Hogan said, speaking casually so as to conceal his sense of superiority, "this here monkey business gives you some idea of the small reverence them louts has fur the dead. No sooner is the service at the graveside over than they want to race it fur town. Tsk-tsk-tsk." Hogan leaned toward Mrs. McHugh. "Now don't you worry none or get excited, Mrs. McHugh. Just take your own good time. We'll bring you right to your buggy."

Hogan had had a reason for supplanting Cassidy as Mrs. Mc-Hugh's escort. He walked importantly along the narrow sandy path, guiding Mrs. McHugh with his left hand and holding up his broad right hand in gestures of warning to each of the many drivers who were trying desperately to get their teams out of the line on the road.

"Wait a minute—wait a minute—wait a minute," he would yell, "fur the love o' God, man, don't you see the little lady here? What do you want to be doin'? Runnin' us down?"

Though Hogan's position was quite unimpeachable, several rebellious drivers glared and muttered bitter execrations under their breaths. They did heed his warnings and checked their horses until Hogan and his group got by. But then, to make up lost time, they pounded their steeds furiously, clucked with their tongues, pulled their reins, backed and seesawed until they were out of line and off the road with a straight, unimpeded course for the gate.

Hogan was in no hurry. His pace was that of one terribly aware of his own righteousness. After all, there was something to be said for a man who, in face of all the distractions about him, remained steadfast to the task of escorting a little old widow woman who had to pick her way so slowly. Tom and Denny and Cassidy were close behind Hogan. More wild crashing of sagebrush caused Tom to look once again toward the lower side of the road. He saw the head of the roan and, also, Weeshy's whip flailing back and forth.

Above the road, to the right, Donner Gribbin's mare and Derg Finley's team were rattling swiftly along a steep hillside. The wheels and the hoofs of the horses made sharp staccato sounds as they struck rocks and patches of gravel. When at last Hogan and his group neared the gate, Tom heard some wild yells and he observed that Donner Gribbin was standing up in his carriage. The cause of the yelling was quite plain: Donner was blocked by Mrs. McHugh's carriage from getting through the gate. He had stopped on the hillside and was bellowing his frustration and anger to the world at large. At that instant Weeshy O'Toole's roan clattered out of the sagebrush, blowing heavily. When Weeshy pulled it to a stop, it reared and then began to stamp and buck and shift restlessly. Derg Finley sat glumly silent in his carriage which was right behind Donner Gribbin's.

Donner Gribbin yelled to no one in particular,

"Get that goddamned buggy away from that gate. Who in hell put that buggy there?"

The friend, in the seat next to him, plucked Donner's sleeve. Hogan, now even with his carriage, shouted,

"Gribbin, you oughta get a pastin' fur that kind o' talk here in the place of the dead. Close that big mouth o' yours 'til I take Mrs. McHugh to her buggy."

Weeshy's high-pitched voice carried to the group.

"Hogan, you lout," Weeshy called hotly, "get that buggy away from that gate and be damned quick about it or somebody'll lay you out good."

Hogan merely sniffed, not even deigning to answer the innocuous Weeshy. To Cassidy, he murmured,

"Take Mrs. McHugh to her buggy now, Cassidy, and pull her horse just far enough ahead to clear the gate. Let her wait there. The poor little woman won't want to leave until the crowd thins out a bit anyway. I'll get into my buggy now and drive up and stop right in the gate 'til you get in. Then we're off, Cassidy, and we'll show Mr. Donner Gribbin a thing or two!"

Hogan's voice trembled from intense delight.

Cassidy moved ahead with Mrs. McHugh. Tom and Denny took the back seat of the surrey as Hogan, in the front seat, was gathering in his reins. When Hogan's brilliant maneuver became revealed at last to all the eager men behind him in the carriages, a general howl of rage went up that might have been heard in Butte itself. Above that howl one voice fairly shrieked,

"Hogan, you dirty son of a bitch."

It was none other than loud-mouthed Donner Gribbin who shouted it and Hogan, flaming with wrath, stood up in his surrey.

Big and paunchy, he looked like an outraged Roman senator and his face was the color of a peeled beet.

"Gribbin," he roared, "fur the love o' God, have you no respect fur the place where you're at? One o' these days someone's goin' to kick them outdoor teeth o' yours down your throat."

Gribbin answered Hogan with a tearing noise through his lips as he moved his surrey close behind Hogan's. As Derg Finley pressed toward Donner, the frenzied yell of Weeshy O'Toole came from below the road.

"No, you don't, Finley!" Weeshy screamed. "Hogan gets out first and Gribbin second, but by God I'm third. You just hold back a minute."

Derg Finley thumbed his nose at Weeshy and called,

"We'll see who gets out third."

Hogan loosened his reins and clucked with his tongue and his surrey moved forward. Cassidy put Mrs. McHugh into her carriage and then led her horse along the fence at right angles to the road. Hogan placed his own surrey in the gateway the instant that Mrs. McHugh's carriage cleared. He stopped his horses and when Cassidy climbed into the surrey, Hogan cut the right-hand horse viciously on the rump and the team bolted from the graveyard down the county road.

Tom looked around in time to see Donner Gribbin take Minnie out of the gate at a fast trot. The gate was blurred by a cloud of dust which Minnie the mare raised when she came off the hill. Through the dust Tom suddenly caught sight of Weeshy O'Toole's big roan dashing at full tilt for the gate. Tom did not see Derg Finley's team at all. He heard a rumble, a swish of sliding dirt, something roaring down the hillside and a horrible crashing and splintering of wood. Weeshy's big roan reared and plunged forward and Tom saw a buggy wheel roll waveringly along the inside of the fence and topple over. Weeshy's carriage tumbled on its side and the force of its falling pitched Weeshy clear of the tangle of wreckage. He catapulted through the air and when he came down he landed, with widely spread legs, squarely on his behind in the sand.

Derg Finley's team had charged down the hill behind Donner

Gribbin's buggy. It was sheer folly for Weeshy to try to beat Derg to the gate. But apparently he felt certain he could get out of the graveyard before Derg's team came off the hill. The left-hand horse of Derg's team had shouldered Weeshy's big roan against the fence post. The roan had stood on his hind legs and then had thrown himself forward, dragging the buckboard with him until the left front wheel caught the post and was ripped off Weeshy's carriage. Derg's team and carriage apparently had come out unscathed. When the dust settled Tom saw Derg's team roaring down the road at a furious speed. Derg was making a desperate effort to overtake Donner Gribbin. He had not wasted even one glance back at Weeshy who still sat, stunned and spread-legged, in the sand.

Hogan had no time for the drama that was unfolding behind him. He lashed the rumps of his team with his whip, leaned forward and shouted like a man gone mad, flapped his loose reins, making no effort to guide his horses as the surrey rolled and swayed and the narrow wheels bit into the crumbly road ruts. Tom saw the small farmhouses sweeping by and felt the rush of wind and the fierce sting of small rocks and pieces of dirt flung against his face. A drumming of hoofs behind caused Tom to turn again. He saw Minnie, the little mare, skimming gracefully along the road, her ears back, her head pushed forward, her nostrils flaring and crimson. She lifted her feet high, running smartly and with excellent form and she was gaining. Each time Donner's whip cut her she shook her game little head and pressed even harder. Tom's heart went out to the poor animal, making such a gallant fight. She was coming on. She might even pass Hogan's surrey at the next wide place in the road.

Behind Donner Gribbin, a short distance, was big Derg Finley, standing in his buggy, beating his horses unmercifully and yelling at the top of his voice. An uneven motion of his own surrey attracted Tom. He discovered that Hogan's right-hand horse had broken into a clumsy lope. Prince kept up his slashing trot but his teammate was slowing him down. Hogan kept yelling, "Come on, goddamn you," as he beat the rangy horse with the butt of his whip. Tom looked ahead and was alarmed to see that they were nearing the town. They would be on a street of South Butte in a few minutes and there was great danger the horses would fall when their hoofs struck the slick surface of the cobblestones. There was danger, too, for any pedestrians that happened to be on the street. But Hogan and Gribbin and Finley made no effort to slow down. They whipped their horses even harder. At last Gribbin yelled loudly to Hogan,

"Pull over, goddammit, pull over!"

When Hogan turned and saw that Minnie's black nose was now even with the hub of his left rear wheel and was gaining, his face became livid with rage. He could have pulled over easily and given Gribbin clearance but he did no such thing. Instead, he deliberately pulled to the left so that the rear of his surrey struck Minnie on the shoulder and almost knocked her from her feet. She lifted her head, fighting beautifully to keep her balance. She did not fall but was forced to slow down because her feet were sinking ankle deep into the soft soil at the side of the road. This reckless maneuver gave Hogan the advantage of a splendid lead. His team reached the first street of Butte without having slackened its speed in the least. The hoofs of the team striking the cobblestones sounded like the rattling of giant castanets. Hogan laughed exultantly and yelled over his shoulder,

"I guess we showed Mr. Gribbin a thing or two, eh Cassidy?"

A wild clatter behind them cut off Cassidy's answer. Gribbin's mare, Minnie, and Derg Finley's team had reached the cobblestones together and Tom looked back and saw a neck-and-neck race between Minnie and the team that Derg was driving. The little mare was more than game. She just would not be beaten. She lowered her head and lengthened her stride and drew up past Derg's team. The three carriages whirled and careened up the hilly streets of Butt with pedestrians fleeing in all directions, around the twists and turns of Anaconda Road and into Dublin Gulch with Hogan first, Donner Gribbin second and Derg Finley third. They reached Grogan's in that order, the horses in a lather and blowing noisily. Hogan, Gribbin and Finley all stood at the hitching rail in front of Grogan's tying up their horses. None of them said a word for quite a time. At last Donner Gribbin broke the silence.

"Hogan," he said, "you're a dirty cheatin' son of a bitch."

He snorted angrily and stomped into Grogan's.

Hogan turned and winked at Tom and Denny who were just behind Cassidy. Stubby Cavanaugh climbed out of Derg's carriage and they all went into Grogan's in a group.

" 'Lo, Chaunce."

"Give us a straight one."

"I'll take a straight one too."

Chaunce wiped the bar carefully and nodded as each order was given. Tom and Denny ordered straight whiskeys. When he had received all the orders, Chaunce leaned over the bar and said in a low tone,

"A good turnout fur Toss?"

"Splendid, splendid," said Hogan, "none better."

"Good, good," murmured Chaunce as he brought out bottles and horns. The ceremony of pouring ensued.

Hogan lifted his horn.

"Well boys, here's to the one that ain't here. To Toss O'Hara and may God rest his soul."

"Ah."

"Ah."

"Ah."

"Ah."

"This one's on me, now," said Derg Finley.

"Well, boys," said Stubby, "here's to Toss O'Hara, the best that ever came to Butte."

"Wait a minute—wait a minute. . . ." said Hogan.

"What's wrong, Hogan?"

"Not only the best fella," corrected Hogan, "but the best goddamned miner that ever drove a pick into Butte Hill. Here's to Toss."

"Hold on, hold on . . ." interrupted Donner Gribbin.

"Now what?" asked Hogan.

"Just this," said Donner, "Stubby says that Toss was the best fella that ever came to Butte and that's all right. But you, Hogan, are tryin' to say that Toss was the best miner that ever came to Butte. Now that's takin' in a hell of a lot of territory, as I see it. There was a fella I knew that could get out as much ore in a day as Toss O'Hara could in a month and . . ."

"Fur the love o' God, man," shouted Hogan, outraged, "what are you sayin'? There never was a better miner than Toss O'Hara and you all know it goddamned well. I'd stake the very name of Hogan on that. . . ."

"Hold on now, hold on now," insisted Gribbin, "Toss O'Hara was the best fella, I'll go that far. But there was one fella . . ."

"Why goddammit, man," yelled Hogan, "what's eatin' you . . ."

"Shut your big mouth 'til I'm through, Hogan," bellowed Gribbin, "I'm tellin' you about a fella you're damn proud of. . . ."

Hogan slammed his open hand on the bar and faced Gribbin. "Now you just look here, you windy-gutted . . ."

"It's about Mike," shrieked Gribbin.

A sudden silence fell upon the room.

"Oh, it's Mike, is it?" Hogan said softly, his words vibrating with awakened pride.

"Yes, Hogan," said Gribbin, "your own cousin Mike."

"What about Mike?" asked Hogan eagerly.

"Why, that cousin o' yours," said Gribbin stoutly, throwing back his shoulders, "that same fella Mike could get out twice as much ore as Toss O'Hara ever could."

Hogan's face beamed and he coughed delicately.

"Well now, mm-mm," he said, meditating smugly, "now that you bring up the name of my dear cousin Mike—mm-mm, well now, maybe my cousin mighta had the edge on Toss O'Hara. I'd forgotten about Mike. Well Gribbin, fur once in yur life you're right. Mike is a damn sight better miner than Toss O'Hara ever was. Come now, boys, let's drink to my cousin Mike."

By Wilson O. Clough

ON A NAKED HILL IN WYOMING

On a naked hill in Wyoming,
Mike Phillipoulos from Macedonia, lying under the thin, gravelly
    sod,
And next him Pavlovitch from Serbia, the wooden cross slanting;
And other miners of coal. For accidents will always be.
And Maria Pinelli, aged three, dead of a fever;
The mother gone now to Napoli,
That last day scrawling across the granite stone,
In shaken pencilled letters, half blurred even now by the wind and
    the rain,
O carissima mia, addio.

The dark forested hills of Dakota face westward,
Backing the naked hill, the low promontory,
Looking sunward on leagues of gaunt, marginal land,
With strange buttes rising, apart, far distant, mysterious,
Against the glistening afternoon sky,
Like great ship-bulks, forever stranded on a static sea;
And the graveyard lying lonely on the stark headlands.

Three miles going on a crisp short grass, the landscape gently
    tipping,
And there the abrupt pause, the ugly gash yawning;

178

The hundred rotting wooden steps, lurching down the steep, grassy
    side,
The rusted rails, the tottering trestles,
The empty shafts, like a throat that's been slit,
The chutes, black-clotted with dust,
The lateral gorges, the streets reclaimed by the swift-running
    streams,
The houses, now bowing to earth,
The hollow, echoing hotel, the boss's big house;
And the bird within, beating vain wings upon the window-pane.

Phillipoulos of Macedonia, Pavlovitch, Kronstadt, the others,
Meagerly entrenched against Time and his gnawing,
Under the simple stone and the anonymous grass they lie,
Peripheral sparks, flung off by the forges of trade;
Spent spray from the whirlpools of commerce, the long trajectory
    ended.

And *O carissima mia, addio,*
Fading in the sun, on a naked hill in Wyoming.

JOURNEY TO DENVER

THE HARD-PACKED emigrant road winding along the Platte was called by the Indians the holy road. Thousands had sought this path. Markers on the widely distant trees, lines scratched in bone marked where they had died, their graves to be despoiled by wolf and Indian. Man, woman, and child had wandered here, in droves like animals and singly. On foot, pushing hand carts, in palatial schooners rocking westward, they carried what could be transported only in heart and mind and skeleton, to be despoiled of that too at last.

Wind was blowing on the last day of March, 1867. Sun, rifting the clouds, cast wedges of shadow over the plains. A cloud of yellow dust far in the southwest corner of the horizon might have been the cloud of a buffalo herd. Toward the northwest sprawled the river, which sand-choked and treeless like a solitary wide eye gave expression to the blank earth. Sun and shadow moved in quick succession, in turn graying and brightening the distance.

The emigrant road was on this, the south side of the river. Beyond, at first unseen and yet, once visible, permanent as if it had been there always, moving toward the river but with infinitesimal slowness as of an insect—beetle or fly—crawled a black speck. Yet that speck, tiny as it was, was the center of the great plain tipping in four massive directions away from it. With the speed of stone it crept or crawled toward the river.

As the plain tipped into smaller compass the moving **dot in-**

creased in size until it might have been a jack-rabbit cradled in the lonely brush found in the hollows, loping with unconscious animal intent after its food, eventually descried by hawk or eagle or magpie, with one thrust deprived even of the unconscious, to lie rotting on the plain. Over the red guts spread above the gray fur would circle the birds of prey, and the magpies magnificently black and white would feast on the red entrails. But this as yet had not happened, for the speck moved on, ever increasing in size, as if metamorphosis were taking place here on the plain with no eye to witness.

It might have been an antelope deprived by distance of its speed, though antelope commonly move in herds and this spot in all the wide horizon was the only moving object, save for the shadows which the sun still flung in sweeping circles over the plain. Now the object, whatever it was and however fast or slowly it moved, waded deep in gray while beyond in bright stripes glittered the sun. Now with light full on it, it crept, unconscious that the intent of all the laws of time and timelessness were culminating in this moment of floodlight when, with no eye to see whatever of animal or insect it proved to be, this speck, this dot, this moment of life moved toward the river.

Shadow and light, shadow and light swept on the plain and through their change, oblivious, crept what slowly evolved into a human form, one of the poor Indians perhaps abandoned by his tribe to die alone of his disease, or battling with the wolves to die in solitary grandeur.

Indian or white, male or female, the figure was wrapped in cloths which scattered about it with the wind like the careless wings of a bird. Slowly it moved down to the river and stopped.

Low bluffs were on that side of the water, which like the shadow-striped plain was striped with sand bars. Whatever trees had grown here had been long since felled by beavers and burned by emigrant trains, so that now not even a vestige of beaver house remained. Only a succession of small rivers, separated by islands of sand, floated between the figure on the opposite bank and the emigrant road, along which sooner or later some vehicle must pass.

It was evident now that the figure was that of a woman standing in dark loneliness on the edge of the hostile Indian country—a sentinel, an outpost, a squaw perhaps who having lost her child to the

white man's magic, tuberculosis, had journeyed alone across the
Indian country into the white domain with what tragic design of
revenge or immolation.

The wind at last blew the clouds completely over the sun and
suddenly the entire landscape was sullen, grayed with a film as
repellent as grease.

The dark figure in the ragged draperies stood motionless on the
bank of the river, if that low shelf of sandy bluff could be called a
bank. Larger now than life, so motionless and so alone she stood,
tall, slight, rather more delicately made than the ordinary Indian
woman. In every line of her figure, in every fall and fold of cloth
about her was written weariness, despair, as if having come this far,
with that energy of intent that had brought her here burned out,
she must fall now like a shadow over the plain and, unseen here
with her purpose all but reached, as she was unseen on the long
journey wherever in what remote village it began, fall like the
shadow of the sun on the plain, lifted and moved and stayed by the
wind until the sand should cover her.

A few miles east, unseen because beyond a rise in the plain, one
of the last of the stage coaches was speeding along the emigrant
road. Four mounted cavalrymen rode beside it. The driver on the
box curled his whip over the backs of his six mules, the two lead
animals perfectly matched, white as doeskin.

Inside the coach sat two ill-matched passengers.

One was a German named Sebastian Rische, a shoemaker by
trade, humble in his broken English. A graying beard, tobacco-
streaked, rounded his sad-eyed face. He sat bowed slightly, one
hand on either knee, eyes bent on the empty seat opposite, one of
those failures of life, still seeking.

His companion was a young man twenty-three or -four years old
named Robert Foss. His people had lived in New England. Long
before the Indians there had given up, his ancestors had fought
King Philip and the French; had burned their witches and codified
their good until it became rigid as the skeletons that lined the
emigrant trail.

He had the open face of the intellectual, gray eyes, dark hair, even and conventionally handsome features. A geologist, he was the first of a party from Harvard College planning a survey in the Rocky Mountains for the following summer. Born in New Hampshire, he had lived along a narrow strip of seacoast all his life, save for three years in Europe and his years at Harvard College. The third of a family of four children, he had one sister, a brilliant and beautiful girl. Of his two elder brothers, one was a journalist in Boston, one a professor of modern languages.

The sad, patient-faced man spoke scarcely at all. The young man stared through the little windows of the coach. Having read of the West, the lurid newspaper accounts, the travelers' tales filled with dirty or picturesque Indians, he was not prepared for the cleanness and softness of this landscape.

They were coming down into a pocket between bluffs along the river. Foss, who had been ill as a child and so had had thrust upon him that role no human being willingly assumes, that of the spectator, sensed the melodrama of the lurching coach with its cavalry escort.

As they came up the incline again out onto the open plain, before them on the bluff across the river stood the figure of the woman.

Each of the seven men saw her almost at the same moment and each of them recognized her as a white woman.

The brakes ground at the wheels. The soldiers spurred their horses forward, stopping, a knot of indecision at the river bank, before one of them, prancing a little back and forth to find a crossing, stepped into the water. The crossing took longer than would have at first appeared necessary. The rivers were wider than they had seemed and each had to be swum. The gray head of the horse reared above the water and then laboriously the animal clambered up the sandbank, took a few steps and walking daintily, plunged again into the water, pointed ears swimming above the river, upstream as the rider forced him against the current.

The sky behind the woman was taking on a rainy cast, bruised with blue.

She stood against that sky, taller than she had seemed before now that they were closer in, skirts and shawl blowing a little in the wind, but as before motionless as if unbreathing.

The coach stopped at the crossing, and the two passengers alighted. The driver dismounted, and the strangely assorted company waited on the bank of the river for the horseman to return.

The soldier crossed the last strip of sand and turning to the left mounted the bluff from the side and rear.

High above the river with its tawny and slate strips of sand and water, dominating river and plain, stood the unmoving figure. She gave no sign to signify she had seen her deliverer.

Foss walked downstream and back again.

The driver spit and wiped his mouth with the back of his hand. "She don't want to come."

The soldiers held their horses in check. The jingling of bridles, the uneasy tread of hooves were sharp sounds against the long sweep of wind and the almost soundless river.

The woman did come. She lay like a bundle flung before the rider over the horse's neck, as he made the descent carefully now with his burden.

Now that the woman no longer stood there, the bluff that had seemed a promontory jutting over the river, was only a poor bank of sand.

Foss, oppressed by what he instinctively felt was melodrama or what was in danger of becoming melodrama because the human beings involved would not be equal to its implications, arched his neck to loose it from his collar, braced his feet in the sand beside the river, felt the wind, fresh with rain, blow down against him from the north over how many miles of treeless land, and thought what a poor figure in his eastern clothes he himself must cut, holding his hat on against the wind—trim, inadequate, somehow young and untrained, however radical he might have been in Cambridge, here conventional as his grandfather and as unequal to events.

The German in greatcoat and shawl, square and stocky, stood like a monument beside the coach, his sad bearded face almost wrapped out of sight in reefer and shawl.

Foss felt impatience again with the actors. The three soldiers, still mounted, were joking among themselves. The whole scene was unkempt as though badly rehearsed. The driver seemed not to know his role at all, busying himself suddenly as he was with the harness

of the lead mules, whose intelligent faces and pricking ears alone
seemed aware. Foss could only guess that events like this rescue, if
rescue it were, had become more or less routine during the eight
years the stage line had been in existence. And if this were a special
scene, unique in its import for the protagonists at any rate, how
could the supporting cast know this, who had at least three hundred
and fifteen times, in one-night stands in the remote wastes of the
prairie, ridden to the rescue of a woman?

The soldier, splashing up out of the river, deposited the woman
safely on the shore.

Strangely diminished, standing before them, she was almost small.

For a moment it seemed she would fall, and the driver, Tom Mac-
Intyre, turning suddenly from his preoccupation with his mules,
steadied her against his arm.

"Ma'am, can you a ride a spell? There's a station eighteen or
twenty miles on and a woman there.

"A white woman," he added impotently, for she was looking from
face to face, but with no recognition or acknowledgment, not even
with fear.

Around her, wrapped like a cloth or a scarf, ragged and dirty
and all but hiding her dark hair, hung a shawl. A permanent horror
seemed to have been stamped on her face, shrunken, wizened behind great dilated eyes.

The driver was a large man with huge shoulders and head, and
he jutted beside her like a rock on the plain.

Her garments must have been worn a long time; they were
weathered and dirty, streaked as if with rain or snow, grayed and
rusty. The shawl she wore over her head fell down instead of a
coat below her waist. Whatever age she might have been was lost
in the sorrow and terror of her staring eyes, so that she seemed
less woman than actual terror; and the men standing before her,
men who had served at Bull Run and wintered at Vicksburg, could
not speak, could not offer even the simple suggestion that she be
lifted into the coach; for though she stood alone, that she could
walk no farther was evident.

The silence lasted probably no more than sixty seconds, if as long. A horse stamped a foot, and the men resumed their human burden of thought and action.

The romantic and sentimental Foss was the first to see that the woman was barefoot. Crying out, he threw down at her feet the cape of his coat, blushing violently afterward at the Raleigh-like gesture.

Her control must have been an act of will, for she wavered and collapsed completely. She would have fallen had not Tom Mac-Intyre caught her. And then the men realized that she was exhausted from lack of food, sleep, rest, from strain, from whatever sorrow it was that stared out of her face.

One of the troopers, a man with wife and grown children, kneeling beside the figure in MacIntyre's arms, who half crouched, half lay against the wheel of the coach, forced a little whiskey between the woman's lips, and the death pallor in her face lifted slightly.

In repose, with the eyes closed over their terror, the face was that of a woman perhaps in her early thirties, perhaps younger. The shawl had fallen away from the face to show the dark hair plastered against the skull, so that the whole bony structure was revealed—beautifully neat, small, wide at the eyes, delicate where the jaw joined the chin, completing a line curved yet pointed. Under the eyes were great scooped circles as if a hand had modeled them.

The young man Foss pored over the face with the awe he had known once when he had seen a bat's skeleton, more delicate than filigree, poised, perfectly articulated, with a design not quite geometric, not quite conceived, beautiful in its perfect imperfection. And so he pored over the woman's face, the person behind it like the design in the skeleton of the bat, not quite hidden, not quite evident, curtained in flesh, caught in bone, vulnerable in its unconsciousness.

The eyes lifted. A struggle began.

The driver said: "There, ma'am, it's white people."

Horses and mules in wise unconcern waited for the moment to pass, ears patiently pointing at the horizon, long faces calm.

With buffalo robes the troopers had improvised a bed on one seat of the coach and there now MacIntyre laid the woman.

Foss had been designated to watch beside her, the German Rische electing to ride outside on the box with the driver.

And so the cavalcade started again.

Foss, tumultuously deprived of all the precise analytical New England defenses he was used to summoning in crises, sat watching the figure under the piled buffalo robes. And before him, untenable, nearer than anything vision had managed heretofore in his life, closer to him than his own breathing, was the print left by a woman's bare foot on the sand—long, narrow, and devastatingly personal. Of the actual foot under the dragging skirts he had caught only a glimpse, but the imprint it had made on sand would remain with him as if he held it in his hand, fetish cast in bronze, or, the more desirable because unattainable, articulated in the living bone.

The woman, if she were not still unconscious, was asleep; or, too exhausted for anything more than breathing, she lay inert beneath the robes.

The eighteen or twenty miles to the station MacIntyre had mentioned were a matter only of a few hours. For Foss they were hours that in his present extravagant state he felt were to change his life, as a bomb, destroying a road or line of communication, is responsible for the ultimate change in that road's course, not passing through the valley as before circuitously to its destination, but directly over the mountains; or like the shock of electricity, which changing the psychological pattern, mysteriously corrects the psychosis.

In the narrow room of the coach he was alone, for the woman in a sense had not yet been created. Inchoate, he reached his arm for the spark that would create him too simultaneously with her.

The robe deformed whatever of charm she had. That charm was mystery to him.

In a whirl he sat attempting to solve that mystery, still enough under the control of his old faculties wryly to comment to himself on his dizziness. And as he had felt, watching the soldier ford the river, waiting for him to return with the woman, impatient with what he had erroneously assumed would be the inadequate reaction to the seriousness of the moment, and mostly impatient with his

own inadequacy, so now he once again felt impatience with himself
—that he could be so divided as to comment wryly on his dizzy
state, like an old man.

For some reason he couldn't remember, connected no doubt with
the chronic bronchitis he was just beginning to break, he had spent
his eleventh winter with his grandparents, a luxury unattended by
cousins or immediate family. It had been matter-of-fact, the winter
in the old house; matter-of-fact however only because all of it could
be taken in. No exciting edges were allowed to escape his careful
map-making of events, feelings, people, discoveries. There had been
no schooling, he remembered, of a formal nature. Books of course,
anything that would feed an extravagant taste he was just beginning
to form and that could be found in the Eighteenth Century library
his grandfather husbanded. They drove on Sundays to St. John's in
Portsmouth, he remembered. He recalled the Christopher Wren
church, steep at the end of the street, as though God and with Him
the past incomprehensibly were being crowded up and up and over
the bluff into the river. His stiff-necked grandfather bent his head;
and he, the stiff-necked boy beside him, refused to bend his, watching the meekness of his fellow beings with scorn, Sabbath after
Sabbath defying God to strike him dead and thus pronounce His
Actuality.

God had not so inclined his majesty—unless the one event that
had not been mapped by the youthful cartographer, that had never
belonged, that in its dangerously exciting edges had come near ex-
ploding the entire matter-of-factness of the winter and of all subsequent winters, unless that event could have been considered an
act of God.

Actually it had not been a part of the winter at all, but of the
spring, still uncousined and unfamilied, busy as they were with
their school and all the pursuits of health and community, from
which he was temporarily disbarred.

He had been allowed the run of the fields and the house by his
grandmother, who was a rather flighty and still beautiful lady; and
from the cupola at the top of the house with its view in all directions—so useful to a map-maker—he had watched and dreamed over

the miles of land and sea visible to his eye. From this vantage point
had his ancestors watched the whaling vessels coming into Portsmouth harbor. The Point, black with evergreens, lay below him.
The white steeple of the church, the white façades of the old houses
in their bare gardens, the white gulls were the only break in blackness until he came to the sea. In the far distance he saw the harbor
rolling slate-colored and smooth like water in a cup.

All this and a log kept by a whaling grand-grand-uncle were a
part of the map of that winter.

In the spring, however, in April when he began pushing into the
woods, coming on gardens he did not recognize, having seen them
only in their summer fervor, or breaking suddenly through a bracken
of hemlock and pine to find himself hung high above the rocks on
the edge of the water, there began happening in him something a
little frightening because unadmittedly he sensed its wild and uncontrolled nature. He was eleven years old and he was frightened,
excited, and seductively attracted as by evil—that witch-thing he
had read about not quite with understanding.

On this particular day he was inland on the other side of the road
that divided the Point into two halves—land-side and sea-side. The
woods were black and deep, starred occasionally down gloomy
alleys with dogwood just coming into bloom. White clouds moved
languidly in the blue sky above the treetops as if raggedly torn on
their black branches. There was no wind. The air was fresh, watery,
and sweet. Glitters of sunlight pushed into the woods. Everywhere
was white. There was more blossoming than he imagined possible—
like the skirts of girls running down the woods ahead of him where
there were no pathways, to be lost in the distant blackness. Like
laughter the white blossoms teased him farther and farther into the
woods, or like a web that was winding him round and round until
he could see only the white flowers, hear the distant laughter.

And so he went farther than he had ever gone before, even with
the oldest cousins, and came into a strange section of the Point.

A field opened and he crossed that, his feet pressing with pleasure into the knobs of soil not quite broken down into dirt. In this
open place he could see a whole section of the sky with its great
continents of clouds floating, and his map-making mind began

charting that expanse; but only so long as it took him to cross the field, for ahead were the seductive woods beckoning him with their unchartable danger. And he went into them again. Their black closed round him as if never to relinquish him.

Vividly all his life long, on those days he unsuccessfully repressed the memory, he was to recall every flower he then saw, every feeling he then felt, as though after all he had made a small map of that unmappable land—or rather it was as if having made the map he was never afterward able to fit it into any state in the known world, having unwittingly stumbled onto territory thirty feet in the air, over the state of Maine but not of it; a floating intangible country no stable mind would admit to the union.

He was a little boy and he was pushing through what seemed to him an impenetrable thicket like those in the fairy tales, growing faster as they were torn.

At last he pushed through it, hair scuffed over his eyes, cheek and chin torn with the brambles; and he saw a small clearing open before him, wedge-shaped like a triangle.

He was standing at the base. At the apex standing before a half-circle of white trees, and not so much standing as floating, dancing, was a woman. Her arms were raised in a circle over her head and whatever garment she wore was never afterward clear in his mind— so struck was he by the pure grace of her body, half flying, half floating before the bank of white. And her face so arrested him with invitation that he stepped into the clearing.

Apparently it had been a garden once, for vestiges of box still grew along one side as if a hedge had grown there. And what must have been the pedestal of a sundial stood slightly to the left of the smiling woman.

Too charmed, too enchanted to move, the boy stood before his beguiler, who seemed about to run off into a distant part of the wood, beckoning to him to follow.

Sunlight poured into the clearing in shafts of gold. He remembered its bright warmth, rising around him, the warm smell of the grass, the damp warm earth, the perfumed flowers, and the silken smile of the woman that held him so bound he could not move.

Finally, not so much disenchanted as blinded with terror, he

turned and tearing his way in frenzy back through the thorny
hedge, he ran through the woods, ashamed, betrayed, inadequate,
and weeping.

When he came at last into the road dividing the Point into its
two halves, and passed the steeple of the church, chaste, white, restrained, and cold, he still was trembling with his fear and shame.

So terrified was he, he never again walked on that side of the
road unless fortified by an assemblage of cousins; and when years
later they came—without him it happened—on to a half overgrown
clearing and told him of a figure they had found, half wood, half
statue, the figurehead of a boat they guessed, he refused to incor-
porate that knowledge into his memory; and all his life was to be
spent in the search for that clear and perfect moment he had
known, before, betraying it, he had let terror break it.

The Indians called the station Dirty Woman's Ranch, MacIntyre
had told him. And it had seemed a fitting name after his first introduction to the place.

They had come up the long slope by the river at dusk. The clouds
had broken in the late afternoon, and the buildings of the station
were black and delicately solid before the apricot sky, with that
delicacy and reality of substance certain Italian painters get in
painting or rather modeling the flesh around the eyes.

In the living part of the buildings, however, they had come on
a quite different scene.

The tall gaunt wife of John Acres, the agent, was standing in the
middle of the room wielding a broom, her gray hair wild on her
head. Underneath a table, peeking out, crying and screaming, were
two unbelievably dirty small children. Snot hung almost to their
chins; their faces were so begrimed with food, dirt, and tears, not
one scrubbing by any means would be sufficient to clean them.

In the middle of the room was a cream jug, dancing a jig, and
out of it, cause of the excitement, protruded the rear end of a pig.

When she saw the travelers, the woman stopped batting at the
animal. She thrust her hair back out of her eyes, but without
anchoring it, so that it was again over her face in the wildest disorder. She wiped her hands on the dirty rag at her waist, which

served as apron, and ushered them into the room where they had
sat ever since.

But she had been kind to the woman when MacIntyre had carried her in—a look of such sisterliness and compassion coming over
her face that Foss never forgot it, and only felt that here again
were two opposites residing in one person, somehow to be recon-
ciled; as a scene here on the edge of the Territory of Colorado had
been of the same stuff nursery rimes were made of in England
centuries before—one more tight link with that past from which he
felt himself being cut loose.

The family of Acres were drawn up in a line the following morning to see the stage coach depart.

Foss again sat inside the coach with the woman, Rische, unaccountably diffident, still electing to sit outside with MacIntyre.

The cavalrymen had gone on, the night before, to Fort Sedgwick,
and the coach lumbered on its southwesterly course unattended
now save by the usual jack-rabbits, prairie dogs, and hawks. The
sweep of the great birds in the sky had a wider rhythm than the
smaller eastern sky would have afforded, as if they drew there the
pattern of the earth as they saw it unroll beneath them.

Her name was Mrs. Sadler. That much had been ascertained. But
where the Indians had taken her or what indignities she had been
made to suffer, more than that they had killed her child, a girl
three years of age, she had not been able to tell.

That she was tall came as something of a shock to Foss, seeing
her stand beside Acres' wife. Yesterday she had seemed small and
fragile.

Under the ministrations of Dirty Woman or following a natural
bent of her own, she somehow managed to look miraculously
cleansed even in the garments she had worn the day before. Mrs.
Acres had given her a pair of Indian moccasins to cover her feet.
The same shawl was around her face, which no longer held the
wild look of the previous day, retaining only its sorrow and a mask
of deep impenetrable quiet, so that Foss felt that even one word
would be an intrusion and sat in a silence, which on his part was
anything but deep and impenetrable.

Toward noon they had to stop for a buffalo herd to pass.

Far in the north had risen the yellow cloud, and soon there came the telltale shaking of the earth as of an earthquake.

"Buffalo," the woman said, her voice astonishingly round and clear, precise.

MacIntyre on the box, beating the mules into a gallop, was standing up and yelling at them. That he could outrun the oncoming herd was a chance, but he was taking it.

"Have you a gun?" said the woman quietly. "If the driver doesn't succeed in outrunning them, sometimes you can divide the herd by shooting into it."

On rattled the coach, on came the animals, broadside.

When he could see the first shadowy black forms in the dust, MacIntyre stopped the stage and jumping to the ground faced the herd.

"Get out," said the woman, "and stand on the ground."

Foss stood beside the coach.

At first he could hear a faint peppering from MacIntyre and the German, but the rising roar of the herd washed that out. The black waves came on. He saw red eyes, tongues, foam, shaggy rolling heads rising out of the dust, which parted in two streams just in time, and he knew the ruse had worked; but for all he could hear or tell he was alone in the middle of the pounding stream.

"Keep firing!"

The woman must have been screaming into his ear. He stole a glance from the moving sea. She was out of the coach, standing on the ground beside him. Gone was the supernatural calm of her face. Glee almost maniacal replaced it, as she stared all but laughing at the pounding animals, so much more terrified than she, their great heads shaking, their bodies swaying, with the herd motion, up out of the dust for one moment of reality.

The stampede took two hours to run out.

"Sometimes it takes all night," and though she said no more, Foss felt that these words linked her with a whole ramification of past events, persons, emotions; and she began to take on for him a human wholeness. He remembered—what he had not had time to remark outside facing the buffalo—that her shoulder had touched

his, that together they had faced whatever it was bearing down on
them. He had hardly had time to feel the terror before he felt the
comfort of her presence.

That community now that it was over could not be easily broken.
They sat side by side in the coach. Their eyes met. And if she were
to retreat again into her calm, into her quiet, he had these few moments to remember: that they sat side by side, their shoulders with
dear unconcern touching in the natural swaying of the stage coach,
her eyes opening like windows in her face as she said the quite
commonplace words.

"Mr. MacIntyre's mules are well-behaved beasts."

It was so human, the remark, so remarkably human that he
laughed, realizing that he had invested her with a non-human identity he was struggling in his mind to recognize—some dream perhaps—he couldn't say, but the investment still hovered round her,
lending charm to her own slowly dawning reality, like a charming
birth he was somehow fortunate enough to be witnessing, as charming as that of Venus rising out of the sea or Eve's birth in Eden.
Madness at any rate was coursing in him, and he felt that the
stage was a chariot bearing them together, the first two of them,
through the deserts bordering on paradise.

In the late afternoon the mountains appeared in the west, a few
piled peaks of blue cloud.

She pointed to these and said: "The mountains."

He had not seen them before, he told her; he had seen the Alps.

She had lived there, she said, pointing to them again, inside the
mountains in various mining camps, and though she vouchsafed no
more, he felt elated at that much discovery, as if he had set himself
the task of mapping this territory—seeking, finding, establishing,
and identifying towns, forts, camps, mountain peaks, rivers, and
waterways, formations under the surface as well as strata above—
a kind of celestial geodesy. On the neat bare surface of his map he
marked now an indefinite number of mining camps resting on those
unreal piles of foam in the west.

Elated at so much small success he planned his campaign. She
might have been a medieval torture-racked saint sitting by his side,
or one of the Greeks, Antigone wailing for her brother's soul. He

felt impatience with these literary flights and longed for a moment
of reality, like that almost unrealized yet perfect moment inside the
buffalo herd, when disaster pounded its shaggy head down on them
and did not descend.

Too much thinking, he scored himself and timidly essayed one
foot forward into speech: like walking on water, he thought, still
warily watching himself, the overcautious New Englander. To assault reality, he found, took more courage than to dream. Yet he
felt there were the two poles, dream and reality, both existent, having to be brought somehow into relationship. That was the crux, he
told himself—to join them in a kind of violent matrimony, as good
and evil must be mated to produce a meaning. But only by violence,
he said, finding himself in the anomalous position of being the
timid, the wary, advocating force.

He turned and faced the cold, calm, sorrowing figure beside him,
almost severely plain in the gathering dusk, and said:

"You are from New England?"

"From Augusta," she said. "I am named for it." And again over
her features was the soft melting as the clear precise New England
tones fell in the coach. "My father had a stone quarry outside
Augusta and I lived there. With him."

"I know the country around Kittery," he said gravely. "My home
is Portsmouth."

"Yes?"

Whether the "yes" were dismissal or not, the conversation ended,
geography not being a topic she would sustain, and he was too
delicate to broach the West, afraid of harrowing the too recent hell
she had experienced.

"You have been in Europe?" she said after a pause.

"I lived in Germany three years when I was a boy."

The faintest smile crossed her face, so faint he could scarcely feel
shame for that word *boy*; and if there were disparity in their ages
he could not tell. It could so easily have been only disparity of
experience.

Side by side they were walking in this halting conversation, each
helping the other as with a sinking kindness sensing their mutual
need.

"Mining! Tell me," he said, suddenly bold, "was the mining boom actually all that it was reported to us in the East?"

"We never struck it rich," she said.

"My husband and I," she said, avowing simply the relationship he had dreaded having to admit, "moved from camp to camp as the new strikes were made. There were rich strikes, but not every man in a gold camp strikes a bonanza."

The clear detached voice, almost with the detachment of a textbook, made these pronouncements. That they had anything to do with her past and intimate life he could not feel. And so the tocsin announcing the end of this dream voyage could still be stayed.

The stop that night was at a station one day's ride removed from Denver, on a flat cactus-grown plain beside the river. The station was kept by a man named Pat Colliston, who by his own account was a friend of Buffalo Bill and Wild Bill Hickock. A pompous dark-haired little man with walrus mustaches and high-heeled Mexican boots, he was full of tales of which he was always the hero, the bad brave gunman and the scout appearing in minor roles as ineffectuals. Even his walk was offensive, as with stomach slightly protruding he pushed his ego before him like a small round egg he proposed hatching at some propitious and unexpected season.

He had been a Pony Express rider, he said, when Buffalo Bill made his name, by innuendo implying the name far overrated. The mean little eyes of the dandy darted fire at his listeners, defying them to doubt him.

Chewing a sliver of wood with which he had been picking his teeth for an hour, MacIntyre sat in silence while the high voice rushed on, and Colliston, like a nervous woman, reiterated to himself his own importance, as if the semi-occasional arrival of the stage were the only time he had any identity whatsoever, the remainder of the week being shut up in a box on a shelf like an unbought pair of boots.

Mrs. Sadler had retired to whatever quarters were provided for the women.

Restless and constrained, Foss walked out of the room, leaving the voice to its sad compromised journey against discovery.

The moon had risen. The earth was a black shelf jutting into blackness cut by that sharp disk. Barred by cloud it was like a bright metal button pushed halfway through its buttonhole. And that was all there was to see. He felt under his feet the flatness of the plain, and in the dark felt that he would trip, not that his feet might stumble against unevenness but that the flatness was too flat even for gravity to operate.

When the moon rose out of the clouds and he could pick out a faint edge of horizon, he lost the feeling, which in its emptiness had been the loss of all subjectivity; he had not been able to decide, being absent, as it were, whether that were the perfect state or not, as if a person being dead had been called upon to judge the state of death.

He walked toward the river, his night fears of Indians gone. This return, after absence, to himself was like an unexpected homecoming and he walked with a conscious feeling of erectness, of swiftness, and of joy; and felt adequate in the dark to anything that might happen, walking among the bare trees with the assurance that something would happen. In this grove of silent trees shining in the moonlight like a silver wood, he was moving toward some expected event, of the nature of which he had no notion but to which he would be equal and with its meaning crack open the meaning of life.

He had left his hat back there in the room with the querulous insistent voice and had only a muffler tied around his neck for wrap. The evening was neither cold nor warm and out of no season, certainly not spring, nor yet winter—a breathing space between them, perhaps the only evening of the year with an identity of its own, a queerness of moonlight and darkness and air that no other night or day would know.

In the dead leaves of the last year his feet made sounds and those were the only sounds.

His hair, cut short in dark thick layers he tried to keep smooth, ruffed up in the motion of air he made, moving.

At the end of the grove he saw strips of light on the river. The current was so still there seemed no motion in the water. He himself was motion. The grove in its silver and black took on identity from hundreds of places he had known in reality and imagination. Bud, leaf, and flower burst in a thickness of memory he did not try with definition, content to feel the fairy quality around him. Stillness was so deep he tiptoed. The moment was glass and he could break it. Danger was he, himself, not coyote, wolf, or Indian.

She was standing at the edge of the water, in shadow so that at first he did not see her. He perhaps would not have seen her at all had she not moved slightly for moonlight to catch her white face.

They did not speak, he remembered afterward.

The water was at their feet. When he had at first taken her hand, she had not resisted. He had known no surprise at her being there, nor any in her warm response.

The next day in the coach sitting beside her, she was like the river, he thought, steely in daylight, at night warm, her mystery dissolvable in moonlight.

They spoke little on this, the last day before Denver, and he came to feel like his own uncle, somehow unaccountably in possession of all the facts, sitting in judgment on his rash nephew for his behavior of the night before.

And flippantly in the dialogue that continued for miles, he replied: Well, it was good while it lasted; though those words were not a description of the event. He thought of it as something isolated in perfection, the memory of which, like a sealed package, he carried with him now. And the woman, whatever she was like by day, sitting beside that censorious uncle, by night was wayward, most like that witch-thing he had courted and feared as a boy. She had run away from him finally through the trees. He remembered her laughter returning like a bell she was ringing at the edge of the grove, as if, witch or devil assuming Christian attributes, she summoned sinners to their early prayers.

In the afternoon, still together and silent in the coach, they came onto the plain ascending to the mountains. Steep and silvery in the sun, it tipped to the blue barrier and to Foss's excited eyes the snowy peaks came out from the surrounding hills and in ring and ring around them knelt on the plain, their snow touched with blue and sun, their slopes grooved with shadow.

He turned to the woman. Tears were streaming down her face.

And in loneliness and estranged, he sensed the home-coming this must be for her.

The approach to the frontier town was like a royal entry over the ascending plain with the tremendous, snowy, and astounding mountains at its door. Golden horns seemed playing, flags waving, crowds shouting—so exciting was this sense of arrival. Yet arrival to what? Foss could not yet admit he had got nowhere. The town was small, a few rows of pasteboard boxes set on the diagonal beside the sandy river, a few broomstick trees, a church tower, once in a while the more imposing edifice of a brick building. Like the elevation of a child's village, it lay exposed on the plain between its two streams.

Mrs. Sadler began adjusting her shawl and they entered the town. Foss helped her, still unwilling to admit this was not a beginning. They sat side by side—the young man from New England and the sad woman with tears unchecked falling on her hands and skirt. She had asked the driver to let her out at an address she had named; and only when the stage stopped before a two-story frame house painted gray with scroll work on its eaves, incongruous among the plain clapboard and log houses and even tent dwellings of the town, did his belief in the night and the mystery begin to fade. He knew nothing of her really. She was gone like the moonlight. Had it been some mistake of his own, some failure to grasp what had been obtainable? She turned and touched his hand, and he heard the round precise voice saying good-bye. Erect, with no appurtenance except the shawl which covered her, she walked away from the coach toward the house. MacIntyre whipped his team into a gallop and they jolted on through the rough streets where Indians in blankets and feathers strutted, their faces painted vermilion.

The stage stopped in a drama of dust and shouts and helping hands.

Foss stood at the edge of the crowd watching MacIntyre unload the mail and luggage, and seizing his own bags, he walked in the designated direction of the hotel. The streets were wide and vehicles of every sort crowded them—carriages, carryalls, pack trains, long freight trains of covered wagons. There were the groaning and screaming of animals through the dust, the crack of whips, the cries of people.

At a store front he stopped to watch a crowd of Indians, mostly squaws and young girls, who were half laughing, half terrified at the antics of a monkey a swarthy man held on a string.

The young man watched the sardonic animal face.

Dressed in red flannel jacket and cap, clever and undaunted before this human motley, the monkey was as uncomplaining of his own queerness here as he was of the gibberish the terrified girls chattered, unwilling to remain, yet powerless to run away.

Over the heads of the Indian girls Robert Foss of Portsmouth, New Hampshire, faced the gesticulating monkey. The animal looked at him and cocked an eye. But whether a glance of recognition passed between them of knowledge and dismay he could not tell. Picking up his bags, he continued on to the hotel.

THE ONE AND ONLY APPEARANCE OF
JEEZ CHRIST ON SUN MOUNTAIN

IT's EIGHTY years now since Jeez Christ made His One and Only Appearance on Sun Mountain, and already His appearance is so hedged around by tales that it's hard for a person to know what's a lie and what isn't. The Sun Mountain Gospelers, down in southern California now, say that He was killed, but got up on the third day and went to heaven, leaving behind Him, so they put it, His Words for the Latter Days; they say He revealed His True Gospel then, which is that man should live closer to nature, build homes in trees, eat nuts and raw vegetables, and have sex only in the spring. The Reorganized Sun Mountain Gospelers, which took off from the others, agree about nuts and homes and sex, but claim that Christ wasn't shot at all, that He turned the bullet around in midair and killed "Red" Powers and then went up in a blaze of light. They put much more weight on the miracles He did on Sun Mountain. They say He held out His hand and stopped the wind, that He brought the 'Frisco Kid back to life after he was shot by a card-sharp in the Sawdust Saloon, and that He fixed up the eyesight of several miners blinded in a mine explosion, and that He worked lots of miracles of all kinds, and drove out lots of devils.

Of course, as it always happens, there are those who poke fun at the whole thing, saying that it wasn't Christ at all, but a prospector that went mad in the heat of Forty Mile Desert. That's what Grampa used to say, but I don't know that you can trust him either, even though he was there, for he never was much of a church-goer. Besides, he had an eye for making things tall, as I've seen. Some of the stories he used to tell over and over again, and I could see that he changed them from one time to the next, adding bits here and there and dropping other bits out, all of which didn't seem to bother him any. He'd say, "Yes siree, every damn word of it's true, every damn word. That's just the way it happened."

I was about thirteen when he told me the Christ story. It was a cold winter day on our Idaho farm and Grampa got tired sitting around the house and wanted to get out. I had to help him get on his coats, about four or five of them—that's not counting the sweaters—all of them old and ragged with about half the buttons missing. He always wanted the longest one on first and then the others, ending up with the shortest. He said it gave a man room around the shoulders that way. When I started to tuck his two pairs of trousers inside his galoshes, Grampa said, "Take 'em out. They don't look good thataway. Messy, that's what it is!" Well, we went out to the barn and I threw some hay down for the horses, and Grampa curried Old Pete, so old he really ought to have been shot for coyote bait, but Grampa wouldn't have it. "Why, he's the best damn horse on the place. That's one horse yuh can't even balk on a dead pull." After he finished fussing around with Old Pete, we went into the harness shed and Grampa asked me to get his rifle down from a couple of nails on the wall. It was an old piece that had been handled so much one couldn't read what kind of gun it was any more. I never knew what caliber it was, but it had a muzzle that would make a .30-.30 look like a beebee gun. With all his coats on he couldn't hold it up to his shoulders so I helped hold it up by the barrel while he squinted along the sights. "I ain't a braggin' man," he said, "but in them there days I could shoot the white out of yer eye at two hundert paces. But at that, I couldn't hold a piss-pot up tuh Brewster Howes. The time he had it out with 'Red' and 'Bonanza' Johnny, yuh couldn't even see 'im draw. . . ." And that brought Grampa around to the One and Only Appearance of Jeez Christ. I couldn't hope to tell the story exactly as he told it, sitting there with that old rifle across his knees, for he went at a story like a dog worrying a snake, jumping around and around, not quite knowing where to tackle it, and making lots of false starts and getting tied up with dates and names that really didn't matter much, but he wouldn't give up, no matter if in getting things right he had to trace a man's family tree back to Adam—no matter how many "let's see now, that musta been 'bout the time that Will Smith got kicked in the back by that spavined bay mare of his—no, that wasn't the time, 'cause . . ." But once he got all the dates and names right he would quit worrying around and jump in and grab and shake like hell. Anyway, this is what Grampa told me about the time Jeez appeared on Sun Mountain.

Sun Mountain's in Nevada. About as godforsaken a mountain as you'll find anywhere, nothing but sage, alkali dust, coyotes, and lizards, with the sun hotter than hell by twenty degrees and the wind strong enough to rip your pants off if you'd ever be so careless as to leave your fly open. Washoe "zephyrs," the Virginny City boys used to call them. The Chinks up there who did the washing for the miners used to fly kites, but they had to use cellar doors for kites and log chains for strings. Why, one time Pete Stringham was sitting in his stocking feet on his porch when he looked up and saw his only burro flying through the air on a high wind. It saw Pete, switched its tail and brayed, but there wasn't a damn thing Pete could do, but watch with tears in his eyes till it flew out of sight. On account of that mineral dust and wind there weren't any birds up there, so the boys called the burros Washoe "canaries." Washoe's the name of the mountain range.

Everything upon Sun Mountain was as big as the wind, or bigger. Ore ran to $3,000 a ton, Virginny City clung like a mountain goat to the side of a hill so steep that a man could sit on his pants and slide from one street level to another, and the boys were as wild and tough as they come. They didn't take to any of this sissy fun. They had their badger fights and dog fights, or laid bets on a wild-cat tossed in a pen with a bulldog, or a cinnamon bear against four hounds. Most of the boys liked rooster-pullings too, a dollar against a dollar for any man that could pull a leg off a live rooster. And Jim Beagel, a blacksmith, used to amuse the boys with some tame ducks that got sort of friendly after he'd fed them pieces of raw liver. Then when a good crowd had gathered around, he'd toss

them chips of red-hot iron, and the boys would laugh themselves
sick watching the ducks swallow the chips, for the iron would burn
a hole through their crops and fall out on the ground at their feet.
The boys got a big kick out of that.

When somebody found silver and gold on the side of Sun Mountain in '59, the news spread like fire through dry wheat. Everybody
hit out for Washoe—landgrabbers, cattle stiffs, desert rats, paisanos,
coolies, muckers, bartenders, gamblers, and flocks of lawyers and
doctors. Anyone who had a horse or could steal one dashed for the
new diggings. One of them was Brewster Howes, who came, so it
was said, from a gambling dive in 'Frisco. A tall, young fellow with
gold hair and a gold beard and the cleanest blue eyes you ever
saw. He already had six notches on his gun butt when he got there.
He was a gunman, but not one of those dirty little killers, for he
never killed except when he had to. But that was often, because of
his reputation. He was a "Chief" and there were lots of other little
chiefs around that wanted to get him, but all of them were scared
after they saw what he did to "Buckskin" John. Buck was out to get
him and jumped out from behind the Wells & Fargo building with
his gun drawn, but before he could shoot, Brew' had plugged him
twice right through the heart. Jumping out like that must have
startled Brew', for he wasn't a man to shoot at the same thing twice.
Even shooting from the hip he could take the leg off a fly at thirty
paces. Most of the time he didn't even draw, for he didn't use a
holster. He had a little knob welded on his six-shooter just back of
the cylinder and this knob fitted into a slotted piece of metal on
his belt. Nothing like it had ever been seen around Virginny City
before he came.

They say he was a Harvard man and came to 'Frisco after he
got into some trouble back East, but nobody knew for sure. He was
a soft-spoken fellow, and always wore a long-tailed coat and a
stovepipe hat except when he was working in the Gentry as a
broadtosser. He was a square dealer, though, and nobody was ever
afraid of being cheated when he was dealing. Everybody liked
Brew' for he minded his own business and did everyone a favor by
shooting a lot of people that needed shooting.

"Red" Powers, though, was a pea of another kind. He killed just because he liked it, kept his own private burying ground and went around boasting how many he had there. Red used to walk into a bar, pick a quarrel with some friendless miner, grab him by the throat and slit his guts open with a bowie-knife. Then he'd take a nap on a billiard table. Everybody said, but not to his face, that Red never picked on anybody that could stand up to him. His hair was kind of carroty and he had a long red beard which he braided and tied under his chin. Whenever he walked into a saloon with his big Spanish spurs clinking, everyone stopped talking and pretended they weren't there. But Red kept out of Brew's way, though he boasted plenty what he was going to do to Brew' if they ever tangled. It must have made him madder'n hell to know that everyone knew he was afraid to mix it with Brew'. Red had a sidekick, a greaser called "Bonanza" Johnny, who liked to share in Red's fame and do a little killing for himself on the side. Bonanza boasted too that he was going to kill the "Chief," but he was never seen looking for him. If it hadn't been for the appearance of Jeez Christ they might never have got mixed up with Brew'.

Frank Baldy—he used to run a six-horse stage between Carson and Virginny City till he got himself bunged up when his stage turned over just below Gold Hill. It wouldn't have happened if a tug hadn't broken and scared hell out of his leaders, for, though Baldy was a loose-rein driver, he couldn't be beat. Well, Baldy and Dick Munson were coming up the Geiger Grade herding a pack of burros loaded down with barrels of whiskey for the Crystal Bar, when up ahead around several loops in the grade they saw something white moving. Neither one of them could think what in the hell it could be. In about fifteen minutes they came up to it, and it turned out to be a man. Baldy and Dick pulled up their horses and stared, for the fellow didn't have a stitch on but an old sheet. Not even a hat and it was hot enough to fry an egg on a rock. He was an old fellow with long hair and a beard as white as snow. He was caked with alkali dust from head to foot.

"I'll be goddamned," said Baldy. "Where yuh headin' fer, stranger?"

"Knowest thou not," he said, "that thou shalt not profane the name of thy God? I go unto the Mount of Olives."

"I'll be goddamned," said Baldy, looking at Dick, and then staring at the stranger again. "Well, yer headin' the wrong way, pardner, 'cause this here is Sun Mountain. I've never heerd tell of any Olive Mountains in this here country."

"Tarry me not," the old man answered, "for I go to speak unto multitudes." And he started walking up the grade, wading through dust up to his ankles.

"He's plumb locoed," said Dick. "Crazier'n a sheepherder. Look how he's talkin'."

Baldy jabbed a spur into his horse's flank and headed the old man off. "Say, stranger, I ain't one tuh be buttin' intuh other folks' business, but what's yer name and where yuh from?"

The old man looked up from under his heavy eyebrows like a horse under a shaggy forelock. "Have ye not heard a voice out of the cloud, which said, 'This is my beloved Son, in whom I am well pleased'? For I am Jesus the Christ who came down from heaven, not to do my own will, but the will of him that sent me."

"Well, I'll be damned," said Baldy again and swung down off from his horse. "I've heerd tell once that Jeez came ridin' intuh town on a mule, and us Washoe boys ain't gonna be skunked. We ain't got no mule, nothin' but them desert canaries, but I reckon yuh kin ride one of 'em." Baldy took off the bedding roll from one of the burros and tied it up on back of his own horse. After several jumps Jeez got on and said, as quiet as you please, "Even so, that it might be fulfilled which was spoken by the prophet, saying, Tell ye the daughter of Zion, Behold, the King cometh unto thee, meek, and sitting upon an ass."

Baldy and Dick went up the grade herding the whiskey and the old man. They had crossed the summit and were coming down the other side into Virginny City when Baldy and Dick got to talking it over and decided they could have some fun with Jeez and maybe pick up some change too.

George Lieber, who was running the Melodeon then, used to put on shows for the boys and he was always hard put to it to find something their size. When they didn't get what they wanted, they usually got into fights and broke up everything they could lay their hands on. Lieber's place had a bar along the south side and a stage made out of sawhorses and planks at the back. The seats were nothing but old benches that he got out every time there was something on, leaving just enough room alongside the bar. That bar, though, was one of the prettiest anyone ever laid his eyes on, real mahogany and every stick of it had been packed in on burros. The mirrors at the back, too, and a big chandelier with glass drops and a dozen or so coal-oil lamps.

Well, Baldy let Dick take the whiskey into Virginny City while he and Jeez cut up the side of the mountain and circled around till they got to Baldy's cabin between Gold Hill and the City. He wanted to get the old man inside, so nobody could see him. Baldy explained it all to Jeez, telling him that in these parts it would take a couple of days to round up all the people. Then he could give his speech.

Baldy worked it all right with Lieber. He was all for it, and plastered the mountainside with signs reading:

THE ONE AND ONLY APPEARANCE

OF JEEZ CHRIST

IN

"SERMON ON SUN MOUNTAIN"

MELODEON

Admission—$1.00   Saturday—8:30 P.M.

He put ads in the *Territorial Enterprise* and the *Gold Hill News* and had signs painted on rocks all the way down the mountainside to Gold Hill. The boys coming off shift gathered around the signs and you could hear them shout above the racket of rock crushers, stampers and punchers and the cussings of teamsters. Here was something their size, almost as big as the Washoe zephyrs. By Saturday night there wasn't a bad egg or anything rotting or dead that could be had, not even for a poke of gold dust. Those that couldn't find anything else filled up their pockets with jagged rocks from the ore dumps.

Saturday night everybody that was able to get in was there and fighting to get drinks at the bar. What few women there were in

Virginny City, not counting squaws and Chink women, were there too, sitting on front benches. Red and Bonanza were leaning up against the bar near the stage, and everybody was giving them a wide berth. It seems that Brew' must not have worked his way in till much later. When one of Lieber's bartenders lit the lamps, there was a rush for the benches, but there weren't enough seats for half the crowd. They were standing up all around the sides and packed together near the door like bolts and nuts in a box.

Lieber pulled back a little bit the sheets that he used for curtains and started talking. He was one man who had the gift of gab. "You boys know I've never been one to spare labor or money to bring you the best shows in Virginny, or for that matter in the whole country."

"You're a damned liar!" said one of the boys.

Lieber pretended not to hear. "Tonight we have a fellow that I'm sure is the most famous—" Just then one of those zephyrs started up and blew all the lights out. After a lot of fussying, they got the lamps all lit again, but had to turn them down low because the wind was blowing so damn hard it was about to take the roof off. The whole building was shaking like an outhouse in a tornado. After the boys stopped swearing and growling around, Lieber shouted above the wind, "Boys, as I was saying, before one of you bastards sneezed and blew the lights out, tonight we have something extra special. This is our guest's one and only appearance on the stage." Some of the boys started laughing and those sitting down began putting their eggs and ammunition between their feet in a handy place, afraid they might not get a shot in before it would all be over.

"Our city ought to be honored, for our famous guest, none other than Jeez Christ, has come to . . ."

"We didn't pay a buck tuh listen tuh yer crap!" somebody shouted. Everybody laughed.

The wind kept getting stronger and stronger, and Lieber had to raise his voice a notch or two.

"As I was saying . . ."

"Shut up!" someone shouted. "And fetch Jeez out 'fore we plaster yuh!"

"Yah, that's tellin' 'im," others said. "Get the hell off of that there plankin'! We come to hear Jeez preach."

Red took a step or two toward the stage. Lieber heard his spurs jingling and scurried behind the curtains like a jack rabbit that has just seen a hawk. He shoved back the sheets and there was Jeez, old and tired and kind of sad, like a man who's had lots of tough luck in his time. His eyebrows, the same color as his hair and beard, were so bushy and long that his eyes just looked like dark patches in his bony face.

"Christamighty," someone yelled, "has he lost his tongue!"

"Jerus'lem Slim," Baldy said. "Sic' Old Nick on 'im. Serve 'im right." The boys roared and stamped their feet.

The old man gazed as if he hadn't heard. Then he raised his right hand, palm out and said in a loud voice that could be heard above the zephyr outside that was still about to blow Sun Mountain over into Utah: "I charge thee, winds, blow no more!" That struck the boys so funny they knocked each other off the benches and shouted and stamped their feet until you couldn't hear the wind outside. They laughed till there were tears in their eyes. Jeez Christ and the Washoe zephyr!

Baldy jumped up and yelled, "Since Jeez is gonna git rid of our wind, maybe some of us boys could talk 'im intuh puttin' grass all over the top of Sun Mountain and maybe he'd show us how to turn water intuh scamper juice by prayin'." But Baldy had no more than had his say when the wind did stop. No one let out a peep. The boys all had their heads cocked to one side listening to make sure their ears weren't playing tricks on them. Of course, those zephyrs came and went all of a sudden once in a while, but its happening just then made it seem kind of queer.

Jeez lowered his hand and looking over the heads of the boys as if he didn't see them, he began, saying:

"Blessed are the poor in spirit:
For theirs is the kingdom of heaven.

Blessed are they that mourn:
For they shall be comforted."

Everybody's eyes were glued on him. He seemed to say everything as if he meant it in a kind of low voice that made you listen whether you wanted to or not. He went on and on, and no one said anything but Red, who was heard by those near him urging Bonanza to pelt Jeez with some rotten eggs. He kept telling him there was nothing to that wind business. It just happened. But Bonanza didn't cotton to the idea at first. And Jeez went on: "Ye have heard that it hath been said, 'An eye for an eye, and a tooth for a tooth.' But I say unto you, 'Resist not evil: but whosoever shall smite thee on thy right cheek, turn to him the other also. And if . . .' "

By now there was a little whispering going on among the boys, and Red and Bonanza kept arguing and talking until Jeez got to saying: "Take no thought for your life, what ye shall eat, or what ye shall drink, nor yet for . . ." Then Red fired a shot into the ceiling and got everybody's attention.

"Boys," he said, "if Jeez is gonna go spielin' on like that he's gotta have somethin' tuh wet his whistle with. He must be mighty dry by now and I aim tuh fix that up by settin' 'im up tuh a drink of Lieber's best.

"Barkeep," he said, "a shot of yer best red-eye fer Jeez." The bartender jumped to pour a drink. Red took the glass, still holding his gun in one hand, and with his Spanish spurs clinking he walked up to the old man, who gave no sign, except he'd stopped talking, that he'd either heard the shot or what Red had been saying. Red climbed upon the stage and jabbed the whiskey at him, "Jeez, here's somethin' you'd better drink fer yer health." Jeez stood looking sad and tired-like, paying no attention to Red. Red began to feel foolish, standing there holding out the glass, and a few of the boys began laughing. He pushed the glass right up in his face, but still Jeez made no sign that he even knew Red was there. The laughter got louder.

"Well," said Red, "since Jeez has lost his hearin' I reckon he won't be needin' his ears." Stepping back a pace or two, he took aim and shot off part of one of the old man's ears. But Jeez didn't even flick an eyelash, he just stood there with that sort of sad, tired look and the blood running down the side of his face into his beard.

"Boys," said Red, turning around, "I ain't much of a hand at doctorin' but I'll betcha anything yuh wanta bet that that fixed up his hearin'. By God, it's made 'im better-lookin' too." Red shoved the whiskey into the old man's face again, but he didn't pay any more attention than a horse does to one mosquito. By then Red had worked himself into quite a rage.

When Bonanza saw that nothing had happened to Red for shooting off Jeez' ear, he took a couple rotten eggs and went up near the stage.

"Maybe it is that his smeller is aworkin'," he said, and splattered a couple of eggs against the old man's stomach. Jeez still didn't budge. He seemed to be waiting until this was all over so he could go on with his speech. Then some of the boys started getting their ammunition out, and some of them were laughing at the egg sliding down the sheet and dripping on Jeez' feet.

"Nah, Bonanza," said Red, "he ain't got a smeller either. I'm bettin' he ain't got guts either.' He stepped back, waited a second for Jeez to say something, and then fired two shots that struck him right in the middle of the belly. Jeez doubled over as if he were going to fall on his face but then he pulled himself up again. There were two little splotches of blood on his sheet and the blood was mixing with the yellow from the eggs. Jeez held up his hand again, palm out. The coal-oil lamps almost flickered out. Then he fell over dead.

Grinning, Red was still standing there, smoke still coming out of his gun barrel, when he saw Brew' in his long-tailed coat and stovepipe hat edging his way from the back of the room. Those that were near the door beat it outside and the rest knocked each other down trying to get away from the bar and under the benches. If there'd been a mousehole around some of them would have tried to crawl into it. Some of the boys knocked out their teeth and gouged up their faces trying to flatten themselves out on the floor. The women huddled together like sheep in a storm.

Brew' made his way almost to the front, then leaned with his back up against the bar. "Red," he said, calm as you please, "you were saying something about guts. I say that old man had more guts than a hundred white-livered bastards like you and Bonanza.

By God, you started the fracas with Jeez but you're gonna finish it with me. Step outside, so we won't hit anyone else, and I'll prove it."

Red still had his pistol in his hand but his arm was hanging down at his side. Evidently he figured that since they were two against one they'd have a better chance if they got outside where the only light was that from the gambling joints and saloons along "C" Street. Bonanza went first, Red behind him. When they passed Brew', he followed them about five paces, the butt of his pistol sticking out over his coattails. Just as he stepped through the doorway, Red spun around quick as you please to catch Brew' off his guard. But he didn't even get to pull the trigger, for Brew', like greased lightning, plugged him right between the eyes. Red went clean over backwards, rolled over the boardwalk and fell into the dust in the street. Bonanza had made a run for it the minute he'd got outside, but Brew' got him in the back before he could dodge in between the Sawdust Saloon and O'Neill's assay office. It only took him one shot.

Then Brew' walked back into the Melodeon where the boys were beginning to crawl out from under the benches. He walked over to where Jeez was lying on the stage in a pool of blood and rotten egg. Brew' took off that hat he'd been wearing all that time, and said, "Boys, I don't know where he came from or where he's going, but he was a brave man and died like one. Tell Brown to fix him up, and give him the best casket he's got in the house. It's on me." Then Brew' added, "Old man, you Christs shouldn't always be getting yourselves killed." There was lots of argument about that afterwards.

Everybody on Sun Mountain, including two Piute chiefs and a dozen Chinks, turned out the next day for Jeez' burial. Hugh Fitzpatrick and Tom Beasley were out with their two volunteer fire companies, hand pumps and fire hats. And the Virginny City Bugle Corps. Most of the mines—the Ophir, the Yellow Jacket, and lots of others—closed down and all the boys went. They buried Jeez in real style, and put up a marker for him, a marble one, saying: "He made His One and Only Appearance on Sun Mountain, Aug. 4, 1863."

Grampa sat there that day fingering the trigger of his old rifle. "I always had it figgered," he said, "nothin' much woulda come of them Sun Mountain Gospelers if Red hadn't killed Jeez, and if it hadn't been fer what happened after Jeez was buried. Baldy and Dick was both killed the next day on their way out fer another load of red-eye. It was on the Geiger Grade, just about where they'd said they'd met Jeez. A landslide knocked 'em off of the grade. Tom Beasley found 'em, half-covered with dirt. And I'll be damned if on the very next day there was no sign of Jeez' grave. The earth just up and swollered it. That got people to worryin' and there was lots of confugalties." Grampa looked at me, kind of proud he could use a big word like that. "Yes siree, but I figgered that it just happened thataway. Just like it did to Beasley's cabin a couple years later. Back he comes from Piper's Opera House one night, and his house was gone, swollered up. That hull mountain was nothin' but a honeycomb, it was, what with all the tunnelin'. Yes siree, that old man, no matter what these Amen-snorters say, musta went loco crossin' Forty Mile. That's the way I always figgered it. But I'm tellin' yuh, ever' damn word I told yuh is true. Yes siree, I'd swear to it 'fore a judge."

DESERT GHOSTS

THE LIGHT flowed up out of the east, driving the night before it. The stars dimmed. The sky dissolved from a cold slate blue to a pale blue; the clouds in the east were first yellow, then orange, then red, and the sun edged up over the cut-out mountains on the horizon and one more day had dawned over Coarse Gold. At the south edge of the town was a slight rise of ground. It afforded a view north across the business district toward the hill. On this rise there had been one short street, and the district had been known as Cactus Flat as there were several acres of flat land on top of the hummock studded with prickly pear cactus, bull's tongue, and beaver-tail. These cacti had been cleared away in 1895 and several houses had been constructed on this vantage point. Since the hummock had a desert vista in all directions and had the whole town between it and the mines and the stamp mill it was the most desirable residential district. Four frame houses had been built on Cactus Flat, but only one remained. And back had come the prickly pear and the bull's tongue and the beaver-tail. Three of the houses had gone forever and the cactus growth concealed the traces of their foundations. The fourth house, having the most prominent location in the town, had been built in the winter of 1899–1900 by Colonel Martin Earhart. It was Colonel Earhart who finally came to control the Coarse Gold Mines, Inc., through the dummy parent company known as the Western Consolidated Mining Corporation, and which, in turn, became a subsidiary of and was controlled by the Great Divide Mining &

Milling Company. Colonel Earhart owned (along with his daughter) fifty-one per cent of the stock of Great Divide and therefore was the power behind the gilt-edged paper. Of this last corporate body the jest was made that those who owned securities in Great Divide never could get the company to declare any dividends to divide among the common stockholders. But this jest was unfair. The company did declare a dividend of one half of one per cent but unfortunately it was going through a process of litigation at the time so that when all the reports and briefs and contracts and complaints and cross-complaints and answers and statements and affidavits and depositions and writs and judgments and attachments were finally put into a sequence of logical jurisprudence, it was found that there was nothing left to divide, and furthermore the company was operating in violation of the Sherman Anti-Trust laws and was thus no longer a legitimate corporation. There seemed to be enough left to meet the attorney fees—in part—but nothing else beyond the physical assets and property of the corporation itself, and by 1913, when the legal fog was finally cleared, there was no remaining value to the rusted and rotted, or stolen mine machinery; and as for the real estate, the property itself was worth only a dollar and a quarter an acre and Coarse Gold Mines, Inc. owed the county a considerable sum in delinquent taxes. Colonel Earhart, moreover, had died. And so, very quietly, did the Great Divide Mining & Milling Company cross the great divide into the limbo of corporate oblivion.

Like the rest of the buildings in Coarse Gold, the house of Colonel Earhart was merely an abandoned shell. The original plans, as drawn by a firm of San Francisco architects, had called for an elaborate house of two stories and a central tower, designed to afford a view of a wide expanse of the desert in all directions, with the active town of Coarse Gold in the immediate foreground. Had this edifice ever been completed it would have been an arresting architectural monument to the rococo predilections of the late Colonel, or an affront to good taste as an eyesore on the landscape, depending entirely upon individual architectonic interpretation. It was designed to give the impression of jagged, broken angular sections, fitting together like a Chinese puzzle in wood—sharp-pitched roofs, recessed façades, cupolas, long eaves, one flying buttress, and far too much scrollwork, gewgaws and gimcracks decorating every available surface. The tower, rather fortunately, had never been completed (the Colonel's interest in Coarse Gold having fallen in direct proportion to the diminishing gold content in the failing veins near the turn of the century) and therefore had not been present to collapse in some desert gale and come crashing down bringing the whole house with it.

Just below the Earhart mansion, however, was a domicile of considerably lesser effort in its attempt at decorative impression. It was a house which could only have been designated as conservative. It had no scrollwork, no gewgaws, and certainly no place for any contemplated and incompleted tower. It was merely a two-room house with a front porch.

Before it stood a Ford truck.

It was not a new Ford truck, for its green paint had peeled and its fenders were dented, but it was obviously in service, as its tires were in reasonably fair condition, and its open truck body was loaded with cartons, crates, and packages. Indicative of life as was the Ford, even more positive was the stovepipe protruding from the house itself. For puffing from its tented top came a steady eruption of smoke. And from the open doors of the house, both front and rear, came the unmistakable odor of frying bacon. Perhaps, to knowing and acute ears, the sound of frying eggs—soft pop-pop-spatter-and-pop—was evident, and as the spatter and pop became unduly loud, the sound of "Damn" would readily have been heard.

Presently the frying noises ceased, and only a few rapid footsteps, occurring now and then, took their place. And then came coffee— the warm, rich, mellow fragrance of pre-roasted and now boiling coffee.

Then nothing.

The attractive noises and the compelling odors ceased. It would have taken coyotes' ears to have heard the sounds of munching, chewing, and drinking, until a chair was pushed back over a rough board floor and the quick footsteps occurred again.

A man appeared at the front door of the little two-room house. He walked briskly out into the clear morning desert air and went to the Ford truck. He knew exactly what he wanted and he reached into one of the cartons and hauled out a sack.

"Forgot my sugar," he said to the desert sunlight, and with that he turned and went back into the house. For half an hour there was no further activity in or about Coarse Gold. Even the smoke from the tented stovepipe dwindled to a wisp. And then the man appeared at the door again. He stepped out and looked around, not at the Ford truck nor at the immediate foreground, but instead he looked far across the desert toward the Funeral Mountains in the west, and then, stepping farther out from the house, he surveyed the town before him and the hill to the north. The expression on his face was one of satisfaction. It wasn't quite a smile, but it was nearly a smile, and it might conceivably have been there for no better reason than the grip his teeth held on the mouthpiece of a large corncob pipe with an amber stem.

He was tall and spare, with straight shoulders and slender hips, and he wore a pair of nondescript pants and a woolen shirt open at the throat with the collar laid back over a mussed and thoroughly worn-out leather jacket. He had a battered hat on his head and from under the brim long whisks of gray-white hair stuck out. His features were homely and strong, with a firm jaw-line, a large nose and a three-day growth of gray beard. But his clear gray eyes were at once kindly and shrewd. He took the pipe from his mouth, spat carefully, and put the pipe back.

"Good morning, everybody," he said pleasantly to the crumbling town. The smile widened and the eyes twinkled and something like a chuckle came from his throat.

"And a very good morning it is," he said and walked around and inspected the Ford truck. He reached over the side and gave a carton a shove or two. He inspected the contents of a crate. He looked from the loaded truck to the house and back to the truck, and then definitely and pleasantly abandoned the idea.

"Too early in the morning," he said to the truck, and then he turned to the house and whistled. When there was no response he whistled again.

"Here, You," he called—and when there was still no response he added in a tone of deprecation, "Oh, You. Too many females!"

He started out at a walk, neither fast nor slow, but because of the stride of his long legs, moving briskly over the sandy desert road. He followed the tracks of his Ford down the slope from Cactus Flat to the first of the ruined houses at the edge of town. The street became Branahan Avenue, but the tracks of the Ford ignored it. They veered off to the southwest and followed what could be called a road only by a stretch of the imagination. This tortuous trail twisted and dipped across the desert floor for seventeen miles to the inconsequential town of Bateman on the highway. The man left the tracks and walked through the sagebrush to the sandy remains of Branahan Avenue.

He strode on, leaving wisps of blue-gray smoke in his wake, only removing the pipe from his teeth for an occasional spit, and that rarely. He was being followed—pursued, in fact—but he didn't know it. About the time he had passed the collapsed rubble and few porch uprights of the doctor's residence, a large brown dog with black spots on his back and a white chest and white feet came out of the two-room house up on Cactus Flat and trotted around the Ford truck. He sensed at once that his master had gone on without waiting, and he bounded into a run and cut down the side of the slope, threading his way in, among, and around, the scrub desert growth. In front of what had been the Reverend Mr. Wilcox's church, the striding man looked back. He and the dog saw each other and the man waited until the dog came racing up, smiling, panting slightly, and tail-wagging considerably. Its ancestors had been Shepherd and Collie and a dash of Setter.

"So you got up, did you?" They walked on, the dog bounding ahead and bounding back.

"Well, you're a funny fellow. But I was your age once." The dog barked and leapt up on its hind legs.

"Sure I was. But I never chased any female coyotes all night. Not by that name, anyway. Are those pups of hers yours, do you think? I doubt it. I think she's got a coyote husband some place up in the rocks and she's just been smelling around with you. Or has she got a sister? Is that it, You?"

The dog trotted ahead.

"Well, don't answer if you don't want to. None of my business—

except I knew you were planning to be out all night. Couldn't wait to get home from Bateman, could you? Couldn't get out of our Ford fast enough and go scootin' off in the dark. Well—I hope she was worth it. And most likely you think she was. When a man, or a dog either, believes he's having fun, then he's really having fun. If you believe it—well, then maybe it's so for a while. Then maybe the illusion has reality. It's not the thing itself. Chasing a female coyote all night is great stuff for you; but it's nothing I can quite see myself doing. So fun, just like everything else, is all relative to individual values. What do you think of that, Mr. Dog?"

The man walked on, cutting across the desert floor at an angle which might have taken him through (or at least into) the walls of buildings had any buldings been left standing in that section of town. He was making a wide tour of the skeletal remains and his stride brought him around the east end to the abandoned railroad station. The chief incongruity here was that there was a station but no railroad. In its heyday the town had been proud of its depot, and justly so. In 1941 it was the best preserved of the buildings left standing. Only one window had blown out; the roof had remained secure; and even the chrome-and-mud-colored paint had remained on the walls. N. & C. G. S. L. was stenciled in black paint over the chrome, and above the entrance to what had been a dreary and poorly lit waiting room the impressive title to the line had been spelled out: NEVADA & COARSE GOLD SHORT LINE. On each end of the building up in the triangle made by the sloping roof appeared:

COARSE GOLD
El. 2400
San Francisco 342   Salt Lake City 486

A platform extended about fifty yards southerly from the station, and there had been tracks on either side of it. Both tracks had ended at the ticket office and waiting room as Coarse Gold was the terminus of the N. & C. G. S. L. The road had been only a spur connecting the town with the transcontinental main line. The rails had been salvaged long ago, and the salvage crew had even taken most of the ties, leaving only the old or rotted or damaged at the side of the roadbed.

The dog reached the platform first and ran the length of it to the waiting room before the man strode over the sand where once there had been a siding. The siding ran on beyond the station to the wreck of the stamp mill. Here it ended, but was met by the remains of the narrow-gauge line which ran partially around and partially up the hill to the entrance of the largest mine.

A quarter of a mile to the south of the station, as alone in the desert as a single spar in the broad Pacific, stood a signal tower. Two semaphores stood out at right angles from the upright superstructure. They had been standing that way for almost forty years.

The dog waited at the entrance of the building.

The man marched down the platform, leaving a vanishing trail of tobacco smoke behind him.

"And what's more, not only is fun a relative thing," he said, "but *everything* is relative." And thinking as he walked: "This man Einstein—and all these modern scientists—they all know that nothing is what it seems to be. I think this is a town; I think this is the old railroad station, and that that's my dog waiting up there, and that we're taking a walk—all relative conclusions. Nothing to 'em. Not a damn-blasted thing except a mind to believe them. If it weren't for the mind, they wouldn't be. And a mind from some other planet made up of sense perceptions different from mine would see something else—no town, no dog, no station. Maybe this other mind would just see a lot of atoms bumping around in a chaos instead of an order. Well, that would be just as real as what I see. We'd both be right, as far as we went. But the true reality would be something way beyond us both. So what is truth anyway?

"Truth," he said.

"'What is truth? said jesting Pilate, and would not stay for an answer,'" he quoted aloud. "Some word, that. The totality of everything—that's truth. But the position and qualifications of the observer have to be taken into consideration. And if an event has two observers, like me and the man with a mind from another planet, then it's got two meanings. Each relative to the other. So neither is the truth. But both together they might be the total truth, mightn't they? Only that makes a third man necessary to correlate 'em. So relativity pulls the props out from under everything. Nothing can be a fixed base for a certainty. All is relative to all. So how in hell can you start from anywhere in order to get any place when you can't depend on anything—not even your own point of view? I wouldn't mind asking you that, Mr. Einstein, if I just had you in the waiting room of the Coarse Gold railroad station. I wouldn't mind a bit, because I think I could suggest the answer."

The man came to the waiting-room door. He grasped the knob and let himself in. The dog followed. The man closed the door.

Twenty seconds later the pair emerged from the opposite door, closed it behind them, and marched on across the desert. There had been no point to it; they had merely passed through the station as a train might pass through a tunnel. But it was a rite of sorts, for the dog knew that it would be done and had raced ahead to wait at the proper door. The man was whistling, and while there were indications of levity, the walk was unquestionably serious. More than serious, it was episodic and even pragmatic. His pipe had gone out.

A hundred yards ahead was the east end of Main Street, and west toward the Funeral Mountains this thoroughfare ran in a straight line past the bank, the newspaper office, and the establishment of M. Fink, "Mining Supplies and Undertaking."

The next objective of man and dog was obvious. At the east end of Main Street, two blocks from the station, stood the shell of what had been the Great Western Hotel. It was a three-story building, windows gone and doors askew, but still possessing a lobby and registration desk, furniture, and two spittoons.

The dog reached the entrance first, and as the door hung agape on one hinge, he trotted on inside without waiting for the man. When the man arrived he shoved the door a little more askew and walked into the lobby. He went straight to the registration desk, around to the rear, and assumed the position of a hotel clerk. He opened a drawer and took several matches from it and stuffed them into the pocket of his leather jacket. Then from under the desk he hauled out a large book and opened it. It was the hotel register. He hummed a bit to himself as he turned the pages bearing the vari-styled signatures of the one-time guests. There were flamboyant signatures and delicate signatures; there were signatures printed and signatures smeared; there were some faded and some bold; some plain and some illegible. There were signatures covering half the width of the page and there were others inscribed in tiny letters with meticulous care.

The man knocked the cold heel from the bowl of his pipe by rapping it on the desk top, and while still scanning the pages of the registration book he blew the charred remains of tobacco off the desk onto the floor of the lobby.

The dog stood waiting before the desk, panting slightly.

"It was quite a parade," the man said. "Quite a first-rate parade of 'em." Then to the dog: "And what do you bet most of 'em are dead? Maybe they're all dead, except you and me. What d'y' think of that? Or—and get this, You—maybe they all were born out of this book and you and I are still here dead, but waiting to be born. What d'y' think of *that?*"

The dog lay down.

"I don't see but what being born and dying aren't just one and the same thing depending on whether you're playing it backwards or forwards. And since you can't have one without the other—no birth without death and no death without birth—why that shows they are relative to each other, meaningless in themselves, and dependent upon a third observer who may be able to see that they are both one and the same thing after all. Yes sir"—he turned a page —"both the same thing after all."

He continued to look at the list of names, turning the pages slowly and pulling a much-worn tobacco pouch from his pocket. He loaded the pipe automatically, scratched a match on the heel of a shoe, and drew a few puffs.

Finally, he came to the signature of the last guest ever to register in the Great Western Hotel. "Powell R. White," it read in a neat script with no undue flourishes and no sprawling bombast. "2/6/02, Denver, Colorado."

"Powell R. White," said the man, musingly. "Well, Mr. White, you just got on board. For after you there isn't a living soul for days and days"—he flipped some pages—"until we come clear from 1902 all the way up to 1921. Then there seemed to be a bird named Chris

Wick who was pretty prominent around here." And to the dog: "Ever hear of him?"

Near the final pages of the book some new entries had been made. They were all in pencil. The first read "Christian Wick—any old place, Sept. 1, 1921." Then there occurred various signatures of Mr. Wick, some dated and some undated. The handwriting was essentially the same in all instances, but the quality of the pencil had varied. Then, too, the signer had chosen to experiment. There was one sequence of signatures beginning Christian A. Wick, and continuing through Christian B. Wick to Christian Z. Wick including in order, for the middle initial, all the letters of the alphabet. Then there was a gap indicating that the registrant was at a loss, but originality came to the fore and there appeared the last of the dated entries which read, "December 25, 1938, S. Claus Wick."

There followed the signatures of three distinguished gentlemen who had inscribed not only their names, but had affixed a comment therewith. All three statements, however, as well as the signatures themselves, appeared in the same chirography as that of Christian Wick. They read:

Yea, the first Morning of Creation wrote
What the Last Dawn of Reckoning shall read
OMAR KHAYYAM

The world's a bubble, and the life of man
Less than a span.
FRANCIS BACON

I could be bounded in a nutshell and count
myself a king of infinite space.
WILLIAM SHAKESPEARE

"M'm h'm, that's right," the man said; and to the dog he added, "It's been a long time since we had any celebrities here—a poet, a scientist, and a—well—let's call Mr. Shakespeare a psychologist. In fact all three of them were a little bit of everything. We might introduce a new one today. Somebody right up to date. Maybe Dr. Einstein. Think he'd like it here in Coarse Gold?"

He opened the drawer again.

"Matches getting low. We've got to put some more in here or there won't be any when we want 'em. Good thing we stocked up in Bateman yesterday. Wasn't it?"

The dog looked up eagerly and unknowing. The man took a pencil from the drawer and held it poised above the page. He frowned.

"Trouble is we can't quote Dr. Einstein offhand. And I can't recall the relativity formula just exactly. Now let's see. Well—I tell you what we'll do. We'll just pinch-hit for Dr. Einstein ourselves. Let's give 'em a good one. Let's give 'em one for their money and two for their show."

Slowly, beneath the quotations he wrote:
                "This atomic thing called a universe
                Is a universal thing called an atom"
and signed it "Christian Wick."

"All right, gentlemen. Put that in your pipe and smoke it." Then he added the date, "January 10, 1941."

"By God, do you know what day this is? It's fifty years after. It's the fiftieth anniversary. Almost slipped by us, didn't it? Here you and I are so busy getting our teeth into Dr. Einstein's relativity that we almost forgot what day it was. I guess we'll have to walk down and give old Sam Branahan's grave a kick or two just to let him know we haven't forgotten him. Think he'd like to know there's somebody still here? I believe maybe he would."

Mr. Wick leaned on the hotel desk and surveyed his signature. The dog got up and shook himself.

"Fifty years," said Chris Wick to his dog, "since Lucky Sam struck it rich. That is, he struck it rich all right but he never made much money from the strike. And when he died the citizens had to take up a collection to pay for his funeral. In a way we're something like Sam. We're rich, all right, but we haven't exactly got a lot of money. There's a big difference. I'll bet Old Man Wilcox could have preached a sermon or two on *that* sure enough. Probably he did. What do you think?"

The dog looked up blankly and waved his tail slightly.

"And fifty years later to the day, here stand you and I. We own a hotel, we own a bank, we've got gold mines, and a railroad; we've got a house and lot and a whole town. And we've got more than any of those things. We've got peace of mind. So we're rich. But we haven't got any money. So you don't need money to be rich, do you see?" He laughed at the dog. "Get that in your head and tell that to your female coyote."

He picked up the pencil again.

"We'll make this a special day, that's what we'll do. And we'll write it down right here in the book for everybody to read." He wrote: "Lucky Sam Branahan, Jan. 10, 1891—fifty years later—You and Me, Jan. 10, 1941."

He closed the register.

"Funny thing," he said, "if somebody should be writing *our* names over again fifty years from now. It could happen. And it would be somebody we don't even know and maybe isn't born yet. After all, we never knew Sam Branahan, did we? Well, let's go to the bank."

Chris Wick came out from behind the hotel desk. He puffed on his pipe, ran his finger through the thick dust on a table top, spat accurately into one of the two remaining spittoons, and walked out of the hotel into the sunlight on Main Street.

The dog followed.

The pair walked west on Main Street, passing the bank and the newspaper office.

"Banking business is over," Chris said as he went by. "After all, the bank's closed. This is a local holiday. And as for Ed Robbins' *Coarse Gold Standard,* it should have a holiday edition with pictures and all that—you know, pictures of the desert before the town was laid out, pictures of the first settlers—maybe a picture of Sam Branahan's jackass—and then pictures of it up to date which would include the mayor and the leading citizens (that's you and me) and a few words about the future. So let's let on that the *Standard* is all out and pretty, maybe on pink or green paper just to show it is a holiday issue. Shall we?"

They walked past the shambles of Wing Sing's laundry and the establishment of Mordecai Fink.

"I always figured his name was Finklestein. Fink doesn't sound right, somehow. Bet that was it. Oh-oh—look here!"

Chris examined the paw marks of the female coyote in the sand.

"Here's your girl friend," he called to the dog. "She must have been looking for you last night while we were still banging our way home."

The dog came over and sniffed.

"Rabbit, too," explained Chris. "She almost got him. There they go, straight down the street. What do you bet he got away? We're going that way, so let's follow them."

They walked on, guided by the imprints of the coyote until they reached the end of the street and encircling raw desert of greasewood and sagebrush.

"Funny business," muttered Chris. "Rabbit went straight ahead like a smart rabbit, but your girl friend began to veer off this way as if she had something in her mind. By God, I do believe coyotes think. See how smart she was? She was figuring on the rabbit making a quick turn, and sure enough, he did! Look here."

Chris whistled through his teeth, lost the grip on his pipe, nearly dropped it, caught it again, and bit down firmly on the mouthpiece.

"Man alive, that rabbit didn't have much to spare there. Looks to me like he's never going to make it. Bet he could feel her breath on his tail. Say, You, bet you couldn't hunt a rabbit like that. She's a smart girl."

They walked through the sagebrush and down a small dry wash.

"Of course, if Mr. Rabbit just keeps to a straight line he'll tire her out—maybe. But—anybody's race."

A few paces later Chris lost the trail.

"Looks as if they've both outsmarted me, now. Tracks disappeared. Hey, You!" He whistled again and the dog appeared on the embankment six feet above the sandy bottom of the wash.

"Up there?" asked Chris.

He scrambled and clawed his way up the steep side of the wash. Sliding in the loose shale, and panting and grunting, he pulled himself up to the firm ground and got to his feet.

"Now where?"

The dog had run on into the abandoned cemetery. "Fit spot,"

said Chris. He walked over a fallen barbed-wire fence and in between the leaning weather-beaten headboards. The dog was sniffing the scattered remains of rabbit, though there was little that was
left but a piece of the skull and a few wisps of fur.

"So she got him. Nice work. Very smart hunting indeed. Your girl
friend earned that supper. She ate him almost on Sam Branahan's
grave, too."

Chris gave the headboard a few taps with his foot.

"How are you doing down there, Sam?" he called. "Do you know
what day this is? If I wasn't so contented at home, I'd trot out here
and have lunch with you. Fifty years, Sam, since you found it up
there on the hill." Then quietly to himself he asked, "What's that
marker say? 1827–1900. Sure enough." Then he addressed Mr.
Branahan again, letting the tone of his voice fall to normal. "And
forty-one years since you changed worlds, Sam. Didn't have long
to enjoy your glory and your few dollars, did you? Only nine years
out of your whole lifetime of seventy-three. And listen, Sam—I'll
bet the wrong end of a double-jack you weren't happy after you
tried to settle down and live on the ten thousand dollars you
thought was so much money. You didn't know what to do with
yourself. You hung around the mines like a lost soul. And when you
finally got rid of your last dollar you breathed a sigh of relief. You
didn't really love money, Sam, or you'd have made a lot of it. What
you loved was looking for gold. When you were broke again you
got your old pick and some bacon and beans and two burros and
went prospecting just once more. So I say you died happy out in
those desert hills, Sam. Too much sun and ran out of water, some
people said. So they brought you in and gave you an honorary
public funeral. But you died, Sam, doing the very thing you always
wanted to do."

Chris stood with his hands on his hips and stared down at the
grave.

"From all I can piece together you were a good sort, Sam. They
pointed you out to me once when I was a lad of twenty-one. I went
through Coarse Gold in my younger days just about the time you
were setting out for your last prospecting trip. 'That's Lucky Sam
Branahan,' people would say. 'He discovered Coarse Gold. Made a

fortune.' I looked at you with worship because I had ambitions to
find gold in those days. But there wasn't any left around these parts,
and I moved on. It took me twenty years to get back—and when
once I did I stayed on for another twenty. And Sam, let me tell you
something: I'm not sure I'll ever die at all. Can't see any reason for
it. I like it now better than ever. Life, I mean. By God, Sam, it's
exciting if you just stop and look at it.

"Now a lot of people would say I was crazy, Sam. Just a lunatic
who lives all by himself in a ghost town and talks to himself—or
even worse, talks to you. But to tell the truth, Sam, I have so much
to do—so much to think about—that I hardly have a free moment. I
was thinking the other night, here I live in a ghost town and I never
have a minute to myself. Isn't that a funny situation? It's true."

Chris grinned broadly and looked around at the shambles of
headboards and graves. The mid-morning sun was burning down,
no breeze stirred, there was not a cloud in the pale blue sky, and
on the horizon the distant mountains appeared to be made of
cardboard.

"Let's see what I can do to amuse you, Sam, seeing as how this
is a municipal holiday. Well—I think I'll tell you a story."

Chris sat down on the sandy soil between the headboards. He
faced Sam Branahan's and leaned his back against the marker reading "Rosie—? of Maiden Lane." Rosie's headboard leaned slightly,
and Chris adjusted his position.

"You're none too comfortable, Rosie," he said. "I'll have to bring
a hammer out here and pound you down a little." He began to re-
pack his pipe.

"I'm putting this story together just as much for myself as for
you, Sam. It's one for you and two for me, and it has to do with
some fine goings-on and shenanigans, as you will plainly see. It's
the causality principle at work, Sam. Some people call it karma.
But I don't like that word very much. Some of these modern
scientists might call it an illustration of the Principle of Indeterminacy. That sounds like a mouthful, doesn't it? All it means in
an everyday sense is that if I inhale smoke from this pipe nobody
in God's world can say just how much or how little smoke I'm going
to draw in, nor how much or how little I'm going to exhale or what

the exact effect that will have on the molecules of air it comes in contact with—and so on, with one thing leading to another until you wind up in China. So this story is a kind of chain of cause and effect. When you see the actions of human beings, cold and from a distance in space and time, it's like working in a laboratory. You begin to want to know what makes 'em tick. It's not so much what they do, as what it is that makes 'em do it.

"You see I've made friends in a way with a lot of people right here in this town. Only they don't know it. They're all back in 1900 and I'm forty-one years in their future. But I was back there too— and I can look back from 1941 and see myself as a young fellow prospecting for gold because I thought I wanted it—just as all of those people back there" (he waved at the town) "were pursuing something or other. Maybe it was gold or fame or politics or love or happiness or salvation or getting drunk—but they all wanted *something*. And I get a great kick today out of piecing all that together that happened way back there because I want to know what makes men act the way they do. I'm looking for the meaning. I'm trying hard to understand things, Sam. I'm not looking for gold any more. I'm looking for truth. Hope this doesn't bore you, Sam. One nice thing about talking to you, and that is you can't do a damned thing about it. So you might as well listen and like it, Sam, because here goes."

Chris lit his pipe and tossed the match away. He half closed his eyes, puffed smoke and relaxed.

"Just two graves away, Sam, is the last resting place of a China girl called Sing Loy. *Born in China, died in Coarse Gold,* it says on her headboard. If you could rise up you could see it, but you'll just have to take my word for it. And this is the story of what killed her. But it is a lot more than that. It is a story of what seems to be reality. This is life. This is what man considers factual, material, real, day-to-day existence. The story of Sing Loy is so infinitesimally real, that the same kind of thing in another dress is going on somewhere today. It's commonplace. And yet, Sam, just between you and me, it isn't real at all. Its only reality lies in being too close to it and accepting it for what it appears to be. An atom of gold was real to you, Sam, but if your mind can conceive of the interior of the atomic structure, you've got a new universe. Just one atom, Sam—any atom anywhere—the least common denominator of matter, is when you penetrate it with your mind and put yourself inside it, a whole new universal system. Hang onto that for a while, Sam, and I'll get back to it."

Chris exhaled smoke and slid down against the headboard. He pulled his hat over his eyes to keep out the sun. His dog lay beside him, waiting, ready to continue the walk, or willing to pause for the time being if that seemed to be the order of things.

"There was a little China boy in this town who had a laundry. His name was Wing Sing. Now the Chinese weren't held in any too high regard in pioneer days, and Coarse Gold was really a crude pioneer desert town where nobody wanted to live from choice, but only to make money and get away. You know how that is. Chinamen were often run out of Western towns, and kids used to throw rocks at them.

"Wing Sing saved his money, and according to the custom of his race, he bought himself what amounted to a slave girl. From the gold rush days of '49 on up to the Twentieth Century it was possible for a Chinaman to buy himself a girl and the main clearing house for this traffic was in San Francisco. There wasn't anything particularly bad about it. In fact it was, for the yellow men, a social institution. But it was fair game for a lot of psalm singers and reformers—that, however, is aside from the story.

"So Wing Sing spent about two hundred dollars and had a China girl sent to Coarse Gold from San Francisco. Her name was Sing Loy. Nice name, wasn't it? This must have been around July or August of the year 1899.

"He was happy as he could be—and why not? A good business, a new girl, plenty of money and enough to eat. Yes, indeed, his ancestors were smiling on him. I think the two hundred dollars he paid for her was all he had at the time, but people had to have their clothes washed, so there was money to be made. He never actually married her, and I suppose that gave the Reverend Mr. Wilcox and his flock something to be shocked about. If Wing Sing wouldn't give up his heathenish customs, at least he accepted some of the white man's institutions, because he put his money in the bank. He had just discovered that it brought interest that way, which it couldn't do under the mattress.

"Remember, Sam, I'm putting this story together from bits and pieces, but a good bit of it you can read between the lines of the back numbers of the *Coarse Gold Standard* if you scratch for it. I may have a detail wrong here and there, but for the most part it is accurate enough.

"So nine months went by from the time Sing Loy arrived as the wife or property, or whatever you want to call her, of Wing Sing. And in that time, she is due to have a baby. I imagine their yellow skins were tickled pink. For don't forget they were the lowest of coolie people making their way along in the world. Probably they said prayers and burned joss sticks to make their first child a boy. I understand the Chinese don't welcome girl babies. But don't ask me why; they've got to have a few now and then to keep the race going. Also don't forget these two are the only Chinese in town, so they never saw anybody apart from themselves and the customers across the counter. In China the girl would have had a midwife attend her, but here there weren't any midwives, and Wing Sing was so pleased with the way the gods had blessed him, that he decided the best was none too good for his spouse and he planned to call in the doctor—Dr. Warren Scott Mayhew, none other. And not a bad man in spite of his love for hard liquor. More of him later on.

"So all is well until somewhere around the night of May 5, 1900. On that night there was a certain respected citizen of this town who was pretty close to a nervous wreck. He was the president of the bank. Mr. Roland Fredericks. Mr. Fredericks was what might be called an opportunist. He wasn't a thoroughbred in any way. He had a stripe, and it wasn't a very pretty color. He was the kind of man who could be honest and a good friend up to a point, but temptation was right beneath the surface of his character and the surface at that point was so thin it couldn't stand much strain. He might have been a very honest man if he hadn't had the opportunity to be dishonest. So when a man like that is exposed to other people's money—when it's right under his nose day after day—he is inclined to borrow it for his own use, planning, of course, with the very best of intentions, to put the money back as soon as he can. Nothing very unusual in that, is there, Sam?

"But, Mr. Fredericks had the bad luck to gamble with his depositors' money in a stock called Western Consolidated Mining Corporation, which had no assets in itself, but was simply a parent company which controlled a number of mining interests around the West. One of the groups of mines it controlled was Coarse Gold, Inc.—and you know *that* story, Sam, for Coarse Gold, Inc. was the group of promoters to whom you sold your claims for something like ten thousand dollars. That seemed like a nice sum to you and you considered yourself rich. At the time even you couldn't have guessed that in the hill there was close to seven million dollars in gold and that the little picayune ten thousand you were selling out for wasn't really much of a price for your claims on that hill. And you even let them kid you out of demanding a percentage over ten thousand. But I don't blame you, Sam. It was bird in hand, and you were a prospector, not a promoter. As it was, you came off with less grief than any of them. After all, you could always go prospecting again. But it is ironic to be the discoverer of seven million dollars and die alone and broke in the desert and have to have the town you made possible pay for your funeral.

"So Mr. Roland Fredericks invested money that wasn't his in Western Consolidated without knowing the inside story. For just as you were small fry to the men who incorporated Coarse Gold and then sold out its control to Western Consolidated, just so was Western Consolidated small fry to a capitalist named Colonel Martin Earhart. Seven million dollars is a hot hillful indeed, Sam, and it attracted an awful lot of flies—to say nothing of crows and buzzards and vultures and finally the giant condor himself.

"And remember, by 1900 seven million had just about been taken out, and for all anybody knew there was another seven million still there in the hill. That was a scramble indeed. That became a battle of the giants and most of the generals planned their campaigns from an office in Wall Street called the Great Divide Mining & Milling Company, a huge trust that never mined or milled a damned thing except the hope out of the hearts of the little fellows like you and me and little crook Fredericks and Ed Robbins and Wing Sing and a whole townful more.

"The big condor had many plans. And if some unimportant mining bloc in San Francisco called Western Consolidated had picked up a seven-million-dollar hill in Nevada—well—Great Divide decided to pick up Western Consolidated and thereby grab the hill. In order to do that it would strangle Western Consolidated in Wall Street and buy the corpse in Nevada. You and your jackass sure did start something, Sam. You were following the Principle of Indeterminacy all right, even if you never heard of it.

"Naturally, it looked to little banker Fredericks, who had only a worm's-eye point of view, that Western Consolidated was a good thing. He invested heavily in it—with his depositors' money. He never heard the wings of the giant condor flapping west from Wall Street to Coarse Gold. He never knew that when Colonel Earhart arrived and built his corkscrew house up on Cactus Flat that the Colonel only did that because he intended to have it all—everything from the gold in the hill to the blood in men's hearts. Banker Fredericks never even knew that Colonel Earhart was fifty-one per cent of Great Divide Mining & Milling. The Colonel said he had come out here and built his house for his daughter and his health. Maybe that was the truth; but it wasn't healthy for anybody else.

"All little Fredericks knew was that he was getting deeper and deeper into Western Consolidated, pouring more of his depositors' money in to protect what had gone in before, and that for some reason beyond his ken, Western Consolidated was going down and down. It practically drove him crazy because he knew the gold was there in the hill—carloads of ore coming out of those mines every day—and where was it going?

"Then came the inevitable day, May 5, 1900, when Western Consolidated hit bottom and died and Great Divide was standing by ready to pick up the corpse simply because the corpse was still controlling a little jewel called Coarse Gold. But by this time all reason was driven from Roland Fredericks' mind. He had ruined himself and his depositors and the Coarse Gold bank was insolvent. He had two ways to get out: he could kill himself or he could run for it. For one thing was certain, the Coarse Gold bank was never going to open its doors after that fatal Saturday of May 5, 1900. And it never did, as you well know, Sam.

"On Sunday, May 6, Mr. Fredericks jumped out of the frying pan into the fire. He took what cash and clothes he could stuff into one suitcase and he disappeared. And nobody missed him until Monday when the bank failed to open.

"Wasn't that some Monday, Sam? You can remember that, all right, and so can I. And in all the excitement with everybody in town in a panic over losing his money, nobody cared if a Chinese laundryman was one of the victims, or that his wife was about to have a baby.

"So the little Chinese was so confused when he was told that all his money was gone that he couldn't understand it. He had been counting on that money to pay the doctor to attend Sing Loy, and suddenly the money wasn't there. And this little yellow fellow didn't know where to turn. The church group looked upon him as a sinner. Kids jeered at him and threw rocks at him on the street. He never dared walk past the schoolhouse—you see, he had it in his head that he was just a despised Chinaman. He never knew that he could have gone to Dr. Mayhew and asked for credit on that yellow baby. He never knew that Dr. Mayhew was made of the salt of the earth and would have delivered that almond-eyed baby out of its mother's belly for no fee at all. Wing Sing was *too* honest.

"So, being too scared to call the doctor when he can't pay him, he tried to bring that baby into the world himself the day after the bank crashed—May 8, 1900. And that didn't turn out to be such a good idea. Who should be going by and hear Sing Loy's cries but Mrs. Ed Robbins, the editor's wife and number one church worker. She walked in (taking it as her Christian duty, no doubt) on a not too pleasant scene in the back room of that little laundry. She screamed and called for help and in a few minutes there was real excitement.

"Dr. Mayhew was called—and he was drunk as usual—but it was too late for any doctor then. So the baby was dead and Sing Loy was dying and Wing Sing was grief-stricken and there was ugly talk going around that the heathen Chinese had deliberately killed

the baby (you see, Sam, it *was* a girl baby after all) and so they
ran this poor Wing Sing off to jail. Ed Robbins wrote it up in the
Standard. "Domestic Murder" he called it and had it all wrong due
to blue-nosed Mrs. Robbins who could see no good in anything
heathen and just naturally jumped at the wrong conclusion. Besides, the town was in a hysterical mood over the bank failure and
had to take something out on somebody.

"And that's how Sing Loy happens to be just two graves away
from you, Sam, as nearly as I can piece that little episode together.
So who killed her? It wasn't Wing Sing—and it wasn't Dr. Mayhew.
Was it Roland Fredericks and the bank failure? Well, not exactly,
because he was ruined by Colonel Earhart—only the Colonel didn't
know it. And how did Earhart happen to be in the story? Because
you discovered a seven-million-dollar hill, Sam. So it all comes back
to you, and impersonally, almost mathematically, Sam, you killed
that Chinese baby—doomed it to death the day you sat down on
gold.

"But that's no criticism of you, Sam," continued Chris, stretching
and rising to his feet. "It's no criticism of anybody. There's nobody
in the story who would deliberately want to hurt another person.
Not one. It just goes to show how men act and react. It shows what
a little gold will do and it shows how far human beings have yet
to go. And you can't tell, maybe that Chinese baby would have
grown up and been a murderer. So you can't regret the past or even
wish it might have been different. It wasn't different, and that's
about all there is to be said about it."

The dog got up and stood watching Chris, waiting to see in
which direction their walk would lead from here.

"But what you can learn from it is that reality of that kind is just
a series of causal effects. You don't surrender blindly to that world
out there; and you don't fight it until you're worn out. You meet it
and weigh it and value it and understand it. You observe it and
you classify it and you enjoy it. Then you never have to be afraid
of it. You've got to avoid the pitfalls of listening to your ego; and
you've got to avoid the traps of materialism—greed for wealth, or
power, or appetites of all kinds. You've got to be pretty damned
near selfless. Then, when you find you don't want anything, you'll

have all you can ever desire in that very freedom from wanting.

"I've lived in this desert ghost town a long time, Sam, and by God, I'm on to something. I'm actually happy, Sam—there's not a thing that can upset my balance and there's not a thing I crave. I really love all you people—you and the doctor and the preacher and the banker and the editor and the laundryman and the whore-madam and Rosie the harlot and the preacher's daughter and all the rest—and the coyotes and the rabbits and the rattlesnakes and the birds and the bugs. I've gone an awful long way on the road to truth from this place. I couldn't ask for more. You see, Sam, I really achieved what I came here for in 1900. I really got rich here—rich in a way that makes gold seem pretty silly.

"Well, so long, Sam, and a happy fiftieth anniversary to you down there."

Chris turned from the grave of Sam Branahan and walked past those of Rosie and Sing Loy and on out into the desert. "Come on, You," he called to his dog. "Let's finish our morning walk."

GHOST TOWN

Here was the glint of the blossom rock,
Here Colorado dug the gold
For a sealskin vest and a rope of pearl
And a garter jewel from Amsterdam
And a house of stone with a jig-saw porch
Out where the prairies are.

Here's where the conifers long ago
Where there were conifers cried to the lovers,
Dig in the earth for gold while you are young!
Here's where they cut the conifers and ribbed
The mines with conifers that sang no more,
And here they dug the gold and went away.
Here are the empty houses, hollow mountains,
Even the rats, the beetles and the cattle
That used these houses after they were gone
Are gone; the gold is gone,
There's none here,
Only the deep mines crying to be filled.

You mines, you yellow throats,
You mountainsides of yellow throats
Where all the trees are gone,

You yellow throats crying a canyon chant:
　　Fill what is hollow;
Crying like thunder going home in summer:
　　Fill what is hollow in the earth;
Crying deep like old trees long ago:
　　Fill what is hollow now the gold is gone;
Crying deep like voices of the timbers,
Conifers blowing, feathered conifers,
Blowing the smell of resin into the rain,
Over the afternoons of timber cutters,
Over the silver axes long ago,
Over the mountains shining wet like whipsaws,
Crying like all the wind that goes away:
　　Fill what is hollow,
　　Send someone down to fill the pits
　　Now that the gold is gone;
You mines, you yellow throats,
Cry to the hills, be patient with the hills,
The hills will come, the houses do not answer.

These houses do not answer any cry.
I go from door to door, I wait an hour
Upon a ledge too high to be a street,
Saying from here a man could throw a rock
On any roof in town, but I will wait:
It's time the people came out of their houses
To show each other where the moon is rising;
Moon, do you hear the crying of the mines:
　　Fill what is hollow,
　　Send down the moonlight.
It's time the people kindled evening fires,
I'll watch the chimneys, then I will go down;
Steeple, why don't you ring a bell?
Why don't you ring a mad high silver bell
Against the crying of the yellow throats?
Wait for me, steeple, I will ring the bell.
　　Pull the rope,

Drift, stope,
Pull a fathom of rock
And a cord of ore
From the higher place to fill the lower,
The Rocky Mountains are falling down,
Go into any house in town,
You can hear the dark in the kitchen sing,
The kitchen floor is a bubbling spring,
The mountains have sealed like the door of a tomb
The sliding doors to the dining room;
Then thump your hand on the parlor wall
And hear the Rocky Mountains fall,
Feel the plaster ribs and the paper skin
Of the Rocky Mountains caving in;
Pull the rope,
Drift, stope,
Pull down the birds out of the air,
Pull down the dust that's floating where
The conifers blew the resin rain,
Pull all the mountains down again,
Pull the steeple down
And a cord of ore
To fill the dark
On the hollow floor.

I am an animal, I enter houses.
Some of the animals have liked this house:
The first to come and go were men,
Men animals who dreamed of gold,
Then small things came and the cattle came.
The cattle used this room for many years,
The floor is level with the baseboard now,
But probably the ants came first
Before the people went away;
Before the children wore the sill
With stepping in and out to die;
It may have been an afternoon

Before the conifers were dead,
An afternoon when the rain had fallen
And the children going back to play,
Did you ask the things the animals can't ask?
Did you ask what made the mountains glisten blue?
Did you say:
                    "The great wet mountains shine like whipsaws"?
Did you say:
                    "We're here and there's the sun"?
Did you say:
                    "The golden mines are playing
Yellow leapfrog down the hills"?
Did you say:
                    "Think what it would be like
To be way up on the mountain top
And see how beautiful it is
To be where we are now"?

The children made this doorstone look
Like a whetstone worked too hard in the center
And the ants went out and the wall went out,
And the rats went out and the cattle came,
But they're gone now, all the animals;
If they were here, and all of us together,
What could we say about the gold we dug,
What could we say about this house we used,
What could we say that we could understand?

You men and women, builders of these houses,
You lovers hearing the conifers at night,
You lovers making children for the houses,
Did you say to yourselves when reckoning
The yield of gold per cord of ore,
Running drifts per cord of ore,
Stoping per fathom per cord of ore,
Filling buckets per cord of ore,
Dressing tailings per cord of ore—

You lovers making children in these mountains,
Did you say something animals can't say?
Did you say:
              "We know why we built these houses"?
Did you say:
              "We know what the gold is for"?
I cannot tell: you and the gold are gone,
And nearly all the animals are gone;
It seems that after the animals are gone,
The green things come to houses and stay longer;
The things with blossoms take an old house down
More quietly than wind, more slow than mountains.
I say I canot tell, I am alone,
It is too much to be the last one here,
For now I hear only the yellow throats
Of deep mines crying to be filled again
Even with little things like bones of birds,
But I can hear some of the houses crying:
   "Which of the animals did use us better?"
And I can hear the mountains falling down
Like thunder going home.

HOMECOMING

"WE'RE ALMOST to Cottonwood, Ma'am," the conductor said in Cora's ear. "You wanted me to tell you."

Cora Gray nodded. She was too tired after the long trip from Iowa to Montana by day coach with three children even to smile at him. She looked out the window at the flat, sagebrush-studded, coulee-scarred country of eastern Montana, bright and dry beneath the late August sun, and tried to realize that in this land would be their new home.

It was so different from the oak-topped knolls of the country she had known that she could in no way identify herself with it. It was a land of brown and gray and white with no green to relieve its glare. Light-brown tufts of grass pushed up from parched brown earth. Parched brown earth was cut through by coulees of still deeper brown, with bits of mica sparkling on their dry banks. Stretches of dead-white alkali land where nothing grew made the glare from the sun more intense. Greenish-gray sagebrush was everywhere—an ugly weed, thought Cora. Cacti—mean, stunted plants that clung tightly to the unsustaining earth and rocks—were almost as plentiful as the bushes of sage.

Cora turned away from the window to meet the gaze of her oldest child, a quiet, thin-faced boy of twelve with her own gray eyes.

"Joe, we're almost to Cottonwood. You wrap up that lunch box, and pick up the children's books and crayons and put them in that basket. Help Barbie into her coat."

Joe shut his book resignedly and turned to his dark and scowling five-year-old sister. "Here we are, Sis. We're going to see Papa in just a few minutes."

Barbie showed no signs of pleasure. "You said there'd be lots of Indians in Montana, and we haven't seen a one yet. You told a big fib, Joe."

Cora leaned over her other son, Jeff, the baby of the family. While Cora patted and shook him into unhappy consciousness, she handed articles of clothing and baggage to Joe to assemble on the seat across the aisle, mentally checked the things they had brought with them, sighed over the things they had left behind, and worried over whether the dishes and bedding sent ahead had arrived.

Cora had thought it was a wild and foolish thing Will Gray was doing when he decided to leave their home and relatives in southeastern Iowa to go to Montana. She had felt a sense of insecurity from the first winter night in 1908 when he came home with a newspaper telling about the thousands of Easterners pouring into Montana to prove up on dry land farms.

"It says the great cattle days are over, but there's still a great new land out there, Cora," he said. "It's got room—lots of room—room fer us. Room fer the kids. Room fer cattle and sheep and wheat. My own belief is that it says right."

She had made her only remonstrance, that a faint one. "You're a carpenter, Will, not a farmer."

"Hell, Cora, farmers need carpenters. All those people—they ain't a-goin' t' live out there long without needin' houses and banks and schools. Then there's this new railroad—the Milwaukee. It'll soon be finished—right across the state. Wherever it touches, towns'll spring up like toadstools. We'll follow it clear across Montana. Maybe clear t' the Pacific Ocean. There'll be more carpenter work than a man ever saw before. And maybe I won't be just a carpenter out there. Maybe I'll hire men t' work for me and be the boss. The country's big. The country's free. No tellin' what'll happen if you git in on the ground floor. Why God-dammit, Cora, I see it all just as clear as if it was right here in this room. We gotta go."

When Will swore like that, Cora knew he was in earnest. Besides he was twelve years older than she was, and she always felt pre-

sumptuous when she questioned anything he wanted to do. She had
had some normal-school education and had taught a country school,
and he had gone through country school only; yet she felt no superiority because of her better education. Cora believed that an education was only as good as the man who received it, and never questioned Will's decisions because of the grammar in which they were
phrased.

So he had told her farewell and had gone out to Montana to follow a railroad across its great length, and, as he predicted, he had
found all the work he could do. He had become a contractor instead
of a carpenter, and bid on buildings, and bossed their erection. He
had just completed a depot, he wrote her; then he had built a
saloon; soon he would be working on a bank. He had teamsters and
lathers and bricklayers working under him. But he had no capacity
for putting aside money, when the building was booming, for the
long winter months when the thermometer was a thirty-five below
and no work could be done. He had sent Cora large sums during
the summer months, and her heart had bloomed; but long winter
months had used up the summer's money. And another summer had
had to be worked through before he could save this stake which now
brought his family to him. All these things Cora turned over in her
mind as she buttoned her two-year-old son into clean rompers,
combed her daughter's hair, settled the navy blue sailor on her own
light brown hair, and lifted bags down from the hat rack and pulled
them out from under the seat. The conductor came and helped Joe
move them to the door. The train began to slow down. She saw
Will's big, slightly stooped figure on the platform, his hat off, the
gray strands in his black hair gleaming in the blistering sun. She
pressed her quivering lips and lifted Jeff to her.

"Joe, take Barbie's hand, and don't let her fall going down the
steps. Barbie, you kiss your father even if he isn't an Indian."

Cora's fatigue didn't leave her as Will gathered her into his arms;
it was too deep for that; but the fear went from her, and was replaced by a deep feeling of peace. At last she was here, with Will;
and everything would be all right. Jeff started to whimper, and they
both realized for the first time that she was still holding him. Will
swung Jeff to his own shoulder, but kept one arm about Cora.

"I'd forgotten how little and pretty you are!" he exclaimed with pleasure.

He turned to the man in overalls lounging beside a team and wagon.

"Jim, you take these here suitcases and things up t' my house, will you? Cora, this is Jim Shaw who does all our draying around these parts. Jim, this is Mrs. Gray."

"I'm mighty pleased t' meet yuh, Mrs. Gray. Bill here's sure had ants in his pants these last few weeks he's bin so scairt he wouldn't git that house ready fer yuh t' move in—" Shaw broke off in a high cackle, rather red in the face and breathless from performing his social duty.

"How do you do," Cora said politely. Then she turned to Will with shining eyes. "Will, you built a house for us!"

Will blushed. "No, not exactly—no. I bought one and fixed it up a little."

"You're jest lucky you come when you did, Mrs. Gray," Shaw said importantly. "I reckon you'd 'a' slep' in a tent or been et up with bedbugs in the Comfort Inn. This house you got was vacated jest in time. Mighty important vacatin' too!"

Will interrupted him, friendly but firm. "You'll be wantin' t' take up them barrels of dishes and things in the freight shed, too, Jim. I reckon they'd better go up now. You drop by the job, and I'll pay you what I owe you. Much obliged. Well, so long, Jim."

"So long, Bill. Mighty glad I met yuh, Mrs. Gray."

"Thank you. I'm glad I met you, too." Cora smiled shyly at the red-faced man, wanting to make friends with anyone who called her husband "Bill."

"My, he's friendly, Will. It's nice he could take our things right up that way."

"Yeah, he's all right. But he talks too much."

"What did he mean about the house, Will?"

" 'Twas the only one in town, Cora, and we're lucky to git it. I never would 'a' got time t' build one. You know the old sayin' about the shoemaker's children goin' barefoot. Well, that's me all right, right now."

"Well, I don't care what kind of a house it is. It'll be home. He said it was mighty important vacating——"

"I told you he talks too much. I'll tell you all about it later. We'll go home, and you'll see the house for yourself." He smiled at his wife apologetically. "It'll be all right." Still she couldn't help but wonder about it.

"I'm glad you're here—you 'n' the kids. By God, I've missed you! Barbie, get out from under that horse's belly! He ain't your grandfather's old mare!"

Barbie came out from under the horse hurriedly. Cora said with feeling, "I've missed you, too." Then she added practically, "And I'm glad you're going to make Barbie mind. She's too much for me sometimes."

The small procession moved away from the red station up a narrow main street, walking on wooden planks laid down on one side of it. The street seemed almost empty to Cora as they started to walk its short length. She was relieved about this, for in spite of having put on a clean shirtwaist and run a chamois over her freshly washed face, she was conscious that her appearance after three nights on a day coach left much to be desired. But her relief was short-lived, for she soon saw that she was mistaken about the deserted street. Women's faces began to appear at store windows, and men began to call greetings from doorways. The small frame storebuildings lining the street were filled with people.

"The whole town's come down t' see you, Cora," Will said jocularly.

Cora was shocked, but as she thought quickly of the size of the town and the number of people she saw at doors and windows, she realized that what he said must be the truth. Loud cries of "Howdy, Bill!" and "So the Missus finally arrived!" were greeted by Will with equally demonstrative bellows of satisfaction. He bowed and waved to everyone, sometimes almost throwing Jeff into the air in the exuberance of his joy. Everyone seemed to know him, and Cora again got the feeling of great friendliness on the part of the people who greeted him from store fronts on both sides of the street. She felt her face redden with a certain pleasure as well as embarrassment. She was glad these people so evidently liked her husband, but she would also have been glad to have felt a little less as if she were being greeted by a brass band.

They came to a new, small red-brick building at the corner of the first of the two blocks which made up the town's main street. It had a plate-glass window in the front of it, like a store. But it also had a green shade pulled down at the window, a swinging door, and gold lettering on the glass which proclaimed that this was "Mike Finley's Bar." A worn hitching rail at one side contrasted with the new brick of the building, as the two ponies hitched to the posts contrasted with a new but slightly battered Model-T Ford.

A tall, lean man with a white Stetson pushed back to show graying hair stood in the doorway. After a day spent staring out of day-coach windows at the Montana countryside, Cora was prepared somehow for such a man. His weathered face was brown as the land was brown. But his face was saved from the harshness of the land by the eyes, a deeper brown and soft and sad as a retriever's, that looked out from it.

"Howdy, Bill," the man said. His words made a great impression on Cora, not because they were unusual, but because the sober way in which he said them struck jarringly on the general paean of joy which had greeted them so far.

"Howdy, Mike," Will said cordially. "Cora, I want you to meet Mr. Finley. Mike, Mrs. Gray."

"Pleased to meet you, I'm sure, Mr. Finley," Cora said nervously. She had never seen a saloon before, much less a saloonkeeper, and she wasn't sure just what the proper greeting should be.

"And I'm pleased to meet you, Mrs. Gray," said Mr. Finley, coming from the doorway to the middle of the plank walk. He swept off his Stetson with a serious, almost courtly air and gave her a slow but not unfriendly smile. "You're getting here just in time to see all these fine buildings your husband's putting up. Mine here—we just moved in a few days ago. And the bank down the street—it'll be the same pattern—the same red brick. Cottonwood's going to have the finest main street in the West, bar none, before we get through with it."

His tone indicated that this would be a great misfortune for Cottonwood as well as the West.

"That will be nice, I'm sure." Cora found herself unconsciously speaking in the same tone of hushed sorrow which he had used.

"Oh, Papa, come on!" Barbie had suddenly come back from her confident stalking. She was almost in tears from fatigue and nervousness, and her voice sounded angrier than usual.

"Barbie, be quiet! There's no need to be impatient; we've got all day." Even as she spoke, Cora realized that she was as tired as her daughter and as impatient to be gone from this sad stranger who talked lugubriously to her from in front of a saloon.

"Don't scold the little ones, Mrs. Gray," Mr. Finley said, and Cora couldn't be sure that he wasn't laughing at her. "Sometimes they die when you're least expecting it." He turned to Barbie. "What is your name, little girl?" Again he lifted his upper lip in a sad smile.

Barbie drew herself very erect. "Barbara Dolores Gray. And I'm going on six!"

"Dolores. Dolores—I once knew a girl named Dolores. Hm-m-m. Never mind. Here's a nickel, Dolores—you buy yourself a box of crackerjack to remember Mike Finley by."

"My name isn't really Dolores, Mr. Finley. That's my middle name. But it was almost Dolores. Mamma named me Barbara for my Aunt Barbie who was dying. After she died I was to be called Dolores. But she didn't die. So now I'm still Barbie."

"Hush, Barbie. Don't mind her, Mr. Finley. She's tired from too much riding on the train. Will, we'll have to get the children home. Good-bye, Mr. Finley."

He bowed deeply once more, and sighed. "I am happy to have made your acquaintance, Mrs. Gray. So long, Bill."

"So long, Mike."

Happy to be on the move once more, Barbie smiled at him angelically. To her mother, she said, "Now may I buy some crackerjack?"

Cora made no reply until she was sure they were well out of earshot. Then she said fiercely, "You just tie that nickel in your handkerchief and save it for your Sunday School! It'll be one piece of whiskey money that's gone to the right place."

Will laughed. "Beer money, Cora, beer money. A nickel wouldn't even get you a smell of a whiskey cork in Mike's place."

Cora had felt only a surprised acceptance of a strange situation when Will had stopped in front of a saloon and introduced her to a saloonkeeper, but now at his casual laughter she found herself feeling both resentful and fearful. She wondered how much of his time in her absence he had spent sitting around the saloon. Vaguely she characterized sitting around a saloon as "carrying on," though, to save her life, she could not have put into more explicit words what she meant by the phrase.

Whatever she might have to say about her fears would have to wait until some other time. Her weariness was beginning to come upon her in recurring waves. Four steps, and a wave would engulf her, weakening her knees, making the small buildings of the street jiggle before her eyes. Another four steps, another wave.

Cora hardly knew how she managed to walk the half-mile which took them to the outskirts of the tiny town. There were no sidewalks, and they trudged down the middle of a straggling road, past small, unpainted houses which she did not see. Sometimes they stumbled over stones or hard clods of dirt. Brief gusts of a high, sweet wind made shifting eddies of dust about them. Fortunately they met no one with whom Will felt it obligatory to exchange more than a "Howdy," or a wave of his hand.

"Here's our house, Cora," she heard Will say, and she opened her smarting lids.

Before them was a small house covered with black tar-paper held in place by strips of lathing. Two little windows, placed rather high, shone in the sunlight. New, unpainted, wooden steps led directly up to a new, unpainted door. Sagebrush grew around the house, cleared away only from the path leading to a small but necessary building about fifty feet to the rear of the house. A fresh pile of stovewood had been dumped almost at the door. It was a lame duck of a house, if there ever was one, but Cora's heart went out to it as she saw the weeks of hard labor ahead of her—scrubbing floors, shining windows, putting up curtains, clearing away sagebrush— labor which she hoped would make the house look less as though it had been dumped from a refuse cart. Her fingers itched to begin.

Barbie gave a horrified snort. "Gosh, Papa, do we have to live here! This is just an awful old place!"

"Be quiet, Barbie!" her mother said automatically. "Stop your sniffling and just be thankful we're home." To her husband she said gently, "Will, it's just as nice as it can be."

The room was faint with early morning light. Sleepily Cora looked at the unfamiliar walls covered with dirty, faded, blue building paper, stained by the rains from many storms. She lay in a brass bed in the corner of the one large room which was to serve as living room, dining room, and bedroom for her and Will. The bed was battered and bent, but it had seemed completely beautiful to Cora the night before. For the first time in her life she had gone to bed before the supper dishes were washed. Now she became more awake as she realized that she would have to wash them before any breakfast could be served to a hungry husband and ravenous children. She stretched and yawned, and noticed with surprise that the fatigue of yesterday was gone. She felt, without being conscious of it, the exciting tang of the air. It was good to be alive, and she didn't need anyone to tell her so; she felt it in her very bones. Tentatively she rubbed a toe against Will's solid leg. He had always been ticklish, and she smiled as he flinched and pulled his leg away. He rolled over, and opened a heavy eye.

"That's a fine way t' wake up a husband after a year's absence," he grumbled happily, throwing an arm about her shoulder.

"Will, you'll just have to shingle that roof, even if the bank doesn't get finished. See where the rain has stained the ceiling."

He laughed softly. "Up to your old tricks! Wake a man up by tickling him so's you can tell him all the things that need to be done. You wouldn't like that sagebrush all pulled up by noon today, would you?"

Cora giggled. "Yes, I would, but I don't suppose I need think about that for a while yet. I'll put Joe to doing that after school."

"Chains around their necks 'fore they're outa short pants." Will's tone carried both amusement and chagrin. "Your Pennsylvania Dutch blood always shows up early in the morning."

Cora rubbed her hand along his arm with unwonted demonstrativeness, and kissed him hesitantly.

"I was too tired yesterday to tell you how glad I am that we got here."

"I knowed you was, Cora. And you knowed I was. That's the way it oughta be. This is an awful dump t' bring you to, but it was all I could git."

Will sounded so much more apologetic to Cora than the situation seemed to warrant that she found her curiosity of the day before revived.

"You said you'd tell me about the house, Will. How'd you happen to get it? Who lived here, anyway? They didn't take very good care of it."

"Well, Cora, I'll tell you—" Will cleared his throat. "I was gonna tell you yesterday, Now don't git up on your high horse—just re-member it's the only house in town." Will paused again. "Well, Cora, this used t' be a bad house, and some women who weren't— well, some whores had it till two weeks ago. Then some of the wives around here thought it didn't look so good for Cottonwood t' have a bad house right inside the town, seein' that everybody's tryin' t' build the town up to be something. So they made their men tell these women they'd have t' clear out. I heard they was a-movin', and come over and bought the place. That's all there is to it."

Coral lay still, too horrified to make a sound. Here she lay in a house in which, just a short time before, other women had lain for quite a different purpose. She felt suddenly angry at Will, angrier than she had ever been before. Her thoughts were jumbled, and at first she felt chiefly outraged that Will had put her in such an un-fair position before their new neighbors. What would people think of her anyway to come into a place like this one? What would her mother think when she wrote to Iowa? Quickly she decided that she wouldn't write her mother this particular fact about their new home. She looked about the room furtively. In spite of herself, she found that it had assumed a new interest. Her glance traveled up and down the ugly, stained walls wonderingly. She had never thought about it much, but she had somehow pictured sin in more seductive surroundings. This homely room with its board floors and creaking windows seemed a test for only those strengthened by the most hardy virtue. She tried to put her thoughts into words.

"It seems funny women like that would live in a place like this."

Will looked at her in amazement. "Well, I'll be damned! I thought you'd have a fit."

She made a wry face at him. "I feel a little like having a fit," she admitted. "But I don't see what can be done about it. The children can't sleep out of doors with winter coming on, and we can't afford to go to a hotel."

He gave a relieved laugh. "I pictured everything, Cora, but I never pictured you'd see it so clear. Cottonwood's so different from every place you ever knowed before that I didn't know how to tell you about it in letters. Everything's different. Mike Finley now. You thought it was funny I'd stop in front of a saloon with you, and talk to him. But he's a respected citizen here. He paid me good money for building that place of his, and he's always been fine to me, and I knowed everybody'd think it pretty funny if I didn't introduce you right away."

"He acted so sad at my being here I thought he was afraid he'd lose some trade."

Will laughed again. "Well, you kin just put that thought outa yer head. A glass of beer and a game a pinochle's about all he gets outa me. He always acts sad. It's just his way. But he's a nice fella, Cora. Only different from anybody you knowed back home."

"Has he got a wife?" Some of Cora's fear that she might have to be friends with a saloonkeeper's wife came through into her voice.

"Not—not a wife——"

Cora looked at him. "Oh—that." She half turned away in distaste. "I don't have to be nice to *her,* do I?"

"Good God, no! Mike'd be the last to expect it. You don't have t' be nice to him, fer that matter, Cora. I don't want you t' feel you gotta bootlick people because it's good business. I just like the guy. It ain't got a damned thing t' do with business."

Again Cora giggled. "No, I guess I won't bootlick. I'm not much better than you are at that. You know, it's funny, Will, but I kind of liked him, too. Giving that nickel to Barbie, and all. I know what you mean— How many women lived here, anyway?"

"Five, I guess, but that's hearsay. I didn't visit the house but that one time I come t' buy it, and I just saw two." He laughed hugely.

"How'd you think I got any work done with all the drinkin' and gamblin' and runnin' after women you act as if I done?"

"No, that's not it. But, my goodness, five women—in these three little rooms! And at least one of them must have been a kitchen. How do you suppose they managed?" She looked guiltily at the door leading into the room where the children were sleeping. She had wondered why a little house so poorly put together as this one should have connecting doors between its rooms.

Will followed her glance. "I don't know but what it's a good thing them doors is there. Now I can kiss you without having you wiggle away and think the kids are lookin'!"

He put his arms around her, and Cora responded with perhaps more passion than she had shown before in her whole married life. Afterwards she wondered whether it was the talk they had been having, and she wondered, too, why this should be the case.

The sun was considerably higher when the sound of snickering laughter came to them from behind the door of the children's room. Cora got out of bed hastily, and went to the door. Joe and Jeff were on their double bed, watching Barbie, who stumbled back and forth with an affected strut across the tumbled bedding on her cot. Over her shoulder she simpered in an engaging and childishly toothless fashion at her chuckling brothers. Around her neck was a long black lace stocking. Held to the flannel front of her nightgown was a huge bunch of paper violets. On her head, tilted at an abrupt angle, was Cora's sailor hat.

"Where did you get those flowers? And that stocking?" Cora was momentarily puzzled; then, as she thought of the information Will had just given her, swiftly alarmed. She hurried to the door of the small closet which she had not had time to inspect the night before. In the general clean-up which the hotel janitor had given the house before their arrival, he had evidently used the closet as a catch-all. Piled neatly therein were things which Cora knew would immediately delight a small girl—a plaid hair-ribbon, a rhinestone-studded comb, a scrap of a broken mirror, a kewpie-doll pincushion. Kicking at the pile angrily with a bare toe, Cora slammed the closet door shut, and whirled around to her children. They were innocently interested in her behavior, but not alarmed.

Joe held out a postcard to her, still laughing at his sister's antics. "She's trying to look like this, Mom."

Cora took the card as gingerly as if it had been a dead toad. The buxom curves of the beaming maiden on its glossy front made a well-clothed figure "S" across the card. Around her plump back was a feather boa; fastened to her generous bosom was a huge bunch of violets; tilted at a steep angle on her head was a Merry Widow hat with many willow plumes sweeping from its brim. One ankle peeped daringly from beneath a skirt which she lifted coquettishly. The simper Barbie had assumed in imitation of the smile on the face of the pictured hussy was almost too realistic to be borne by her mother.

"The idea! Take off those things this minute, and come wash your hands! Throw those awful flowers and that rag of a stocking into the coal bucket! And, Joe, you get up out of bed this minute, and get dressed. I want you to get some lye and some Dutch Cleanser and—and—well, I'll ask your father what else you're to get. We'll scrub this house from top to bottom before another day has passed."

The first breakfast was over in the new home. Emptying into the teakettle the last of the bucket of water which Will had brought in just before bedtime, she turned to him.

"Now, Will, you show me where the well is, and I'll carry my own water after this."

"There ain't no well, Cora. Not in the whole town of Cottonwood. Ever'body buys their water at fifty cents a barrel. I borrowed that pailful from Labrees' over there."

Cora looked at him for a full minute, letting the fact sink in. It was so startling that there was no well any place in the whole town that at first she almost laughed at the oddity of it. But as the words speeded fully into her housekeeping and maternal consciousness, she realized that it was no laughing matter. She thought of the children's clothes that needed to be washed, and the tubfuls which she had planned to use in scrubbing the house. She looked at him hard, hoping he was joking. As she saw he was speaking the truth, dismay deepened in her face. She mustn't let Will see the extent of her consternation. Forcing a dismal smile, she held out the bucket to him.

"Well, borrow another pailful for me, will you? Then we'll get three or four barrels of water to start with. How do we do that?"

"The water man comes around three times a week. He's due to come t' this part of town today. Rose Labree said she'd make him come here. But you're gonna be disappointed, Cora; he only lets each family have one barrel at a time—and you only get three barrels a week—it keeps him workin' overtime as it is t' keep the town in water. He hauls it from the river about three miles away."

Cora looked at Will unhappily. He patted her shoulder roughly, half-sympathetic, half-amused.

"My poor little scrubber. You just gotta read a book in place a scrubbin' all the time."

Cora pushed out her chin. "Don't you worry about me. The rest of these people seem to have lived through it. But how they keep clean, I don't know."

When Will came back with a bucket of water, he set it down carefully on a rough table beside the stove. "We gotta remember to return this, Cora. It's about as bad as horsestealin' not to pay back water in these parts." He laughed and shrugged. "Well, I'm off. I'll eat dinner at the beanery this noon—then you can just git the kids a bite, and won't have to bother about me."

"You'll do no such thing," Cora said briskly. "Think I came all the way out here to have you eating downtown? People'd think you had a fine wife! You can bring home some meat for dinner, and Joe and I can go down this afternoon and lay in a store of things. You can put up some shelves in the kitchen for me, and build me a bread box. I'll make biscuits today; then I'll get some yeast and bake tomorrow."

"Pancakes for breakfast?" Will wanted to know.

"Pancakes for breakfast."

Although barrels of unpacked household goods still stood in the middle of the floor and the house was in complete disorder, Cora already saw in her mind's eye a clean and spotless home where activities ran on schedule: Monday, washing; Tuesday, ironing; Wednesday, baking; Thursday, mending; Friday, cleaning; Saturday, more baking; Sunday, church and a roast for dinner. White pancakes for fall and spring; buckwheat pancakes for winter. She smiled happily at Will.

Turning briskly to Barbie she said, "Barbie, you take Jeff out in the yard. The two of you can start carrying the little chunks of wood around to the back—I'll show you where. Joe can take the big chunks and stack it later. Joe, you can chop down sagebrush; and Barbie and Jeff can pile it at the back, and we'll burn it. We've all got to work."

"The sagebrush'll make a terrible smudge, Cora—" Will began. He broke off abruptly. "Never mind, honey," he said. "When the water man comes, you'll find a new barrel around on the shady side of the house." He picked up Jeff and carried him down the steps. "Yes, sir, my boy, we've all got t' step lively when your mother's around. She'll make great men of us yet." He smiled at Cora to show that there was no malice in his remark.

In the middle of the morning, Cora heard a team drive up to the door. Barbie shouted from the yard, "The water man's here! The water man's here!"

Joe came to the door and said politely, "Here's the water man, Mom. You'd better come talk to him. Barbie's making an awful racket."

Cora went outside to find a strange contraption resembling a hayrack drawn up to her door by two powerful horses. The vehicle was filled with many barrels covered with wet gunny sacks, held in place by staves. At the front of it, seated on a kitchen chair which was fastened to the frame, was a small man in neat blue overalls, with an oversize straw hat on his head. Through gold-rimmed spectacles, he peered benignly at her.

"Howdy, Mrs. Gray," he said with great dignity. "I'm the water man. Rose Labree said you needed water, and I come right over."

He climbed down from his chair. "You kin hold the reins," he said to Joe, as though he were conferring a great honor on him.

Joe took them carefully and stood at rigid attention, with the reins clenched tightly between tense fingers. Seeing Barbie's look of disappointment, the water man said to her, "I'll need you to hold the gunny sack off'n the bar'l."

"Our barrel's around here on the shady side of the house." Cora led him around to it.

He looked it over with the eye of a connoisseur. "Good. Good. A good tight bar'l that'll last you fer many a day. But it oughta be sunk in the ground, Mrs. Gray. Yes, it really oughta. It'll stay cooler in summer that way, and be handier t' git at any time. I never could git these other folks that lived here to berry their water, but you git Mr. Gray t' sink this bar'l just as soon as it gits empty."

"But the children might fall in," Cora objected.

He began deliberately to fill the barrel from one on the wagon, a bucketful at a time. "No, you kiver it with a tub. An' the children mustn't never go near the water bar'l. Not never! It's a sin that oughta be punished by death er worse."

He uttered these words in the most soft and gentle voice imaginable. Barbie dropped the wet gunny sack she was holding and backed slowly away from the barrel, looking at it with horror.

Cora saw he wasn't joking. "Is there no way I can get more than a barrel at a time, Mr.—?" she asked.

"My name is of no importance, Mrs. Gray," he said rather pompously. "What I bring you is the important thing. I am the water man."

After giving Cora a moment to absorb this thought, he answered her question firmly. "The water man don't know of no way you kin git more'n a bar'l at a time, Mrs. Gray. Everybody does without all he wants so's everybody kin have. It seems awful hard at first, but you'll be glad later, becuz it'd soon run up inta more money'n you c'd afford. There ain't no family in this town oughta be so spendin' with water they have to pay more'n a dollar 'n' a half a week fer it. That's whut three bar'ls come to. Now I know about whut Bill Gray makes; an' he cain't afford t' have me sell you more'n three bar'ls a week, not even if you beg fer it on bended knees."

Cora felt both irritated and apologetic. "I'm not spendthrift with water! I simply need some immediately for a lot of washing and scrubbing I have to do."

He smiled at her soothingly. "You newcomers gotta learn, Mrs. Gray. Now what you do, Mrs. Gray—you make all the kids wash in the same water. Be fair to them. Let the little boy wash first one day, the big boy next, the little girl the next. That way nobuddy's cheated, and all's equally clean. An' tell 'em not t' drink so much. An' use about a third as much fer cookin' an' dishwashin' as you're used to. Peel your potatoes without no water. When you wash clothes, jist wash 'm outa one tubful and rench 'em outa one more. Then you save your rench water from one week to use for your wash water the next."

He delivered all this in a rapid singsong, as though it was something he had repeated many times. Finished with his task of filling the barrel, he turned back to the wagon.

Cora said, "Just a minute; I'll get your money."

"No, Mrs. Gray. Not fer the first bar'l. It comes easier t' pay fer the second. An' life's tough enough these days even when you git the first bar'l a water free."

He took the reins from Joe and climbed back up on his seat. From this height he smiled down at Cora in a kindly fashion. "Don't let it knock yer props from under yuh, Mrs. Gray. You'll git along better'n you think fer."

He paused, then fixed the children with a mild eye, and said slowly and impressively, "An' don't never, never, never let me hear of you little Grays havin' water fights. When you wanta throw water, you go t' the river. You hear me!"

A cluck to his team, and the makeshift water wagon went lumbering off. Though his seat jiggled furiously beneath him, the little man sat very erect. About a block away he turned around and called out something.

"What?" cried Cora.

"Boil it!" shouted the water man. His voice came back on the wind. "Boil—it!" The wagon creaked off.

"Well, I never!" Cora said with a helpless laugh to Joe. "I think we're in a country of crazy people. But he's right about one thing— you children stay away from that water barrel, or I'll give you good spankings."

"I'll never go near it, Mama—never! He'd kill us all!" Barbie spoke with great intensity, enjoying the quivering fear which sounded in her voice.

"I guess I'd have something to say about that," Cora said. "But just the same—and I mean it—you remember not to go near that barrel."

Cora stood for a moment looking at the barrel. A gust of wind whipped around the corner of the house, and it seemed to her that she could see the film of dust deposited on the water. She got a washtub from the kitchen and put it over the top of the barrel.

Her eyes searched the countryside. A narrow road, with deep ruts, wound across the plain behind their house, disappearing between two small brown hills. No tree was to be seen, but in places the sagebrush grew almost as high as lilac bushes. The air was fresh and heady, drenched with the fragrance of the sage; but to Cora the country was as ugly as anything she had ever seen, and she turned to go inside without reluctance. Out here she could do little, but inside she could do much. Sagebrush could be pulled up from the yard, only to expose an expanse of brown dirt. She looked at the barrel angrily. There could be no question of flowers or grass or trees with water selling at fifty cents a barrel.

As she entered her house, she felt an excitement which was always hers when she came within her own four walls. Inside these four walls, she could control the wild shiftlessness of the West. Inside these walls she could bathe her children and scrub their ears and see that they were clothed in clean garments. Inside these walls she could bake bread and apple pie and fry chicken as she had been taught to do back home in Iowa. She hung some pans on nails sticking out from the kitchen walls, and vowed that Will should make her shelves before the week was out.

That evening Cora looked about her again, this time with a feeling of great contentment. She had taken the water man's advice, and had used her wash water for scrubbing her floors and woodwork; but even so, she thought ruefully, the barrel of water was already more than half gone. The house now had a steamed, soapy smell about it; and depressions in the uneven floor still showed damp spots from the recent scrubbing. The children's clothes were hung on nails in the tiny closet, or were sorted into neat piles on kitchen chairs which Cora had ranged along one side of the wall. White lace curtains, still creased from their packing, covered the shining windows. White cotton bedspreads covered the beds, even

Barbie's cot; and Barbie had been cautioned that there was to be no more jumping up and down on it. A huge pile of sagebrush was stacked at one side of the yard, and at least one tiny patch of ground directly at the front of the house was completely cleared.

The mood of close identification of herself with her family was still upon Cora. When the dishes were done, she brought some darning into the circle of light cast by the oil lamp. So sharp was her perception of Will and each of the children that it seemed to her they sat within a charmed circle. Joe was hunched over the table reading a book. Barbie, who was curled up on her father's lap, put her finger on his thoat now and then in an attempt to feel the rumble of his voice as he talked to her mother.

"It's time for you to go to bed, Barbie," Cora said, smiling quietly at her daughter.

"Papa used to sing to me before I went to bed," Barbie objected.

"That's right, I did," said Will. "I used to sing to you. And I'm glad t' have the chance t' be singing to you again. What'll it be?"

Barbie wrinkled her forehead in an attempt to remember the songs her father had sung to her before he went to Montana.

Joe said, "Sing that one about the old man who's going up North to freeze to death, Papa. It used to make Barbie cry, but it's pretty; and she's got to grow up some time and quit crying."

Will gathered Barbie more closely to him. She watched his mouth and throat intently as he started to sing.

> "I'm goin' from the cotton fields,
> I'm goin' from the cane,
> I'm goin' t' leave the old log hut
> That stands down in the lane.
>
> "When the sun goes down tonight—
> Oh, it makes me sigh—
> When the sun goes down tonight,
> I'm goin' t' say good-bye."

Will's voice, singing the plaintive, sentimental white man's ver-sion of the Negro's thoughts, rose full and rich in the quiet autumn air. A patch of moonlight, brighter than the glow from the oil lamp, shone on the floor. The evening was chilly, and no fire was built. Somewhere in the distance Cora heard with great clearness the hoofs of a plodding horse and the turning wheels of a wagon. She looked about her at these people she loved most of all those on earth, and felt a lonesome peace in accepting as home this strange land in which she found herself. She could almost feel the miles and miles of silent prairie stretching out away from her, and she could hear the wind, rushing through space, with never a treetop to stop its breathless speed. She pulled her rolled-up sleeves down over her cold arms.

> "Now Dinah she don't want t' go,
> She says she's gettin' old
> An' she's afeared she'll freeze t' death,
> That country am so cold."

A long, shuddering sob from Barbie interrupted the song. "Oh, Papa, I can't stand it. Truly I can't. It's too sad."

"No, Barbie, you gotta hear it all. You can't just say you can't stand things and not listen when a body wants t' sing a song. You let me finish, and then I'll sing a funny one for you." Barbie put her hand over her mouth, and cowered down against her father's chest. He stroked her hair gently as he finished the song for Joe, and wiped the tears from his own eyes when he had finished. Then he picked Barbie up in his arms and started waltzing gaily about the floor with her as he began to sing his next song:

> "Now McManus loaned a dress suit
> For the ball the other night.
> The coat was much too large for him,
> The pants they was too tight—"

CABIN FEVER

THEY WERE at the woodpile when the first gust of flakes shook down over them, fine and hard as salt. A shawl of white wool was drawing low over the mountains. Wind groaned through the pines north of the house.

McWethy looked up while his axe suspended its syncopated rhythm.

"Blizzard," he said needlessly.

Pride let his saw rest in its thin yellow trough. He thwacked his thigh with a hand that had stiffened round the handle.

"Number—how many?" he inquired. "I've lost count."

McWethy did not answer. He was measuring with his eye the pile of logs that remained.

"I wish I'd got that last load home," he said. "I don't think there'll be much left for building timbers. We'll be lucky if we get through."

The snow was mid-leg deep when they came back from the stables, Pride's lantern spilling a quavery pool around his feet. They could feel the hairs in their nostrils stiffen with the frost, and McWethy rubbed his nose tip with the back of his mitten after he had set the milk pails down by the separator. But the house was warm yet and there was a glowing bed of coals. McWethy nursed it swiftly into flame with fine-split wood. It did not take long to prepare supper. They had learned by experience how to eliminate every waste motion. And their meals were not elaborate. Today there were fried potatoes, roast beef warmed up in its own gravy, creamed corn, and canned peaches. Yesterday, Pride remembered, there had been canned pears, and the day before that prunes, and tomorrow there would be pears again.

They ate prodigiously, and with few friends. Pride remembered suddenly other meals—dinners in cozy city restaurants that had stretched over hours, with many cigarettes; coffee cups replenished and forgotten again until they were scummy-cold; beer that went flat while controversy waxed and waned. That was civilization. Minds met across the table there, and food seasoned with wit and wisdom. Here eating was a deadly serious business. The machine must be refueled so that it could do its work, and nothing was important enough to interrupt that fundamental ritual. Animals ate thus, speechless, greedily intent.

McWethy shoved his plate aside and found a cigarette. The house shivered to a sudden blast of wind; the scrap of carpet by the door bulged and lifted uncannily, and a belch of smoke came from the stove.

"She's a stem-winder," said McWethy. "It'll take us two days to dig out. Lucky we got those cows into the maternity ward this morning. The rest may have to go hungry."

Pride nodded. That was McWethy's way now, McWethy's speech, curt, factual, handling things as solid and positive as the axe helve or the knotted chunk of pine that he was thrusting into the stove. It called for no answer. It was not conversation—not as they had known conversation once.

"Mac," Pride said suddenly, and then paused. McWethy emptied a dipperful of cold water into the dishpan and tested with one finger before he yielded an incurious "Yeah?"

"Oh—nothing." Pride took down the dish towel. They worked swiftly and in silence, except for the rattle of heavy china, the recurrent ague of ill-fated window frames. Two glasses, two cups, two saucers, two plates, two sauce dishes, the meat platter and the potato dish, a handful of silver, the milk pails. Pride tilted the last pail bottom up atop the warming oven and flipped the sodden towel on the line behind the stove. The chores were done, and the evening stretched before them, a Sahara to be somehow traversed.

McWethy reclaimed a towel, wound in a limp snarl across the line, and spread it out smoothly. McWethy was an orderly soul, with the spinsterly orderliness of the confirmed bachelor. He replenished the stove, grumbling at its capacity, and cast an appraising look around the room. All ready for morning: table set, kindling split, oatmeal simmering on the back of the stove. He liked things thus, from long habit, though the need of economized time existed no longer. All life moved sluggishly, stiffened with frost, or lay recumbent in the long winter stupor.

Pride had found a greasy pack of cards and laid out a game of solitaire. At the second turn of the deck he found himself stalled. He said "Damn!" and went to the window. It was a jungle of crystal.

"Thicker than cheese," he growled. He padded over to the stove and stood for a while soaking up the warmth before he ambled back to the table.

McWethy cocked an eye over the top of his book, and a tuck of vexation formed in his forehead. Why did Steve have to prowl that way?

Ten minutes.

"Mac," said Pride, abruptly, "don't you know any other tune?"

McWethy struggled back to consciousness. "Huh?" he queried foggily.

"I said," Pride enunciated, "don't you know any other tune than that?"

"What tune?"

"That thing you've been humming for the last two hours. Doesn't it ever *end?* You go round, and round, and round, like a carousel."

"Oh," said McWethy after a moment's research, "that's 'Springtime in the Rockies.'"

"Yes"—with ponderous patience—"I suspected as much. I appreciate your subtle irony—but I wish you'd enlarge your repertoire."

"Sorry, I didn't know I was humming. I'll quit."

For three minutes there was silence, except for the wind and the fire and the slap of the cards. Then Pride flung up his head. McWethy was whistling softly, and one foot was tapping out a waltz rhythm against the woodbox. Halfway through he broke off, with a guilty start and covert glance at his companion. Pride exhaled deeply. There was silence again, until Pride made his fourth visit to the window. McWethy looked up.

"Steve," he began, and then broke off.

"What?"

"Oh, nothing. Yes. Give me a cigarette. I'm too lazy to go after another pack."

Pride fumbled, vainly.

"I'm out, too. I'll get some."

His voice came a minute later from the pantry.

"Where'd you bury them? I can't find them."

"On the top shelf, with the matches, aren't they?"

"No. Nor anywhere else, that I can see."

McWethy's feet thumped to the floor.

"*All* right, I'll find them."

Five minutes later they faced each other in dismay.

"I remember taking the last pack and throwing away the carton yesterday," McWethy said slowly. "I thought we had two more. I had them on the list the last time we were down to the Forks, I know. You packed the stuff in. Do you remember seeing them?"

Pride shook his head. "I'm not sure."

"God-damn! Did that half-wit forget to put them in? Did you check the list over with him?"

Again Pride shook his head, miserably conscious of guilt. He was aware of McWethy's eyes measuring him; to avoid them he turned for another fruitless exploration.

"Well," said McWethy mildly.

"How long will this last? I mean—how long before we can get down to the Forks?"

"Lord knows. I don't. May snow all day tomorrow—maybe all next day. Then it's likely to be a week before a saddle horse can get through, the way it rolls up in the canyon. If we had snow-shoes . . ."

He broke off and shrugged eloquently.

"Mac, I'm sorry. . . ."

"So'm I."

McWethy walked over to the door and stood for a little with his

hand on the knob. But he did not open it. He came back to the
stove, poked in a knotty stick and watched a minute as the flames
took hold. When he spoke again his voice had that same studied
mildness. "Well—I swore off smoking once. Stuck to it for two days.
Looks like I'd improve my record. Let's hit the hay."

Next morning they stepped out into a maelstrom of white. There
was no sky, no horizon, no earth underfoot. The snow came like a
river. The wind was so thick with it that one could not think of
them separately; they were a single force. They had swept away
barns and sheds and haystacks; Pride had a foolish feeling that any
minute the house might disintegrate under that bludgeoning, go
plunging crazily down the torrent as he had once seen houses borne
in a Mississippi flood.

They reached the barn breathless and weary, and profoundly
thankful for the guidance of the fence. For once Pride forgot the familiar revulsion when the breath of the stable immersed him. It was
warm and it was sheltered. He forgot some of his distrust of the cows;
they were alive, at any rate, and like himself prisoners in this
savage white beleaguerment. Somehow McWethy and he managed
to get the stock fed and watered. Somehow they got the pails back
to the house without spilling quite all the milk. And somehow, in
the early dusk, they did it all again. The storm poured over and
around them with the same tidal brawn. To Pride it seemed already
that it had assumed permanence; there was no term to it, no end
nor any beginning. It was a datum of existence.

Between the morning and the evening chores was a day in
which they stoked the fire and prepared meals and ate them and
washed and dried dishes and put them away and took them out
again, and swore inwardly because the ritual, prolong it as they
would, took so little time. A day in which McWethy finished *The
Case of Sergeant Grischa* and thumbed biliously through the heap
of dog-eared magazines and finally in disgust began rereading
Sergeant Grischa. A day in which Pride laid out innumerable
games of solitaire, and between them trod a lugubrious circuit
from table to window, from window to stove, from stove to table
again. A day in which their hands groped recurrently for cigarettes

and came away empty, in which the tobacco hunger gnawed remorselessly within them.

During the second night the storm died. The morning was clear and white and bitter. The thermometer on the porch read thirty-four below. They looked out on a world of snow. It swelled down across the valley in great billows, a white sea bewitched into sudden sculpture. Barns and sheds wore an exaggerated thatch. Fences lifted an occasional fez and an ungainly harlequin arm. The trees had broken into a new and shining foliage. The range was a mighty upheaval of crystal. It was strange and splendid, and Pride felt the cold sink deep within him as he looked upon it. The landscapes of the moon must be like that—lifeless and sheer and malignantly beautiful.

McWethy looked up to the hogback and shook his head.

"I wouldn't ask a saddle horse to try it," he said. "It'd be up to his withers all the way to the Forks. If we had snowshoes now—or skis '. . ."

Pride, too, looked at the hogback. There had been a road there once—months ago, it seemed. There was no road now, nor any other visible mark to point the way to the outer world, or to prove that there was an outer world. Always Pride had drawn a little gulp of relief when they topped the hogback on their way down for the mail. It was like opening a door; the world widened before them, and it was a peopled world, with slow shavings of smoke in the brittle air, and midge-small nests of buildings where men and women went about their work. Suddenly he felt a desperate need to see them again, to reassure himself of their continued existence. For in these days there had grown within him a grisly conviction that he and McWethy were alone—alone on an alien planet, a sentry post flung out across empty space and abandoned there.

But he said nothing of this as he followed McWethy back to the house and set the milk pails down to stomp the snow from his overshoes and drag the mittens from stiffened fingers. He said nothing of it over the breakfast that tasted flat and inadequate and ended strangely soon for lack of the cigarette that should have followed it. He said nothing while McWethy guided the team floundering across the meadows to the stack where the herd was converging to meet them, a crooked dark procession vocal in many dolorous keys. There had been a time once when he would have spoken. Months ago—or was it years?

Pride came out of the bedroom that night from one last hopeless exploration of pockets that might, just conceivably, have secreted some limp shreds of a forgotten cigarette. He sagged into his chair by the table, shook the greasy cards out of their case, riffled them listlessly and laid them out in seven ragged piles. Twice through the deck; he scooped the cards together in disgust. The chair scraped back; he paddled across to the window and gouged a hole in the frost that lay plush-thick.

McWethy's eyes lifted over the edges of his book, and his nostrils widened and stiffened.

Pride stood for a little with his nose hard against the pane. Then he shrugged his shoulders vastly, turned, and prowled over to the stove. He opened the door and stared biliously into the flame, inserted a fat stick of wood, and closed the door. He teetered indecisively on wide-spread feet for a space; then he ambled over to the cupboard to fumble desultorily among the magazines that littered it. Then to the window again.

McWethy exhaled unevenly, and bit his teeth hard on the words that shaped behind them.

The chair scraped again. Pride picked up the cards.

Five minutes more. An eddy of icy air sucked through the house. The bedroom door banged shut, squeaked, and banged again. Not loudly, but with a dreary eccentric persistence, lacking reason or rhythm, like the sound of an idiot's carpentry. *Squeeeek . . . Bang!* Pause. *Squeeeek . . .* Pause, *Bang!* Pause . . . *Squeeeek . . .*

McWethy's feet thumped down and the book slapped shut. With exaggerated strides he crossed the room. The door slammed and latched. He marched back, sat down with emphasis, and said "Damn!" in a venomous undertone when he found that he had lost his place.

Why couldn't Steve *ever* shut a door behind him? Why couldn't he do *anything* the way it should be done? Why did he always bunch the dish towel in a limp knot across the line instead of spreading it out properly, and tumble the knives and forks helter-skelter into the drawer instead of assorting them neatly, and hang the big frying pan on the hook where the little one belonged? And why did he have to prowl the floor every night—from the window to the door, from the door to the table, from the table to the stove—until a man felt like screaming at him?

McWethy grunted, and returned to his book. Five minutes later he had forgotten his ire; his foot was tapping the woodbox and he was whistling thinly "I Don't Want to Play in Your Yard." The verse, and then the chorus, and then back into the verse again, without pause or variation. Pride knew that the recital was good for hours—until bedtime, at any rate.

The cards were wrong again, with the maddening obstinacy of the inanimate. Pride said "Hell!" and riffled them so savagely that the nine of clubs tore halfway across.

The clock ticked toward nine. The carpet by the door lifted and bulged. A white fungus of frost was growing over the sill and in across the floor; a like deposit seamed the window frame. McWethy, reaching the end of a chapter, shut his book and yawned prodigiously. Stretching to his feet, he came over to the table and dropped into the chair opposite Pride.

Pride was engaged in a deliberation of profound delicacy. If he played the king of spades out of the deck in that vacant place he could free the deuce of hearts that lay under the king. On the other hand, if he played the king of diamonds off the seventh pile he would open up all the rich possibilities of the buried cards. He needed that deuce—but of course the missing ace of clubs might be somewhere in that seventh pile. He was slowly persuading himself that the potential was more tempting than the assured, when McWethy leaned forward and informed him:

"Here's a place for that king, Steve. See?"

"I know," explained Pride patiently. "But I think I'd better play this one and see what's underneath." He did so, and pounced on the ace with a little "Ah-ha!" of welcome.

"Oh, yes," conceded McWethy. "That was better."

Three minutes passed. Pride had progressed. Kings and aces were all in view, and he had built up to the sevens and eights on the upper tier. But there were still three cards down, and he was moving discreetly lest injudicious haste close irrevocably some line of attack that later might prove just the one he needed.

"Look, Steve," McWethy pointed. "You can play the eight of hearts and the nine of clubs here."

"Not yet," Pride muttered, preoccupiedly.

"Why not?"

Pride executed a shift involving the eight and nine, and turned up one of the buried cards.

"I see," agreed McWethy.

Pride riffled through the deck again. Yes, this time the black jack he had been wanting came up.

"Play your jack of spades on the queen of diamonds," McWethy prompted. Pride did so. His teeth were clamped on his lower lip and he exhaled profoundly.

"And now you can move that string over on the jack and find out what's in your last pile."

Pride slammed down the four cards that remained and swept the layout together in ruinous confusion.

"For Christ's sake," he demanded, "are you playing this game, or am I?"

McWethy's bewilderment slowly seasoned with injury.

"Well, you needn't get so hard-boiled about it."

"Hard-boiled? God almighty, do you like to have somebody sitting by and telling you how to play your hand? I may be a cripplewit, but I can lay a black jack on a red queen without being coached."

"Suit yourself," said McWethy frostily. He rose and stretched with elaborate unconcern, and retired to the bedroom. When Pride came in he was furled like a cocoon and his eyes were locked tight. But he was not asleep. His smoldering sense of injury was too urgent. And shortly it had found new sustenance. Pride was snoring.

Pride always snored. He was one of those fortunate mortals who can drop off two minutes after they knead their pillows into shape and pull the covers to their chins. And he had a robust snore, a rich, swelling baritone, that persisted in defiance of nudges and muttered imprecations. It was strange that McWethy had never really dis-

covered Pride's snore before. During the summer and fall he had
been too exhausted for any noise to keep him awake. But now life
was easier, and sleep was correspondingly coy.

That night he lay, it seemed, for hours—shifting recurrently from
left side to right, recurrently opening smarting eyelids to stare into
the darkness, listening to that nasal diapason until he felt himself
ready to scream, until hatred was hot within him.

Hatred. Of Steve Pride.

Pride, swabbing out the potato kettle next noon, set it bottom
up on the back of the stove and flung the sodden towel across the
line.

McWethy jerked it down again.

"For God's sake!" he said, so venomously that Pride turned to
see him spreading the towel out again. He reddened.

"Well?" he challenged.

A little ashamed of his pettishness, ashamed to admit his shame,
McWethy took up the challenge.

"Can't you ever do anything *right?*"

Steve Pride's eyes seemed to sink deeper into their fine net of
wrinkles, and his mouth was flat and ugly. His voice when he answered was flat and ugly too.

"No," he said. "And I don't give a damn. I never made any pretensions to being a model housemaid. I've dried your dirty dishes
until I'm belly-sick of them. I've milked your stinking cows and
shoveled your rancid hay and cleaned your filthy stables until I
never want to see them again. I was a damn fool ever to let you
talk me into coming out to this God-forsaken dungheap of creation,
and by God I'm paying for it."

McWethy was conscious of nausea and a constriction in his throat
and something like giddiness. His fists were clenched; they wanted
to hit Steve Pride. The effort of holding them by his sides was a
physical ache.

"You know," he said, "what you can do."

"Yes," said Pride. "I've been a cripplewit a long time, but I know
that much."

He turned his back and began pulling on his overshoes, with
hands that shook so he could hardly control them. A minute later

the door slammed behind him. McWethy sat down, feeling momentarily as if his knees could support him no longer. Rage burned over him in long prickly waves, and ebbed again, leaving a sickish feeling, a leaden emptiness at the pit of the stomach. And as rage ebbed shame seeped into his consciousness, a swelling torment of chagrin.

After a little he rose, emptied the greasy water from the dishpan, swabbed the pan out and hung it behind the stove. He replenished the reservoir and pumped the pail full again. He fueled the stove with two big sticks and closed the drafts so the fire would keep until suppertime. The familiar tasks steadied him, and performed thus, with dogged concentration, they postponed the necessity for thought.

The kitchen set to rights, he donned jacket and cap and mittens and went out to the woodpile. He had heaved a ten-inch log onto the sawbuck and measured off a stove length on the thick rust-red bark when he looked up to see movement in the lifeless circle of the horizon where there should have been no movement—the dark silhouette of a man and a horse, tiny with distance, floundering across the white periphery of the hogback and vanishing.

He stared while his fingers grew stiff on the saw handle, and profane words formed on his lips and found no utterance. There was a crooked furrow, angling down from the hogback; it disappeared behind the cottonwoods that sheltered the house and emerged to fuse with the track that led to the barns. He traced it with eyes that saw and did not see; gravely, carefully, as if it were necessary to assemble all the evidence before phrasing the inevitable conclusion.

"The damn fool!" he said. "The damn fool!"

He had never dreamed that Pride would really go.

After a little he became aware of the cold. It was a gray, shrunken day; the sky was thick and opaque; it pressed down on earth as if to crush it under an intolerable weight. There was little wind, but it seared the skin and sent a scurry of loose snow along the drifts.

McWethy thumped life into his mittened hand and set the saw eating its slow seam into the log. The tug and thrust, rhythmic,

monotonous, soothed him. Work—you could depend on work. It
didn't play you false. You could get it in your hand, feel it, real,
factual, comprehensible, with no subtleties or ambiguities. And
there was no better medicine for the maddening migraine of
thought.

But the anaesthetic wore off too quickly.

He hadn't thought Pride would really go. All over a childish tiff,
a flare of words by which neither had really meant anything, a
momentary fury blazing up in the tinder of accumulated trifles. An
unlatched door banging with idiot reiteration, the scrape of a
thumbnail on a frosted pane, boots scuffling a fretful parade across
worn linoleum, a damp towel flung across the line in a ropy snarl.
Because of these things two men who had sweated and schemed
and bantered and bickered and wassailed together for the better
part of a decade were suddenly enemies, looking hate out of
narrowed eyes, speaking hate in flat malevolent voices. Because of
these things one of them had ridden over the hogback, not even
deigning to look back at the little domain they had claimed from
the wilderness together.

"The *damn* fool!" McWethy said. "Putting a horse into drifts
higher than his withers. Hope he has sense enough to follow the
rimrocks where it's blown off a little. He ought to make it all right.
Blue's a good horse."

A gust of snow caught him in the face as he turned from the
sawhorse to the chopping block. It thinned and left the air clear
again, but he looked up to the mountain and it was not there. The
sky seemed to have slid down between them, a cheesy sky that
looked as if one might take it in both hands and find it corporeal.
It was darkening fast, too; it must be later than he thought. Time
to be starting the chores; he had them all to do alone tonight. And
tomorrow night, and all the nights to come.

He came out of the cow stable into a seething darkness. He staggered as the wind caught him; milk sloshed from the pails and
soaked icily through the leg of his overalls. The snow in the path
was nearly to his knees. He almost walked into the north wall of
the house before its bulk emerged from the smothering tide.

As he shook the snow from cap and jumper his eye fell on the

clock over the washstand. Not six o'clock yet. And suddenly he
began to calculate. When was it that Steve had started? After they
had finished the dinner dishes; that would make it somewhere
around one-thirty. But no, come to think of it; they'd eaten late,
because he'd had to ride back through the bunch after feeding and
cut out three cows for the maternity ward. It had been one when
they came into the house. And stirring up the fire and getting dinner took time. It must have been well after two—perhaps nearer
three—when he had looked up from the woodpile and seen that
black midge-figure dipping over the hogback. He remembered how
dusk had caught him unawares.

It was seven miles to the Forks. Had dusk and storm caught
Steve the same way?

Seven miles. Steve had been gone more than two hours before
the storm really became bad. He'd had plenty of time. He'd be
toasting his toes by the big base-burner in the Forks Hotel now, or
sitting down to Mrs. Pettigrew's supper, a better meal than he'd
have found up here at Next to Nothing, McWethy conceded ruefully.

Two hours—a little more—for seven miles. It was more than
enough. And yet—he remembered his own words, "drifts ·higher
than a horse's withers." The snow always rolled up deeper than
anywhere else in that flume of a canyon. And to a horse floundering to his belly at every step seven miles was a long way.

McWethy found himself standing at the window that looked east
toward the hogback, the fat of his thumb melting a hole in the frost.
For a minute he stood staring out into nothing. He remembered
Pride's many similar reconnaissances, and drew back with a little
grimace of disgust for his folly.

"Hell," he told himself, "he made it all right."

It was strange how many reminders of Steve there were in every
simple act. First the conscious effort of peeling three potatoes instead of six, cutting off a single portion of steak, setting out one
knife and fork and spoon. Then the blankness of that wall which he
faced when he sat down, where he was accustomed to seeing Steve
Pride's long frame and lean face sculptured in the lamplight. There
was a queer sense of incompleteness when he pushed back his plate.

The meal had gone so abruptly, with no pauses for colloquy and controversy. He forgot how long it had been since they had really paused for controversy, interrupted the business of eating for more than a curt sentence about the weather, a terse comment on the day's labors.

"Damn!" he said fervidly. He had fumbled automatically for a cigarette and found none. Without it the habitual interval of relaxation after the meal had lost its savor. But the dishpan was not yet hot. He tested it with a forefinger, said "Damn!" again, and walked over to the window.

Suppose Steve hadn't made the Forks before the storm? Suppose he hadn't known enough to hug the rimrocks instead of following the road down the canyon? Steve was a tenderfoot, after all, queerly inept in the fundamental skills that seemed to McWethy so simple, because he had learned them in boyhood. Suppose Steve was still floundering through the drifts somewhere down toward the mesa, with the wind whipping the snow around him fifty miles an hour and the night a boiling confusion?

"Lord," McWethy muttered, "I wish we had a phone!"

But the phone was one of the luxuries they had foregone through these first lean years. Next year, maybe, they had said. So many things were on the calendar for next year. A secondhand flivver, and a radio, and maybe water piped into the house. He and Steve had planned these things together, finding solace in the future for the niggardly life they were constrained to live today. And now Steve was gone.

He tested the soapy water again, conscious of an absurd smoldering impatience. Absurd, because the dishwashing was so quickly over. Spreading the towel neatly out to dry, he remembered, and shame welled up in him. Such a little thing to knot a man's fists and urge ugly, blistering words through his teeth; such a little thing to send another man floundering out into the drifts with a blizzard raking down from the range at his heels.

The table was set, the kindling ready for morning, the fire stoked to gluttonous repletion. He drew his chair close to the stove and picked up a magazine. But he could not read. He sat staring at the print without seeing it, conscious of the silence—silence complete and malevolent despite the shuffle of snow on the window, the bay of the wind along the eaves. It was a new kind of silence. There had been hours when Steve and he had exchanged hardly a word, while evenings when each had been immersed in his own concerns. But always he had been aware of Steve's presence. The knowledge of it had existed on the edge of consciousness, fed by trivial tidings that the senses never bothered to translate into active perceptions—the flip of a turned page, the slap of cards on oilcloth, the creak of a chair under shifting weight. He had hardly been aware of these things, or of the presence to which they testified. But he was acutely conscious of their absence.

He threw the magazine aside and strode to the window. The frost had closed over the peephole. He reopened it and peered out for a long minute. And terror rose in him like a fever, the terror he had been denying for two hours past.

What if Steve hadn't made the Forks?

It was useless to repeat the assurance that there had been time enough. He had ceased to believe it while his lips mouthed the empty reiteration. Two hours for seven miles—seven drifted miles. The margin of safety wasn't enough. If all had gone well Steve had ridden into the Forks well ahead of the first greedy tentacles of the storm. But if all hadn't gone well—if he hadn't found clean going along the rimrocks—if Blue had wearied and lagged or played out, tough old warrior that he was—then Steve was somewhere out there now.

McWethy remembered all the lore he had heard or read of blizzards and men they had overtaken. That young couple over in the Badwater country, who left their two kids tucked in the car when it stalled and set out to walk back to the nearest ranch. A sheepherder had found them next morning, huddled together in the drifts, and a rescue party discovered the boys. Cocooned in the robes, they had lived, though one of them had lost a foot.

And old man Corrigan. He'd gone out to bring in a cow that had just calved, in a pasture not half a mile from the house. They found him stiff next day, seventy-five yards from the door.

And it was seven miles to the Forks.

"I'm a damn fool," McWethy told himself. "Two to one he got

there in plenty of time. Storm's behind him anyhow, and Blue'd take him through if he'd give him half a chance."

He scowled into the crystalline jungles on the pane.

"Anyway, there isn't anything I can do, until the storm breaks and the trail's open again."

That was the damnable thing. There wasn't anything to do. Common sense told him that. Even if he *knew* Steve was benighted out there somewhere there wasn't anything he could do. No way to summon help. No neighbors to organize searching parties with lanterns and blankets and hot coffee. And no chance in the world to set out alone and hope to come back, let alone find one infinitesimal speck in a seven-mile caldron of seething wind and snow.

He strode over to the stove with swift, nervous steps, and stoked it afresh. He discovered he was shivering; he must have been standing by the window for minutes. The carpet by the door bulged and flattened again; the lamp flame sent a supple tongue licking up the sooty side of the chimney; the shadows jigged briefly and were quiet again.

McWethy sat down and picked up the magazine. He read a paragraph through and read it again and knew nothing of what it said. He swore dully, without venom, and went over to the door. For a minute he stared irresolutely at the tumbled sheepskin coats and denim jumpers and sweaters and caps hanging there, at the arctics round which the muddy melted snow was congealing.

It was the damnable uncertainty that was maddening. He could have wished, almost, that he *knew* Steve was out in the blizzard. It would have made it easier to decide what to do. Though there was nothing to do in any event. He couldn't start out alone. Not a chance in the world of finding Steve; not a chance in the world of getting back. Two men lost instead of one; or perhaps one man lost for no reason, while the other sat safe and snug at the Forks and gossiped with the Pettigrews and got the news of the valley and the world.

Nothing to do but wait. Tonight and perhaps tomorrow, and maybe another day, other days, before he could know.

He looked at the clock. It was eleven minutes to ten.

"I'm a damn fool," McWethy told himself. "I'm going to bed."

Deliberately he took the clock down and wound it and released the alarm lever so that it would go off at six. He refilled the teakettle and moved the oatmeal boiler forward. The Morris chair squealed under him as he sat down and loosened his boot strings.

He had removed one boot and half unlaced the other when suddenly he stopped. For a little he sat stooped and immobile, the leathern thongs loose in his fingers. Then, slowly, he began to relace them. When they were knotted he retrieved the other shoe and put it on. He picked up the lantern and kindled it. He set it down by the door while he pulled on his overshoes.

He was squirming into jumper and sweater when there was a thud of steps on the porch and the door opened, letting in a swirl of snow, a blast of cold, and Steve Pride.

There was a bib of ice around the collar of his sheepskin. His clothes were a blaze of snow; his face was whipped red except for a chalky spot on either cheekbone, and there were little icicles in his eyebrows and on his mustache.

"It's a wild night," he said tamely. "That fire feels good."

He hunched over it as he stripped off his mittens and fumbled with stiffened fingers at the button loops on his coat. Thus occupied, he did not see McWethy inconspicuously removing jacket and sweater and kicking loose his overshoe buckles.

"I'd never have got there if it hadn't been for Blue," Pride continued. "Plugged alone like a Trojan, though he was over his ears part of the time. We clung to the rimrocks going down, and it wasn't bad. But coming back—Holy Saint Peter! I never knew where we were until he stopped—spang!—at the barn door."

He shook himself out of the sheepskin, and sank into the chair. McWethy saw long shivers shake him like a rag, heard the click of chattering teeth. He pulled off the second overshoe and came over to the stove.

"Reckon you're hungry," he said. "I'll get some coffee. Won't take long. Better rub those cheekbones. They're frosted."

Pride suppressed the chills for a moment while he extracted from his pocket a parcel tied in a flour sack. He thrust it at McWethy.

"Open it. Six cartons; I wasn't taking chances on another famine. And I brought the mail, too. Letters, Mac. And magazines. Open them up. Have yourself a smoke. Then get me that coffee. I can use it."

The chill took him again while McWethy unknotted the sack and emptied its contents on the table. With his thumbnail he broke the seal of one carton and took out a pack.

"Luckies, eh?" he said. "Hell! Didn't they have any Camels?"

By Alan Swallow

WYOMING

1.

The coyotes raise the hood of light,
Inviting darkness with their cries.
It is the prairie dusk, and night
Wavers, then boldly takes the skies.

And falling on the hills, the dark
Deepens the purple cloth to black.
At last there is no agile mark
Of hills for stiffened cardiac.

The stars elude the groping fingers:
The sun has taken all we tasted.
Here in the consciousness that lingers
The coyotes' hunger is not wasted.

2.

Here on the cliff I've topped, my shadow blotting
The edge of stone, the edge of flowing air,
I watch the hawk assuming sky, and plotting
Unpenciled arcs on clouds' ascending stair.

One step, and I'd go preying down to death,
Swooping the towering altitudes I've stood,
Folding my wings complacently as breath
To take with my own beak my only blood.

It is from blood I've climbed. The heart's slim trickle
Has coursed the thoroughfare too long for rest.
And even as I stand, time's early sickle
Gathers the orange grain along the west.

I will remember hawks find sleep on stone;
This is a place to leave a silenced bone.

3.
I cannot number all the pairs of feet
That climbed this hill: many were moccasined,
And some were clad in boots; and some were fleet,
Some slow, some stiff against the pelting wind.

And why should they attain this rising place?
Perhaps to watch the hawk wing-folding sky,
Or take the warrior's privilege, to trace
His tenancy of sage and alkali.

They left no sign, no rock expressly turned.
The ground is smooth with wind and dust and rain,
The grass has often towered, leaned, and burned,
Leaving no single trace. *But never again*
Will earth be quite the same, for after plow
This hill will wear a newly furrowed brow.

4.
Here on this hill I take the coyote stance,
Alert to trace mice-movement in the sage
And stiff, defeated grass. With hovering glance
I read this water-marked old parchment page.

And it is old. It's old with frosted rot.
The slanting light of southward-moving sun
Displays a ragged edge, thumb-smear, a blot,
And faded lines where eyes have quickly run.

There is no movement now. The tale is reaped,
And marketed, and stalks no more. Tonight
Let snow erase it, cold and blizzard-heaped.
There will be other tales to write.

5.
In this almost forgotten valley I
Have stood alone beneath the mountain rim,
Soil under foot, and blanketed by sky,
And watched the western fires turn red and dim:
The light *which suffers blindness* leaves the air
To cold, and to the world-wind's throated sally;
The mountains flatten, are no longer there;
And I am in the universal valley.

O world, I want to etch upon my brain
The unhorizoned earth, the earth that any star
Can know! *It's cold.* And there is war in Spain.
Now bed, and sleep, and hear the wind's catarrh.
Some morning I hope to wake, look up with eyes
Content, and find this valley paradise.

RAIN

THIS IS a story that is minted of the West, and you're likely to hear it anywhere—as well on the High Plains of Kansas or Colorado, in Utah's desert outlands, in Texas or in Arizona, as in the country of the Humboldt.

So the story goes, one day a waddy out on the range incredulously squirted some tobacco juice at the nearest clump of sage. Sure enough, he saw a wagon, drawn by a couple of browbeaten horses. On the wagon box sat a graybearded stranger and in the wagon was a gleaming steel plow.

The waddy rode up and pointed to the plow. "Beggin' yore pardon, dad, what in hell is that?"

"Why, my boy," the old man said genially, "that's a plow."

"A plow. . . . What's it for? What do yuh do with it?"

The old man snorted. "Do with it? Why, you break up the earth with it. I'm agoin' to stop right here, pre-empt myself about eighty acres, fence it and plow it and raise corn, garden sass, mebbe a little wheat."

The waddy scratched his ear. "But look here, don't yuh hafta have a little moisture to raise that stuff—rain, for instance?"

The old man chuckled at this innocence. "Son, you've got behind times. Ain't you heard about this new dry farmin'? You can farm without rain." He filled his pipe and between puffs explained about the new way of using half the land and summer-fallowing the other half to store moisture.

283

"But yuh can't do that here," the cowboy objected. He thought up half a dozen reasons why. But the old man was stubborn; he cal'lated to have him a farm right here. At last the waddy sighed, pushing back his Stetson and mopping his brow with his sleeve. "Dad, I'll tell yuh a story.

"A while back an eastern dude inherited a lot of money. He'd heard about the West and he come out here, right out here, and he started to have him a farm right here. The first year he spent quite a lot of money, gettin' the land plowed, fenced, and planted. Well, dad, there wasn't no rain, and nothin' came up. He was a stubborn galoot, and he tried again the next year, and there wasn't no rain that year neither. He still had a lot of money left, though, and the third year he got a bright idee.

"He went into town and bought hisself a wagon, a big, strong wagon, yuh know, with four-inch tires. He put fourteen-inch side-boards on the wagon, and got a load of good soil—yuh gotta say that for him, dad, he got a load of good soil some'eres around. Nobody couldn't never figger out where he got that there good soil. Then he got a good team of horses, big, fast horses, and he hired a chore boy. Then he planted hisself another garden in that wagon, and he says to the boy, he says, 'Nick, I want yuh to keep yore eye skinned all the time, day and night. And if yuh see a cloud, no matter where it is, no matter anything, I want yuh to hitch up this-yere team and drive like hell till yuh get under the cloud. And if the cloud does percipitate, then the rain'll germinate the seed in the good earth on this-yere wagon, and damn if I won't have me a garden!'

"But the fack is, dad," the waddy said sorrowfully, "that rich dude, he went plumb, flat broke, buyin' oats for the horses and axle grease for the wagon."

Like many of the stories the West tells, this yarn has at its heart an unimpassioned disillusion. Elsewhere in the American wayfaring the land was always conquerable. Some land required a greater stubbornness of spirit, and its yield might be grudging. But soil always could be vanquished. It was not until Americans crossed the 98th degree, west longitude, that they realized how the condition of their triumph had been rain.

Rain! To the West the word is an invocation. Rain is the yard-stick of the land's worth. It is the determinant of the level of life. Rain on the land itself, the rolling, illimitable earth, has, except for stockmen and the range grasses, the significance only of an unexpected beneficence; it is token of the interested, if weak-willed, benevolence of God. In the farther West rain means not rain upon the farmland so much as snow in the mountains, running water in the creeks, ground water from springs and wells. Man himself will bring the water to the farmland, and give thanks for the privilege. All that is expected of the Lord is that He shall precipitate the rain somewhere in the country, "that if not for us, He shall not be against us."

In the beginning none but the Mormons was willing to accept the West on those terms. The price of desert settlement was a lower level of subsistence, a greater measure of hardship and deprivation, a lesser return for the heart's blood. While other Americans went on to Oregon or California, the Mormons settled in the mountain-desert to work out their destiny. And from their center stake of Zion, planted in the valley of the Great Salt Lake, they carried the warfare to the desert.

Down the long valley of the Humboldt the Saints went to plant their western outpost under the Sierras; and in retreat they marched back up this valley to mountain-girt Zion. Save only outcast Peter Haws, in all these years there was none among these greatest of desert fighters who carried the war to the Humboldt earth. It was not only that the Humboldt Valley was America's thoroughfare, the highroad of empire, nor was it only that the Diggers of the West made perilous the whole land, for Mormon outposts dotted the Southern Route to California at oases even so poor and so isolated as Las Vegas, and there were not Indians for whom the Mormons could not feel fellowship. . . . In the Humboldt Valley the desert was enthroned. Mormon frontiersmen never here sought out the antagonist, the old enemy with which they warred even in the badlands of the Colorado Plateau. But in the end, when the pioneer years were finished, Mormons came to the Humboldt.

Bishop's Creek gathers itself from the west slopes of the Independ-

ence Mountains, a rapid mountain torrent eager to reach the Humboldt. This way the Golden Army came to the desert river, marching
out of yellow-walled Emigration Canyon to that great, rolling plain
from which the Ruby Mountains lift, gray-purple and gnarled, snow-
mottled even in summer. The Golden Army could feel a lifting of
the heart at the renewed spaciousness of the world. Even a desert
plain, smelling of sun and dust and sage, was good to see.

Southwest across that rolling plain they went, that valiant, ragged
army. Through giant sage they marched, sage that grew as tall as
their heads, and there was none to think that the trampled earth, the
earth that clothed the day in dust and soreness, contained its own
dream.

With the years, other trails to California scarred the earth in the
valley south, shining rails and dusty wagon roads. Over the flank
of the hill a sun-dreary railroad town straggled about the old Humboldt Wells. Here below the mouth of Emigration Canyon, grazing
cattle listened to the far, thin screech of the Central Pacific engines
sounding their arrival at Wells. Down the river, west around the
shoulder of the Rubies, farms might begin to bulwark Elko, but here
the desert seemed secure.

The West has always had promoters. Sometimes they were called
empire builders, and the presumption then was that, whatever they
cost the country, the country got something in return. Sometimes
they were called speculators, and the presumption then was that the
country paid through the nose for the privilege of knowing them and
had no other joy of their presence. The promoters who in 1911 came
to this spreading land where Bishop's Creek emerges from the mountains called themselves the Pacific Reclamation Company.

Reclamation! It was a flag for men's hopes. Capital could build
dams in canyons, and spread water upon the long-barren land; by
what God and Mormons had failed to do with the desert earth,
capital could measure its potency. . . . Need it be added that the
capital was eastern?

The agents of the Pacific Reclamation Company who came into
the Humboldt Valley to purchase some thirty or forty thousand
acres of land below the mouth of Emigration Canyon were gratified

by the co-operation they received from everybody. Just beginning to
get back on her feet after the destructive nineties, Nevada wished
the enterprise well. The Southern Pacific agreed to build an 8-mile
spur track and a $9,000 depot. The company laid out a townsite,
plotted the streets of the business district and built a $100,000 hotel,
crown of glory for the town. Metropolis, they called it, this fated city
of the desert.

The advertising literature glowed. By 1913 the company could
print pages of pictures—oats as tall as a man's head, ripe and golden;
fenced fields and houses ("This was nothing but sagebrush eighteen
months ago"); spreading vegetable gardens, green and luscious, the
dry mountains baffled in the distance. In nothing the land lacked.
Soil? An alluvial deposit of rich loam, remarkable in its depth and
in the entire absence of heavy gravel or boulders, hardly more than
one-tenth of one per cent alkali. *Water supply?* Water in God's
plenty from the streams that unite west of Metropolis to form the
Humboldt River. The company possessed, in Bishop's Creek Basin,
one of the nation's finest and largest reservoir sites. "The Company's
plans are conservative, and call for storage of more than one year's
requirements, so as to guard against a possible dry year." *Climatic
conditions?* All that could be desired in this latitude, though "we
have not land suitable for orange-growing." *Products?* The finest
varieties of beans, beets, sugar beets, celery, corn, cauliflower, cab-
bage, carrots, cucumbers, cantaloupes, spinach, parsley, parsnips,
tomatoes, squash, turnips, rutabagas, asparagus, watermelons—anything and everything. Apples, pears, peaches, apricots, and berries
all had been grown successfully in the immediate vicinity of the
company's lands. "*At the Four State Fair oats grown on the dem-
onstration farm of the Pacific Reclamation Company took first
prize in competition with Utah, Idaho, and Wyoming.*" Barley,
wheat, and other grains were grown with equal success. *Dry farming?* "The heavy sagebrush growth, the deep soil, with the added
factors of an excellent clay sub-soil and proximity of water to the
surface, with sufficient precipitation, make Dry Farming in this
section an assured success." *Markets?* Nevada had always been dependent on imports for its food supplies; the products of the company's land had "practically no competition that has not at least a

two hundred and fifty mile greater haul." And we would remind you again, gently, gently, that we are served by a transcontinental railroad only six hundred miles from San Francisco, "which in itself provides an excellent market, and upon the completion of the Panama Canal will enable farmers on our project to compete successfully in all the markets of the world."

The company was firm. "Our enthusiasm may entertain you, our confidence excite your interest, but it is facts that you are after if you mean business." It should be understood: "We have no cheap land, if by cheapness you mean low prices. We have a real live project, and this being the case we have no low-priced land that we care to recommend to you. We think the most solemn warning of this decade was uttered by Mr. J. J. Hill when he said, 'There is only ONE crop of land.' The census of 1920 will show at least ten million more people in this country than we had in 1910, and come good times or bad they have GOT to be fed and the food has GOT to come from the soil. Ponder over this little problem in its relation to increasing land values."

This was the word scattered over the West, where land has always been a hunger in men's hearts. Farmers turned over the pages of the illustrated folder and felt their hearts lift to the thought that here was security, heritage for their sons. The pictured hotel, with its two stories of trim red brick and its new awnings, was an earnest of something strong and stable. "Attention is called to the excellent investment offered in lots of the town of Metropolis. There has been for years a crying need for a first-class town in this portion of Nevada, and the opening up of the lands of the Pacific Reclamation Company assured its existence. . . . Reference may be made here to the Hotel, modern in all its appointments; the city water system with its pure spring water under high pressure insuring ample fire protection; school building of the latest construction; cement sidewalks; electric lights, etc." A descriptive booklet might be had by addressing the Metropolis Commercial Club, Metropolis, Nevada.

So a new order of things had come to the West. Mormon pioneers of yesterday had come to the desert land by midwinter pilgrimage, shivering in their wagons as the winter waned, building houses in the fashion of a fort, digging irrigation canals, fencing a Big Field and individual holdings, grubbing out sagebrush, working together and starving together, and at last, with the passing of the years, achieving some measure of security and comfort. That had been the pattern of the past, the face of the war with the desert. But regard the superior technology of the modern age: Today there was benevolent eastern capital to build reinforced concrete storage and diversion dams, railroad spurs, and $100,000 hotels. And to sell the land at a price.

Many journeyed to the new town at the head of the Humboldt to investigate for themselves. The hotel filled with them. Soon homesteaders' shacks could be seen in all directions. The rolling sage plain was fenced off, teams of horses dragging lengths of steel rail to clear the land of sage. Other teams were raking the loose sage from the earth, sweeping clean a way for the plows. Here in the land was a dream to which the Golden Army had been blind, the reluctant earth subjected to man's will. Here amid green fields trees should rise, and houses of stone.

Warfare with the desert is a tradition bred into the Mormon blood and bone, and though this dream at the head of the Humboldt was alien to that tradition, Mormons came in numbers from the far places of the West to take up land below Emigration Canyon. Not all were Mormons who came to Metropolis. But it was the Mormons who stuck.

During the months before the outbreak of the first World War, the population of Metropolis reached nearly a thousand. Some came hopefully to the dry farms beyond the silver network of irrigation canals. This dry farm land was to be bought for prices ranging from $10 to $15 an acre; between that asking price and the information that the land was to be had on the installment plan in ten annual payments with interest at 6 per cent on deferred payments, the company sandwiched the observation that "the average annual rainfall is 13.8 inches." Those who had more money and, out of an intuition of the desert's ways, were disinclined to gamble on dry farms, bought irrigated land at prices that ranged upward from $75 an acre.

Many of the settlers who came to Metropolis brought with them hardly more assets than their will to dream. There was even a philosophy about having too much capital: a farmer must get a large proportion of his living out of the soil, and if he had much capital, he might use it up or waste it, and neglect to raise a garden or to milk his cows. A man should live close to the earth.

But, during the first years, some capital was essential. No crop of proportions, under whatever favorable circumstances, could be expected before the second year. It took that long to subdue the land. Even as Metropolis prepared to boom, decay was working in its bones, men starved out before the struggle was well begun.

At first, however, there was rain. And wheat prices soared as war raged in Europe. Under the sun, round about Metropolis' tall red-brick hotel, wheatfields rippled their gold of the desert wind. But year by year the land seemed more reluctant, the wheat unrelieved by rain from the intolerable sun. The dry farmers began to leave. And though the State of Nevada, beginning in 1917, appropriated $5,000 a year for an investigation of dry farming possibilities, five years' work only turned the land back, at last, to the irrigation canals and to the Herefords and the sheep which the farmers had driven, for a time, north into the hills. In abandoned shacks, buried under the litter the hot wind blew along the floor, the folders of the Pacific Reclamation Company still held forth their promise of abundance: "The average annual rainfall is 13.8 inches." By something like four inches, that has been an optimism of the empire builders.

Retreat, then, to the irrigated farms and entrench in defiance behind the canals. The dream dies hard, and money is strong. Money can build dams in the mountains, canals along the shoulders of the hills; money can build hotels and schools and paved sidewalks strung with electric light. Money is a force the desert farms of the West have never known. . . .

But the prospectus of the Reclamation Company had not provided against the dryness. "The Company's plans are conservative, and call for the storage of more than one year's requirements, so as to guard against a possible dry year." Yes, but if the extra dry years run two, three, and four in succession? That magnificent reservoir site, capacious for all needs—of what use was it unless snow fell in the mountains? And there was something else the company's advertising men had failed to write into their hymns.

To those easterners rabbits were game to be hunted. Here, in the fields around Metropolis, they were a ravenous vermin. Without rabbit fences the farms were no more than a benevolence of God to the rabbit cosmos. Rabbits were fought with the means at hand, and the intervention of predators and plague thankfully accepted. In bad years the farmers continued the stoic fight and could even see the workings of a large determinism in this irruption of the land: "We're going to have another depression in about two years. The rabbits are increasing to feed the poor."

Men gave up in despair, but there were others to take their places. As the sifting continued, Metropolis became a community of Mormons. The help and encouragement by state and federal governments and by the Southern Pacific Railroad had less to do with Metropolis' continued existence, during the years that multiplied hardship and difficulty, than the social and religious organization that bound the people together and gave them hope.

"They were encouraged to struggle along and not give up; their leaders holding before them a promising and truthful picture of beautiful fields and a prosperous community," a Metropolis man has written. "The amusements fostered by the church were many and varied; they served to take the minds of the discouraged farmers off their troubles. There were dances and dramatics and concerts by home talent as well as religious gatherings." Up in the canyon above the diversion dam, where a warm spring bubbles from the south wall of the canyon, the settlers built a low pool, with a bathhouse at the upper end. This shallow swimming pool was also the baptismal font, where the community's children came at the age of eight to be baptized into the Church, the work of God served in the hard-handed desert. . . .

A boy who had been baptized in that pool came back with me in the summer of 1940. It was fifteen years since he had seen Metropolis. We drove north and west from Wells across sage uplands that opened out, eventually, upon farms green in the valley before us. This was the upper part of Metropolis. The nearer farm, gold and green in the hot afternoon, had been owned by a fellow best situated to avail himself of the precious water from the canyon above; something of a water hog, he had gone through periods of social ostracism. Water counted, however, for more than social grace. A group of trees, cottonwoods and Lombardy poplars, flanked his wooden shacks. Beyond were other houses; once this had been almost a community. A mile farther on, standing on the brow of the hill surrounded by Carolina poplars and other trees, was a tall stone house that had been built by the father of my friend. They had planted the trees, "and, Lord, how slow they grew!" There were no other trees in sight, except a scattered few toward the canyon mouth. We drove up a dusty road. A line that ran along the hillside south from the canyon was the canal which watered most of Metropolis. Only the farms in the foreground were watered from the creek bed. Now we saw that the fields and the road were crawling with repulsive life.

Imagine a loathsome grasshopper without wings, a grasshopper leaden black or bedbug red, a grasshopper as thick and long as a powerful man's thumb, a grasshopper that leaps and skitters along the ground or pauses to stare with an unutterable malignance. . . . Looking at a Mormon cricket, you suddenly disbelieve the stories the Mormons in Utah tell of sea gulls that came miraculously in 1848 to gorge upon them and save the crops. It is unimaginable that a sea gull could find courage to look a cricket in the eye, let alone actually pick a fight with one and eat it. A Mormon cricket looks strong and mean enough to jump on sea gulls and rend them limb from limb, feather from feather.

We watched the uneasy movement of the fields. There was no square yard that did not have a cricket or two. The crickets were capable of stripping a field as though it had been scorched with fire. The crickets had come to Metropolis since my friend's family departed. Like rabbits, they were the desert's gratuity to its conquerors. The irrigation canal was speckled with them; some of the crickets had just fallen in, and were still struggling, while others

floated torpidly on the surface of the roily water. In Utah irrigation
canals, bird predators, and hogs and poultry wiped out the crickets
soon after the Mormon occupation of the land. But this cricket in-
festation, we presently learned, was in its sixth year.

We drove on up the canyon, a narrow defile down which a gray
stream plunges tumultuously, water released in constant volume
from the storage dam. Beyond the diversion dam which separates
the water allowed to go down the channel from that diverted into
the canal, we reached the warm spring. Although my friend remembered that it normally contained a few blow snakes, fallen into
the water from the yellow canyon wall above, now it was empty of
them. A few drowned crickets, however, floated in the water, amid
yellow-green moss. We threw out the crickets, and gratefully shed
our clothes to rid ourselves of two days' accumulation of dirt and
salt dust. Down this narrow canyon, within yards of where we
soaked in the pleasant warm water, the Golden Army had marched
for California. . . . Ghosts stalked the afternoon, but we stirred to
no imperative except that of being clean.

Feeling fine, we drove back down the canyon. The valley opened
before us, the distant farmhouses and fields looking unutterably
brave and little and lonely in the late afternoon sunlight, which lit
the rye and alfalfa fields and cast tiny, dark shadows behind
mounded gold hay. Passing again the stone house on the hill, we
drove on down toward the heart of Metropolis. Jack rabbits sprang
out every dozen yards, dashing frantically down the road ahead of
us or into the sagebrush on either side. Now and then a tiny cotton-
tail ran among the jacks. We flushed on a jack who started straight
down the road ahead of us, the sun gleaming strangely salmon-
pink through his extraordinary ears. About every sixth leap he
hopped into the air as though shifting gears, and Lord, how he
traveled! Timed by the speedometer, he was going about thirty
miles an hour when finally, after some three or four hundred yards,
he yielded the road to us.

So we came to Metropolis, to the hotel, the railroad station, the
schoolhouses, the bustling, energetic town. Over the hill the grade
school still stood. The high school, however, was gone. The meeting-
house was gone; some mean board shacks stood on the site. The

depot was gone, and the railroad tracks. Both saloons were gone. The Consolidated Wagon Company building was an empty shell with high hollow windows. Next door south stood the storied hotel. Part of one wall extended to the top of the second story, but most of its red brick had fallen down to the level of the first. Nothing remained within but rusted steel girders. The floor was gone and the basement gaped empty.

We sat in the car, looking about us. Beyond the ruin of the hotel a length of concrete sidewalk ran irrationally under a farmer's barbed wire to end suddenly in the middle of a pasture. That was Main Street. The summer sun, sinking at an angle down the long Humboldt Valley, cast the blue shadows of fence posts and barbed wire across Main Street. The sidewalk once had bridged hotel and railroad station, and sputtering yellow arc lights along the concrete path had been evidence of the redemption of the desert land to the uses of civilization.

The land can have an eloquence outmatching the tongue. In another decade there would be nothing here but a red rubble of brick, nothing but the shacks, the corral fences, the sheds. That was the true level of life here. Metropolis had had the vitality only of a dream. No riches had come out of the earth in justification of this vision; here had reared no Aurora, no Virginia City, no Unionville, no bright flame of the desire and its fulfillment. Man had simply pitted himself against the desert—his energy and desire, his technological expedients, his driving will. The sun's rays threw upon the ground a ragged shadow, the hotel. A wind was beginning to rise; it blew in from the sageland, warm, spiced, sweet. The wind was a little sick with the smell of the sage, and it gathered up whorls of dust beyond the barbed-wire fence.

In nothing had the land been lacking. The soil was good, the slope of the land admirable for drainage, the climate equable. The men who had come to the land were desert-wise men, not easily discouraged or beaten.

Rain is the answer to so many things in the West. An inch or two of rain above the 10-inch mark means white-painted houses, trees tall and green (though perhaps yellowed by the dryness in late

summer), the shocked gold of wheat, oats, and barley, the serried
green of onions, potatoes, beets. Each half-inch loss from the year's
precipitation takes something from the land and from the spirit.
June grass grows where alfalfa once spread green. Sage marches in
from the desert. Dust blows on the wind, a bitterness of the land
ever present on the lips.

At length we left this dead city, driving up toward the benchland
again, the rutted road frenzied at intervals with jack rabbits. We
passed a lonely, dusty-looking building. My friend had lived here
while his father was building the stone house on the hill. "I remember playing in the dusty yard in the hot sun. It looked then just as
it looks now. My mother hated the place." The wooden walls of
the house were warped by the sun. There was no greenery around,
just arid sage and dust. We drove past fenced fields where, even at
the time his family had departed from Metropolis, there had still
been long plots of alfalfa and grain. June grass rippled there now,
obscene in the wind.

A frame house, more pretentious than most we had seen, a few
flowers growing around it, was our destination. A dozen sheds with
open east face flanked the house. Farm machinery was lying around,
and white Leghorns and sandy Rhode Island Reds were running
about the place to the rear. On the east was the muddy irrigation
ditch. Several horses, buckskin, roan, and black, were in a corral
with a couple of frail-legged colts. As we stopped at the side of the
house a young man came out, a handsome young fellow whose
skin was burned red with much sun, his dark blond hair parted
loosely on one side, his blue eyes squinted against the glare of the
sun. The collar of his shirt was folded under so that his Mormon
undergarment was visible; he wore levis, work shoes, and heavy
woolen socks.

My friend had gone to school with him, and they talked, eying
each other across this bridge of fifteen years. The young man now
was the bishop of the Mormon ward here, which had shrunk
through the years to some fifteen families. Presently a younger
brother came out, and then the father. The old man had come to
this country before the first World War as a German immigrant; he
had a wonderfully characterful face, with gray, rather unkempt

hair, straggling gray mustache, and furrowed bronze forehead. A little bent, and shorter than his sons, he stood in the dooryard with all the blunt earthy strength of a German peasant. He and his sons had dwelt here over twenty years.

We were invited inside. The mother, like her husband, was of unmistakable German blood, with long nose, small mouth, work-worn hands and hair, bent and heavy breasted in a print house dress of violet and light green. The young bishop's wife, dandling in her lap a three-months-old baby boy, had the smooth-skinned, feverish fresh blondness, the sun-bleached blue eyes, of so many girls who live in the desert.

For an hour or more we talked. It was a drought year; the Metropolis farmers were hard up for water, though there had been seventeen feet of carry-over in the reservoir. Things had changed over the years. . . . Once there had been grain fields, truck gardening, dry farming a few miles out from the canal arteries. Then the dry farmers, beaten, quit the unequal fight. On the irrigated farms, then, there had been potato growing and dairy farming, with a co-operative marketing association. The co-op had gone, too. But they were still here. They had a hundred head of cattle, part beef and part dairy, and they raised alfalfa, grain, and a sizable acreage of potatoes.

And they had, now, new hope in the community. The number of farmers had decreased until there should be enough water to go around, and the value placed upon the farms and water had been reduced. A committee, during recent years, had been pushing litigation to clear title to the water; only a few weeks ago the suit had ended, the farmers successful in ousting the land-promotion company interests. There had been help from the Mormon welfare organization; the Church had assumed in some way all the debts of the federal land bank, and the process had reduced valuation of the farms and water to about one-third. The refinancing process eliminated land and buildings, and all value of any holding depended on the amount of water right each farm possessed. Grass-hoppers, squirrels, rabbits, and the crickets that had first appeared in 1934 were ever present, but these were the natural enemies of the land.

Listen to quiet voices talking of water and the land. ("I was in Salt Lake eight times last year working on the water suit.") Eastern capital thrown out. Rain could have supported a hotel, a two-story, red-brick, strictly modern hotel; with rain farmers could have paid not only for storage and diversion dams but even for such extravagances as $100,000 hotels. Subtract an inch of rain and the dry farms go; subtract another and the railroad pulls up its steel rails and departs. ("A lot of our people, maybe twenty-five families, went to Gridley, California. I've been there and seen it. No good. Either too hot or too cold or something. Every time I went there I liked it less.") Unpainted inside and out, the house dwells sick within the fetor of sun-hot wood. Across this land had gone the Golden Army, another race of buccaneers. Down the desert river the hosts had marched. . . . In this land there had been a dream, a hard dream. When the old piracies were ended, men had come in pursuit of this dream—capitalists, men with money. ("Mostly, the company was eastern Jews.") Capital, the omnipotent instrument. But though money can be poured out upon the land like water, only by water is the earth made pregnant. Promotion has no margin for survival in the desert. For the desert is an honesty, a realism unchanged by persuasion or chicanery. Dreams, like opalescent soap bubbles, may drift above the sage, but the air is dry and the bubbles burst.

Think upon these things and see the white curtains the windows lift to the desert wind, and see them ranged across the room— grandfather, father, infant son—three generations to toil upon this desert earth and always know hope. And then go out into the wind, saying the words of farewell, remembering smiles in sun-darkened faces, remembering brown-flowing water in the shallow irrigation canal. North in the sage uplands where a campfire leaps brightly in a circle of sage under a world of magnificent stars, you may wonder where fortitude is secure. The desert is patient and near.

WILD WEST IN NEON

THE TWO largest communities of Nevada are respectable, bumptious, and decadent. Each is a village, a frontier outpost, and a sophisticated cosmopolis. Each dominates an end of Nevada. They differ only in size and proportion. With its 23,000 inhabitants Reno is more the cosmopolis. Las Vegas, a quarter as large, is more the frontier town.

Seen as villages, Reno and Las Vegas are the communities of homeowners with the "unsurpassed educational facilities" and "fine, strong church groups" that the booster literature truthfully refers to. Reno has fifteen churches, of which the Catholics, Baptists, and Methodists are prosperous. As you approach Reno from the south, sign after sign advertises "Harold's—World's Largest Roulette Wheel," but finally there comes a different sign: "The Churches of Reno Welcome You." In either town you may get gay on Saturday night and sing, "Hail, hail, the gang's all here!" at a cabaret, and next morning, just as likely, you raise your voice again in "All hail the pow'r of Jesus' name!"

The busy shopping districts are as self-consciously neon-lighted as any Billings or Oklahoma City, but the residential streets are modestly shaded, in Reno by elms and planes, in Las Vegas by poplars and cottonwoods. There are flower beds of asters, cosmos, petunias, snapdragons, zinnias, golden glow, and hollyhocks. There are lilac hedges. In summer the lawns are bright green and often they are shaded by old apple and pear trees. White picket fences enclose the less recent places. The houses, like those in any American small town, range from gewgawed Victorian Gothic through prairie-house types to the innovation from California: Monterey-Cape Cod. Kids play in yards and vacant lots and swim in the open-air plunges. There are Hoovervilles, but no slums. Crime is rare.

On the hill to the north the State University presides over the village of Reno. Despite the sagebrush and barren ridges in the distance, the immediate campus is kin to that of Middlebury College in Vermont or Grinnell in Iowa or of scores of rather old-fashioned residential colleges. The quadrangle resembles that of the University of Virginia. The architecture is colonial, with tall white columns and red brick draped with ivy. The elms, box elders, and ashes, Manzanita Lake with its swans in summer and ice skating in winter, Gutzon Borglum's bronze of John Mackay the miner, the young men and women studying in the library and strolling along the sidewalks with books under their arms—these suggest a side of life in Reno that is in contrast to that represented by the post-frontier gambling of Center Street and the post-Hollywood novelty shops of Virginia Street. A divorce suit brought by a faculty member would be a scandal.

Townspeople are friendly in Reno and Las Vegas. Everybody talks to everybody else. Natives are as genial toward bootblacks and bartenders as toward grocery clerks and milkmen and popular preachers. Two drinkers at a bar brag about their babies. On a cold day a taxi driver at the station says, "Ride up in front. It's warmer here."

In Las Vegas, especially, a new resident isn't a stranger long. Someone will clap him on the back. "You're a stranger here, aren't you? Come on in and have a drink!" Anywhere else such a greeter might be a "con man," but not in Vegas. There he is just a citizen who has a town to share. "Everybody knows everybody else." He walks down Fremont Street, nods to several dozen people, or exchanges joshing remarks, or makes a serious inquiry or two. "How're ya?" "What'd you hear from Bill?" "Hear you smashed your garage door off th' other night!" This social compactness spreads outward to much of Nevada. "Miles mean nothing here," testifies a radio dealer. "Reno's four hundred miles north. You go back East and someone asks, 'Oh you're from Nevada. Say, do you know Bob Jones in Reno?' And the funny thing is you do know him!"

Many divorcees sense this welcome. Those who weep from homesickness on arrival gulp with sincere regret on leaving. They can quickly establish acquaintanceships, if not romances, with natives, and they find opportunities for the sad business of pouring out their life stories or the pleasant occupations of horseback rides, motor spins, and dinners out.

Inevitably there is gossip about private lives. Wholesome village clans have much to say about the activities of fellow residents. All are watched with the friendly sharpness that Carol Kennicott came to appreciate in Sinclair Lewis's Gopher Prairie. So-and-so has left her husband again. So-and-so won't be re-elected. So-and-so was drunk on Virginia Street in daylight yesterday. So-and-so said the other evening that . . . And much more—the conversational traffic in private lives that is conspicuous in villages the world round.

Except for the university circle, culture is simple and unoriginal. Reno unquestionably has the advantage because of its size. Its Nevada Community Concert Association sponsors a season of well-known musical artists. A Little Theater presents dramatic productions. The crowded Washoe County Library displays a reasonable assortment of volumes, and there are women's clubs that print anthologies of Nevada poetasters. The Nevada Historical Society struggles along. An active Astronomical Society has explored the regions of Scorpio and Sagittarius through 5½- and 8-inch refractors and watched Venus and Mercury sink behind the Sierras. Down south, Las Vegas, which is a generation newer, has a much less complicated culture. It has no urgent aspirations at all for culture but does label certain things as such. The movies are culture; so are the high-school plays and the church cantatas. One businessman says, "We have culture here. Rex Bell and Clara Bow have a ranch south of town, near Searchlight." Literature is available for five or ten cents a copy on the drugstore racks. A radio store carries a music side line of from ten to fifteen Decca swing records. No classical records are obtainable in any store in town. The county library is small and cramped. This in the state's second largest community! The fair explanation, however, is that Las Vegans who want cultural matters and luxuries, even some of the important necessities of life, buy them by mail or in Los Angeles.

Much of the social life is bound up in the rituals of fraternities, the Elks, Eagles, Masons, Knights of Columbus, the Eastern Star, the I.O.O.F. Standards of wit and humor are set in the Rotary, Lions, and Kiwanis clubs. Unofficially, an adolescent jest like this will make the rounds:

> A fellow named Wood and a fellow named Stone
> were walking down the street.
> Stone turned to Wood and Wood turned to Stone,
> And they both turned to rubber when a girl walked by.

Or like this: A Nevadan will come up to a friend and say, "You're a bum grocer!"

"Why am I?"

"Why, you don't know the difference between a blonde and a battleship."

"What is it?"

"I don't know either! Never been on a battleship."

Official humor is similar. A couple of Decembers ago the Las Vegas Lions gave Christmas presents to prominent members. The master of ceremonies, who is a man regarded by his fellows as quite a wit, gave a set of poker chips and a rack to a certain Protestant minister. He said he had heard the church services were rather sleepy, and here was a way to pep them up. He turned to a state legislator who had been trying to open up a new area for irrigation and settlement in the southern tip of Nevada. With Block 16 in mind, he said, "We hear you are trying to open up a new district," and handed the legislator a red light globe.

During the annual Helldorado in Las Vegas and the Fourth of July Rodeo in Reno, business and professional men wear beards and Western clothes. In Reno a kangaroo court roams the streets in an open truck. A dozen men are all judges, prosecutors, and executioners. They are disguised in seven-day beards, sombreros, and gorgeous red, yellow, and green silk shirts. They spot a friend on the sidewalk, some hapless optometrist or butane-gas distributor who is clean shaven and in ordinary business clothes. He is looking sheepish and pleasantly uncomfortable. "There's Rod McIntyre!" An eager vigilante, flushed red with the afflatus of village democracy, jumps down from the truck and slips a noose over Rod's ears. The judges call down from above, "Where's your whiskers?" "Where's your cow boots and ten-gallon lid?" "You're just begging for a necktie party, right in front of all these people!" "Get up here and explain yourself!" If a nonconformist is stripped of civilian clothes down to his civilian B.V.D.'s, the reason is he hasn't had enough pep and vim to be a vigilante himself.

Home folks use the telephone exchange frequently and copiously. They call up their friends whenever a question comes to mind or they have a bit of news to distribute. Suppose a man wants to talk to the house mover, gives what he thinks is the right number, and gets the confectioner instead. He chats on for a while, anyhow. Then he calls the operator and tells her laughingly about the mistake. If he likes her voice he asks her for a date. Finally he asks for the correct number and sees about getting his house moved.

Friends borrow cars and new skis and the owners don't mind. Eventually they'll borrow, in return, a shotgun or a riding horse. Everyone waves to acquaintances from his car. A Las Vegan in a convertible rides down Fremont Street and honks at fifty people in four blocks. Salesmen are folksy and genial rather than slick and hypocritical. They know their customers too well to want to cheat them. It is the California cities that are grabbing, grasping places. "Why, damn it all," a young assemblyman says, "L.A. was built to take your money away from you. Go down to their angel city with fifty bucks. They take it away from you. Go with forty. They take it away. Thirty. They reach out to snap it away. Take a dollar. They want it, too. Play safe, and go into town with just a dime or a nickel. They jump up and down and can hardly wait to sell you a two-cent value and clean you out!"

Informality and congeniality, combined with frontier liberality, are symbolized by the free phones at the bars and lunch counters in Las Vegas. If one wants a taxi, or gets to quarreling with a fellow drinker about what the score was in the Rose Bowl last New

Year's Day and wishes to call the sports editor of the *Review-Journal,* he just picks up the handy French phone.

Narrow-mindedness is always potential and sometimes actual. Professors at the university and instructors in the high schools do not speak out freely on economic and political subjects, as they could in a town fifty times larger than Reno. Las Vegas saw mob action in 1940, a year in which hicks and villagers the country over made illegal attacks on the Witnesses of Jehovah, in a wave of religious intolerance unparalleled since the Missourians warred on the early Mormons. Three members of the sect, two men and a woman, were distributing tracts and playing their phonograph records of Judge Rutherford's sermons. A crowd of "war veterans" came on the trio in the car, pulled them out, grabbed their bundles of tracts and several phonographs and burned these in the street. They ordered the Witnesses to leave town and threatened to use branding irons on them if they returned for more proselyting. Police stood by and made no attempt to interfere.

In contrast, naturally, kindness is just as potential, and no doubt it is more often practiced. The people of Nevada's two largest towns, like its other inhabitants, are notably liberal-minded and tolerant. One Reno man says of his town, "Here are probably less hypocrisy and meddling and more freedom than anywhere in America."

Startlingly opposite to the Witnesses incident in Las Vegas are the typical actions of the young, liberal District Attorney, Wisconsin-educated and a boyhood friend of the LaFollette brothers. A Negro was arrested on the charge of a white woman that he had tried to rape her in a back alley. The *Review-Journal* rumbled that the D.A. better do something about this quick, and ardent Caucasian democrats talked of stringing up the outrageous Negro. Cool-headed, the District Attorney made a careful investigation. He found that the woman was illegally approaching men on Fremont Street, she had been a drunken hanger-on in a club the day of the happening, and she had pestered the Negro until he went off with her. When they were together in the alley she saw a passer-by and had a twinge of Nordic self-consciousness. "Rape! Rape!" she cried. The result was that the District Attorney released

the Negro and had the court fine the woman five dollars for solicit-
ing on the streets. Thereafter the D.A. referred to it as the case of
the white girl who got fined for raping a Negro.

Provincial villagers under their surface sophistication, Renoites
and Las Vegans dislike the spotlight when it points at unortho-
doxies: gambling, vice, and divorce. Citizens are reticent about the
"lurid" sources of local prosperity. The chambers of commerce are
noncommittal. The mayors and police chiefs are evasive. Information
and clues must be pried from one Nevadan or another. Some Nevad-
ans are indifferent or disinterested, it is true. The moralists are cov-
ertly hopeless and tired of talking on these subjects or they have a ra-
tionalization which enables them to ignore the indirect source of
their income, wholly or partly, and to dismiss the subject from
their conversation. The Reno *Evening Gazette* expressed this same
attitude at the time gambling was legalized in 1931.

> The great part of Nevada's population is composed of
> men and women who never gamble and are not seeking
> divorce. Their attitude toward both these things is the
> normal attitude of most American communities. They are
> good citizens, uphold the laws, and raise their families to
> be honest, and upright in all things. . . . The real life of
> Nevada is not hectic, and this is something which the
> country ought to be made to understand.

The boosters, hopeful of attracting industries and millionaires,
minimize the moral novelties. Publicity issued by the Reno Chamber of Commerce and the Nevada Department of Highways only
hints at them and stresses, properly enough, things like housing
and living standards, parks, educational facilities, and winter sports.
One colored brochure, distributed by the Las Vegas Chamber of
Commerce, does go further. Besides the usual praise for climate,
churches, and accommodations, it contains puffs for the wide-open
recreations of "this amazing playground" which is "still a frontier
town" and for the advantages of Nevada's " 'modern' divorce and
marriage laws."

Small-town propriety has not been strong enough, however, to do anything about Reno's famous sign. Spanning the highway through town and clearly visible from all trains is a boldly lighted arch:

RENO
THE BIGGEST LITTLE CITY IN THE WORLD

In 1934, after hearing protests that the sign was distasteful and boastful, the City Council voted to change it to a mere modest RENO in four-foot green letters. But the change was unsatisfactory; the one-word sign seemed empty without its subtitle, and shortly afterward the immodest paradox was once again glaring out into the darkness. Six years later a new super-neon arrangement increased its brightness fifteen times.

Certainly the towns have good orthodox matters to advertise. Each has an excellent dry climate, plenty of water, thriving commercial distribution, and normal public institutions, schools in particular. Each is in or near important cattle, farming, and mining country. Each lies close to scenic attractions. Las Vegas calls itself "Hub of the Scenic Southwest." Reno offers "1,000,000 Square Miles of Opportunity." Both hug transcontinental railroads and highways and thrive on tourists. After the Japanese raid on Pearl Harbor, the through railroads were prodigiously busy freighting war matériel to California; new army camps trained soldiers and fliers; local housing facilities were crammed tight. The towns hoped to become bigger and wealthier and more powerful. What prosperous burgs ever thought otherwise?

"Slanderous" and "libelous" attacks, therefore, are grounds for limber activity by town builders angered by a blotched reputation. Both towns have had run-ins with detractors. Renoites have protested against numerous articles in national magazines. Time and again they have had to say what a local judge said in 1910: "This town is really as fine a town as there is on earth. It ain't wicked. It only does things open and above board that San Francisco and New York do on the Q.T. Why, even Reno's gambling is on the square!"

Recently Las Vegas has had two occasions to fight infamy. In 1939 an Idaho legislator said publicly that Las Vegas was the cesspool of the world. The Chamber of Commerce and other civic groups invited him down at their expense. He came, had a good, respectable time, and publicly changed his mind. The following year *Look* published a photo-essay: "Wild, Woolly and Wide-Open, that's Las Vegas, Nevada, where men are men and sin is a civic virtue." It was the hodgepodge of fact and fantasy that Nevada subjects traditionally receive—melodramatic, sensational, distorted. According to *Look*, Las Vegas was "the most cockeyed and self-consciously wicked place on earth . . . the American Gomorrah." Its mayor conducted much of his official business in a bar. The Reverend C. S. Sloan of the Baptist Church slept with his boots handy and responded to a marriage like a fireman, and would perform his leisurely service, eight minutes long, "and in almost any place—Pullman car, hotel lobby or street corner—for $4." A picture showed him marrying two eloping California youngsters outside the cab of a Union Pacific locomotive. Mothers interrupted their shopping to play slot machines in grocery stores. Block 16 (the segregated prostitution section) was on "the official 'fun map.'" A horse was a permissible means of entering a bar if you could get him through the door—a hooliganism considered harmless by the Las Vegans. . . .

This five-page spread drew the wrath of many inhabitants of the town. Letters besieged the Chamber of Commerce and it campaigned against *Look* for a retraction or a future depiction that would show the town as the residents saw it. Members of the Baptist Church, highly wroth, urged the Reverend Mr. Sloan to make the matter a personal one with the magazine. Sloan declared Las Vegas was not as wide open as indicated and was, instead, "a city of clean living and home loving people." President R. J. Kaltenborn of the Chamber declared his organization would attempt to compel the magazine to make some restitution for "the smirch on the good name of Las Vegas." He threatened suit. The Secretary wrote, "This office feels the part concerning sin being a civic virtue was a very unfair statement. We do have a beautiful little city and our schools and churches are as good or better than any in the western country." Las Vegans did not get satisfaction from *Look*, but their protest may have benefited them. An article on Las Vegas commissioned by *Liberty* and entitled "Sin for Sale" did not appear in print.

SAD HILLS

Sad hills, when I chose to leave
    your wild silence
Then I fell on these dour days,
    city-sordid!

They said, another boy-truant
    home
From rolling restless rocks
    down high hills . . .

Impractical wanderer-for-a-day
    wondering
How all yearns never to be quiet
    again, mass-hampered!

Oh, earth's the long-slope,
    precarious-carrying
Down-pull power deeply!

At the bottom one has, lacking
    further to fall,
Some friends, a little money, what
    they call security.

But up-canyon there: that old
    roar rises
From where the world rides
    down deadlier mountains!

THE WAY OF THE TRANSGRESSOR

ONE THING I did was just like another, and I forgot it, except when mother and father talked about it and made me remember. Once mother left me alone to get dinner for father and the hired men, and once everybody left me alone. Both times mother and father talked about what happened until it stayed in my mind.

The first time mother left me, she had to take Teressa to the dentist. She thought it would be hard for me to get dinner, so she told me just what to do. I was to put one cup of rice in three cups of boiling water, with salt, and begin to cook it at half-past eleven. Mother showed me how the hands of the clock would look when I should begin to get dinner, and put a paper on the wall with a picture of the clock-hands that way. I kept telling her I knew, but she made the picture anyway. I did know, except that I thought five minutes on the clock was one minute. When I sat still five spaces on the clock it was twenty-five minutes instead of five minutes. I found that out afterward.

The rice was all I had to cook. Father liked rice, and the hired men could eat cold meat.

I set the table almost as soon as mother and Teressa left in the morning. I built a good fire. We burned cobs. It was summer time, and mother and Teressa always talked about keeping the kitchen cool and keeping the flies out. When the fire was burning hard I went into the front room to look at books. I went every few minutes to look at the clock. The fire went out twice before it was time to cook the rice.

One cup of rice looked too little for four people when I measured it. I thought it might have been three cups of rice instead of three cups of water, so I used three. It made a good deal. It took more water than I had hot, so I put in cold. I put in more salt, but not enough.

After the rice began cooking I went into the front room to look at books again until father came to dinner. He came in ahead of the hired men to see if I was getting along all right. I heard him coming, and went out before he could call me and said I was. He said, "Gee Whiliker, it's hot!"

I said, "Yes, isn't it? I stay in the other room."

Father laughed. He laughed all the time he was eating dinner. He told me to get a large plate and set it under the butter dish, so the butter wouldn't run onto the tablecloth. He got up twice, once to get sugar and once to get water. It was fun to sit at the table and ask people to pass me things.

Dinner was so easy to get I would not have thought about it again, except that father told mother about it when she came home. He said, "The kitchen was like an inferno, and the butter swimming; but the cook sat cool and unconcerned while the dinner cooked itself. She is of the earth, earthy."

Teressa heard him too, and pinched me. She said, "Oh, it is sweet and wonderful when *you* let the butter melt, but when I do it is a different story." She pinched me more, on places she had pinched the day before so it hurt worse. While she pinched she said, "How wonderful to be such a wonderful child, you little simpleton!" Then she made me say I loved her, and held me on her lap and rocked me. She told me the poem:

> See by the moonlight 'tis past midnight
> Time kid and I were home an hour and a half ago!

I liked that poem, because the way she said it made my chest shake.

The day everyone left me alone mother and father talked about it a long time before they left. I did not understand why they hated to leave me. People were on the outside of me anyway, and it didn't make much difference whether they were outside close, or outside farther off. When I told mother this she told me not to be silly trying to act wise.

Something happened while they were away that they talked so long about I cried.

Before they left mother said, "Be a good girl. When it is dinner time put the small tablecloth on the table, and sit down and eat just as we always do. And be a good girl."

Father told me things, too, but they were things not to do—funny things that I couldn't have done anyway like hiding the end of the road so he couldn't finish coming home. Mother didn't think they were funny. As father got into the buggy he said, "And don't hack the knives."

Mother said, "Don't be bitter, Henry. Those things are past."

Father said, "Nothing is ever past."

I knew what father meant about the knives. When Augusta lived at home, before father sent her away to her grandmother, she hacked knives. Augusta was a very bad girl. At least, I supposed she was bad, but when I said, "I hate Augusta," mother was angry. "Augusta was always a good sister to you," she said. "She loved you and took care of you. If you do not love her you are the one to be ashamed. Never let me hear you say that again as long as you live." If I was to love Augusta she couldn't have been bad, so I stopped thinking about it.

Augusta hacked knives. She washed dishes standing on a little stool at the pantry sink, and father scolded her for wasting soap and for dawdling. When he scolded her she would draw her eyebrows together and watch him out of the corners of her eyes. When he wasn't looking she would hack the edges of two knives together. She did worse things. I didn't know what. When father was angry at Augusta, mother would take Teressa and me and go walking through the fields. When we came back Augusta would be studying arithmetic, and crying.

If the knives were hacked father would take them out to the blacksmith shop. I asked mother why, but she said, "Hush!" so sharply I didn't ask again. Father made Augusta go with him, and mother would not let me go along.

After father said, "Nothing is ever past," and drove away, I was entirely alone. I went out to the pig corral. There was a tall corn crib beside it where I liked to climb. I would sit on top of the corn pile and make fun of the pig when he squealed. He would sometimes put his feet on top of the fence below me, and slant his nose up at me, and I would pretend the corn rolled under me and slid me down into his pen. I would pretend I ran for the fence, and the pig caught a piece of my dress just as I climbed over it. If I pretended hard my heart would beat and frighten me. Then I would throw ears of corn to the pig to make him stop looking at me. When father cleaned out the corral he was annoyed about the pig's eating so much.

While I was sitting on the corn I began remembering about the knives. I thought about them, and then I wondered about them. I wondered why Augusta hacked them. There was something exciting and dark about her doing it. The pig had gone to sleep. I climbed down and went to the house, and into the pantry to look at the knife box. It was on the lowest pantry shelf, above my head, so I had to have a chair to see into it. I took a chair from the kitchen, not a cane-seated one, so my feet wouldn't break it.

When I tapped knives together it made little pains run up and down my legs. I wondered if the knives hurt. The edges caught together and it made a rough feeling in my wrists when I pulled them apart. The first two knives were not any fun. I laid one of them down and tried another and another. I changed both knives, but they were all alike; none of them were any fun. I decided to wait until sometime when father and I were talking together, and promise not to do it but ask him to show me how to hack knives the way it was wrong to.

I put the knives away, and the chair, and went back to the pig. He was awake. After I fed him all he would eat it was time for my own dinner. I set the table and ate, and cleared it and washed the dishes. When I dried my knife it caught a thread on the tea towel and puckered it.

After dinner there was nothing to do, so I decided to scrub the kitchen. It wasn't dirty, but Teressa always scrubbed it when mother was away. I scrubbed the first part hard, and the last part not so hard. Each board was worn most in the middle, so the edges stood up. It was easiest to dry them the long way, so I dried them crossways. I thought the hardest way would be most right.

When mother and father and Teressa came home they brought me a present. It was a bag of figs. I had never seen figs before. After supper, mother acted queer. She put me to bed early and she and father talked. They talked the next day, and kept sending me away from them. Teressa wanted to scold me for scrubbing the floor, but mother wouldn't let her. Teressa said it would take three scrubbings to get it into shape again. It wasn't out of shape. The next day father didn't go to plow. Mother sent Teressa outdoors and called me in where she and father were. They asked me why I had hacked the knives. I had forgotten all about it because it hadn't been in my mind. Not understanding about it made it as if I hadn't done it, and I said quick, "I didn't."

Mother said, "You hacked the knives, and that was wrong. But it is a great deal worse to deny it. You must tell the truth about why you did it."

I said I did try to hack them but didn't know how, and father said, "You knew how all too well."

I tried to explain about it, and they asked me more and more questions. They asked things that had not been in my mind before, whether Augusta had taught me to do it. Father's face looked white and thin. He had never paid so much attention to anything I did, before. He said, "If I *knew* she did it to flout me, if I knew she did it in scorn of me, to fling back into my face the villainy of that infernal—"

Mother said, "Stop! There is no mystery about it, except that you should have been so short-sighted as to suggest it to her. It would never have occurred to her otherwise."

They asked me more questions, and mother began to talk about the other time I had been alone and cooked too much rice. She asked if I didn't suppose she knew how much rice to cook. I said I was afraid I had made a mistake listening. They talked to me until I cried. I cried so hard that when I looked at their faces their cheeks stretched out in wavery lines, and if I half-shut my eyes, streaks of light came from their faces toward me. I was so interested I forgot to feel bad, and they were discouraged with me.

Father went to the pantry and got the box of knives. He said, "For your punishment you must turn the grindstone while I grind out the nicks." I thought he was making a joke, because Teressa and I always wanted to see who could turn the grindstone. Usually he let Teressa, because she was less erratic. I looked at him and laughed, but his eyes looked down at me, small and blue.

I turned the grindstone until my arms were tired. When they were tired the wheel went slower and slower until it stopped. Father said, "Keep on turning."

I explained about my arms. He said, "Indeed!" He looked at me, whistling, and said, "Indeed!" again. "Tell your sister to come here."

Before I could start he turned and called her. He called her Dick. He said, "My son, Richard, will you turn the grindstone for your father?" He called her Richard because she was Richard the Lion-Hearted. Teressa said, "Yes . . . baby." She meant me. Before she began to turn the grindstone she reached back with her heel and stepped on my foot.

Father sent me to the house to talk to mother. I went. I explained about my arms, and she said I must learn that the way of the transgressor was hard, and that I should be ashamed to let Teressa do my work. I smiled because I knew a secret about Teressa that I didn't tell. She liked to do things after she was tired, to see whether she could.

Mother asked me if I thought it was fair to make extra work for father, when he should be out plowing. I asked, "What work?" She said, "Grinding the knives you hacked."

I sat without moving. When I found out things I had wondered about it made me excited inside so I forgot to be sorry for things I had done. I said, "It wasn't wrong to hack the knives." I meant it wasn't wrong in a way I couldn't understand. Mother picked me up by the arms and set me down hard on my feet. She shook me until my head jerked back and forth. She said, "I can not understand your being so naughty." I couldn't either, so I didn't.

She said again that the way of the transgressor was hard, and I must sit in a chair while she thought how to punish me. I picked a hard chair to sit in, not a cane-seated one.

Mother said she would take my own little white-handled knife away from me, and I must eat with a big one like those I hacked. I said, "You can have my little knife for a butter-knife." I had heard her tell Teressa we would have to use it for a butter-knife, because Mrs. Clarington had borrowed ours and not brought it back.

Sometimes when mother was annoyed I didn't know why. She was annoyed now. She took my hand and said, "We will go to the bedroom, and you must kneel down and ask God to make you a good girl."

I didn't want to go. I wanted not to so much that my legs moved in separate parts. I could feel my knees, and noticed where my feet were. I never prayed out loud, in the daytime. I knew quite a good deal about God. Usually I prayed when I was swinging, because I liked to swing. I always thought of God as having a good disposition. It seemed unnecessary to bother him about the knives, especially since it was all over and understood about, and he hadn't in the first place had anything to do with it.

While mother prayed I was so uncomfortable that if it had been any one but God I would have hated him. I almost did not like mother. I thought of a word so naughty that I did not dare say it to myself. Usually when I was naughty it was an accident, but this time I was so tired about the knives I wanted to be bad. I made a real prayer inside me, praying that God would say what I was thinking out loud. I wanted to hear how it sounded in the bedroom where everything was still except us. He didn't.

While I said after mother the words she told me to, I thought of a way I could say what I was thinking without being naughty. I whispered, "God said something to me."

Mother had her hands on the side of the bed, ready to stand up, but she stopped and put her arms around me. "My little girl," she said, "my little, little girl!"

I was afraid she wouldn't ask, "What?" but she did, and I said, "Silly."

It was a very uncomfortable morning. I sat in my high chair

without speaking until dinnertime. I thought a long time about grown people. I thought of them as if they were wrapped in thick quilts, only not quilts, that kept them from understanding how things really were.

SECOND HOEING

"O GOD. O GOD, I can't stay. I gotta go," Hannah prayed. "Olinda's home. She can help Mamma. And Papa can hire some one. He can hire Jake. He won't. He'll keep me. He can't. I'll get a job in town. He'll take your wages." Round and round went Hannah's thoughts as she rode the harrow across the freshly plowed ground. She braced her rough work shoes more firmly on the wooden cross plank.

The wind tugged and sucked at her blue overalls. It beat against her thin face, whipping loose strands of pale gold hair from under her boy's cap. She gritted her teeth and faced into the chilly blast. The two horses kicked up little puffs of dust as they plodded up the field and the wind blew the dirt back into her grim face.

She looked at her father sitting hunched down on the little beet drill, his straight-sided black cap just showing above his sheepskin collar. Up and down the field he went, driving the black and the gray, seeding the beets.

The factory field man stopped his car at the side of the road; Adam went to the fence, leaning there, talking and gesturing.

"He can rest and visit while he works us kids to death," Hannah thought, even though she knew the field man had stopped to see whether the ground was properly prepared for the beet seed.

Hannah watched her father and the field man walk slowly over the field inspecting the soil. Checking up on her work, she thought savagely. The sugar factory was always sending its men to keep an eye on the crops. The farmers had signed contracts to grow so many acres of beets at a certain price to be paid in the fall of the year. Nothing but work, work, work.

She'd never forgive her father. Never. He coulda just as well let her gone to school to finish her eighth grade.

Every jiggle of the harrow over the freshly plowed beet ground added to her hate and resentment. In her mind she went back over the sixteen years of her life, as far as she could remember, as she fought the wind and dirt.

She'd been just four years old when she was left at the end of a beet field to look after two-year-old Tabia, and two-months-old Alec. There, in the shade of a gunny sack stretched over four upright sticks, she had tried to hush the squalling Tabia, and the wailing Alec, while her mother went up and down the rows of beets chopping with the long-handled hoe. Hannah had cried for her mother who could not stop work. The beets had to be thinned.

"Yeah, an' now he cries about how hard he's worked, and how big a succeed he's made. We all worked an' Mamma worked harder than all of us put together, and he'll work her in the beets this year too!" Hannah savagely yanked the horses around at the end of the field. She slapped the lines smartly across their backs, shouting, "Gid-ap."

She thought of the time when she was six, big enough to crawl behind her father and mother and Lizzie and Mary, who swung their hoes up and down, blocking the tiny sugar beet plants.

On the ground among the dirt and clods, she had crawled on hands and knees, grasping the plants with dirty fingers, pulling the extra ones out so the biggest and strongest would be left to grow.

Her fingers had become stiff and dirt-caked. Sweat had run down her body. There was no rest. Adam eternally yelled that the beets had to be thinned. He got them up before daylight and kept them in the field until it was too dark to see.

It was when she was ten that she'd cut her knee with the bright-bladed beet knife while haggling the top off a big beet in the harvest. She'd been too little to lift the heavy beet; so she'd held it on her knee. Swish, the knife had cut through the beet into her knee.

That same fall Fritz had broken his arm when he was thrown by a runaway team. Adam had cursed day and night because Fritz couldn't top beets. It took two good arms and hands to top a sugar beet.

Adam had driven all the rest of them, screeching that the beets would be frozen in the ground.

"Yeah, and he still drives us. He thinks we're cattle that he owns!" Hannah spit the words into the wind. "And he'd buy us gum and break the stick in two pieces so we'd work harder. No wonder he saved money so he could rent!"

Hannah looked bitterly into the south. "Nothin' but a dump," she thought, as she compared their place with the Boswell house across the road. "The Boswells got it easy." Then she saw Jim's coupe turn on two wheels into the circular driveway.

Hannah went sprawling across the harrow. She got up quickly, yanking at the horses to turn them around. They'd stopped suddenly at the end of the field.

"All I'm good for is to grub in the field," she half cried as she rubbed her barked shins. "I bet the hide's took off," she said aloud. "I'm not gonna stay here. I'll leave. Papa can't keep me till I'm twenty-one!" But even as Hannah spoke she thought how he'd kept Lizzie and Mary, and how he was still keeping Fritz.

It was getting dark. She hurried her horses from the field before Adam could speak to her.

As she came into the barnyard she met Alec and Solly bringing in the two cows. At the same time Ana, white kerchief tied over the head, came out of the house carrying two milk pails.

Hannah called her. "You go back, Mamma, I'll milk."

"Ach, Hannah, all mine life I am milk the cow."

"All her life," Hannah muttered as she threw hay to the horses. "Papa'll work her till she drops in the field."

At the table, that night, Hannah helped Reinie with his food.

"Drink your milk, Reinie," she coaxed.

"Me want some milk," shouted four-year-old Chris.

"Me, too," chimed in six-year-old Coonie.

"Ach, eat the supper. The pigs, he don't got milk enough so he grow good," commanded Adam.

"He even puts the pigs before us!" Hannah thought. She watched her father as he shoveled his food into his mouth. As he chewed, the ends of his straggly mustache moved up and down across his leathery cheek. His sharp beak of a nose wiggled. Industriously, he piled potatoes onto his knife blade, using his fork as a pusher. Raising it to his mouth, he stopped the loaded knife in midair, and roared:

"Solly! Drop that cat! We don't eat mit cats on the tables!

"Hannah, tomorrow you drill mit beet seeds, und Olinda, you ride the harrow. Hannah, she got you skinned one mile for work. Gott, I wish it rain, oncet."

Hannah couldn't sleep after she went to bed. She felt gritty and dirty all over from the dust of the field. Her mouth was parched and dry. Dirt-caked. She slid out of bed and crept down the narrow stairs.

Feeling her way to the water bucket, she stopped. Adam was praying in the bedroom off the kitchen.

"Gott, make it rain so mine last beets come themselves up. Gott, you make it rain and next fall I pay twice over mine church dues. Yah, I make him up mit you. Too many acre I think I am farm, und I worry so I don't can think, und I need the rain so I raise good beets. Make him rain and I praise you all mine days, Gott. Sure, I done it."

Grimly Hannah dipped her cup into the water bucket. "Hypocrite," she muttered. "His word don't mean nothin'. He won't keep his word even with God. All he wants is something for himself, and he's scared to death he's gonna make a failure, so he can't crow to everybody how swell he is."

The next morning she started drilling. The factory field man had come in March with the contracts and Adam had signed to grow forty acres of beets. Twenty acres had been planted the first week of April, then, ten days later, the south field had been planted. Rain had come and the first beets were up in long slender rows of green.

It was dry now and there was not enough moisture to bring up beet seed. Adam held up the lid of the drill box for Hannah to empty the gunny sack of beet seeds, and said: "We got make space between time of plantings so we got time to done the thinnings be-

fore the plants get too big in the other fields, but Gott, he don't
rain, und the beets come themselves up all to oncet."

The big bulky sack sagged against her knees. Adam roughly put
a hand under it, watching the brown, curly seed tumble into the
narrow red drill box. Hannah grabbed for a firmer hold and lost
her grip. The sack slipped sideways and the light, sponge-like tiny
seeds scattered on the dry ground.

"Spill seed, will you?" Adam sent her tumbling to the dirt.

Hannah got up, hating him. She stooped and tried to gather up
the seeds with her trembling hands.

Adam's foot struck her on the hip. She fell flat in the dirt. She
gathered herself up and faced him.

"You hit me again, and I go to the house. I don't work. You ain't
in Russia." Hannah shrank away from him, defiant, but also fearful.

"Ach, mein Gott in Himmel! Make shut the mouth." He advanced
upon her, shaking his fists. "Get the drill on, und get busy! Expenses
I got on mine back mitout spilling seeds. Fifteen cents a pound I
pay for him!"

Sullenly, Hannah climbed on the drill and clucked to the horses.
"I'm goin' to leave. I'm goin' to get out," she declared to herself.
"He's made me dig manure out of the sheep pens and ride on the
old manure spreader. I've plowed and harrowed. I've rolled his old
fields with the roller. And now I'm drilling. He makes us all work,
Fritz, and Olinda and me, and he keeps the other boys home when-
ever he thinks he can get by without the truant officer getting him.
He keeps us all till we're twenty-one, but he won't keep me."

Adam's voice roared up the field. "Hannah! Make them horse go
faster! You hear?"

Hannah paid no attention. "Let him yell," she muttered.

She stopped drilling before noon. She went to the house to hunt
for Adam, and found him mending the pig pen. "I'm outa seed."

"Yah, sure, you spill him on the ground!" As Adam spat out each
word a sunflower seed came from his mouth.

"I never spilled no hundred pounds of seed. The factory says you
gotta plant twenty pound to the acre. It's only half planted."

"Shut the face. Me, I don't plant no more und seventeen pound.
Tell Fritz to get more seed."

Hannah found Fritz sharpening blocking hoes in the barn.

"Fritz, he wants another sack of seed. I'm going with you to get it. He knocked me in the dirt, an' he kicked me." Hannah put her hands to her face and the tears trickled through her dirty fingers.

"Come on, let's get seed," Fritz insisted gently.

They turned into the road beside the red factory, going past the main building to the storehouse. The foreman took Adam's card from the files. There was note of the acreage signed up for, the Boswell dump to which he would deliver his topped beets in the fall, and there was note of the amount of seed allotted, with the amount Adam had gotten and planted.

Fritz boosted the huge sack of seed onto the front bumper of the car and headed for home.

"They sure check up on you," Hannah said.

"Yeah, the Sugar Company thinks when you sign the contract to grow beets that they got the right to know how you raise 'em and what you do. I guess it's all right. Kinda good to have your district field man to run to if you have trouble or want some advice. The Sugar Company guarantees the exact price you get so I guess it's all right. Some people think the company don't pay what they should, but me, I don't know. The old man'll sure cuss. That field won't take a whole sack and the factory don't take back no broken sack nor one with its seal broken. He'll grumble 'cause he's got some seed left over."

"He thinks he owns the earth." Hannah was bitter.

"God, I wisht it'd rain," Fritz said. "I just as soon be shot as irrigate beets up. They don't never do good. It makes the ground hard, and you can't get it fine all summer, and beets don't come up good."

"Quit your worryin', Fritz, the old man does enough of that."

"Yeah, I guess." Fritz stopped at the beet drill to unload the seed.

After supper that night, Hannah washed the dishes while Tabia, grumbling, dried them. Olinda had a date with Henry.

When the last dish was put away, Hannah went out onto the front porch. A car came out of the Boswell driveway and turned toward Valley City.

"Jim," Hannah said, watching the bright lights twinkling above

the city; large clear red ones, smaller pale yellow ones. Above the
little lights there was a soft brightness, like a halo, with the dark
mountains behind. In the darkness between the city and where
Hannah sat, lay the blackness of Shag Town, the beet-workers' city.

"Jim's got the light, the sunshine, while I got nothing but the
darkness. He don't even know I'm on earth. He won't ever know it
so long as I work in the field. But I won't stay. Papa can't keep me
here." Hannah spoke the words defiantly.

"What you say, Hannah?" Ana sat down heavily on the step.

"I said I wasn't gonna stay here and work on this farm forever!
Mamma, I'd think you'd hate the everlasting work an' the dirty
houses, an' the moving, an' the beets, an' babies comin' all the
time?"

"Ach, Hannah, life, he is not hard when you get used to him. We
take him like he comes."

"But I don't wanta take it like it comes! I wanta go places! I
wanta have swell clothes, and have some fun!"

"Good times we have here, Hannah. Be glad you're not in the
Old Country, Russia. We work there, I tell you.

"Up in the morning before day is light, und driving oxen or
camels, two, three, might five miles to the fields. We take the tent
und stay till we get the crop planted und the old man he ride out
in the little light cart mit the high-stepping horse to see if us kids
is working. You think your papa hard, but in Russia the old mens
never work. Sons he want so he get more land from the governments. For every son when he is born, the old man gets five or ten
acre. Five acre if it been good land. Ten acre if it been hilly und
rough.

"You think we crowded here. In the Old Country the houses is
full of peoples: aunts, uncles, grandfathers, und grandmutters. Yah,
they all live in the towns close by each other, und go out in the
country to the farms. The children have to work over there."

"There's no difference. Papa still thinks he can do like in Russia."

"Stop it, Hannah. You papa not for blame. Some day you see it,
und you will been shamed the way you talk."

A car stopped at the front gate. Katie Heist called, "Hannah, I
got the swellest news! You can't guess! I've got a job! A job!"

"Really, Katie? Where?"

"You couldn't guess in a million years! The Boswells! Think of it, right across the road from you. Just think I'll see that swell Jim every day. Boy, won't I make eyes at him!"

"Yah, und lose your job," Adam spoke from the open doorway. "Better you keep your eyes on yourself. That Jim he steps high. If you know him, you don't wipe your feet on him or roll your eyes on him neither. Too much money! Too much car! Und too much girls! Bah, Katie Heist, better you leave his kind alone."

"If he was German, you'd think he was swell," Katie laughed. "Well, I gotta be goin'!" Katie went running toward the waiting car.

"Nothin' but a sassy piece," Adam muttered.

Nothing further was said for several moments. Then Hannah spoke, tears in her voice.

"Katie's got all the luck."

"Ach not, Hannah, you have luck, too. Today the minister come, und I tell him how you want go in high school und he say you come work for his wife this winter and the next three winters. Adam let you go sure, if the minister ask. Yah, you go. Sure."

Hannah felt stunned. Freedom! No more beets! No more dirt!

"I can't go. I ain't finished the eighth grade."

"Yah, you smart. You take the examinations."

"Oh, Mamma, I can't believe it! I'll get my books from school and I'll study. Ooh, just think, Mamma, in town at the preacher's. Oh, it's the swellest place, thick carpets, big easy chairs, and a bathroom even. Ooh! Just think never havin' to scrooch up in a dinky wash-tub to take a bath no more; no more kids a-squallin'! But Mamma, can you get along without me?"

"Yah, Olinda, she help good. She eighteen, und Tabia, she help."

"Mamma! Mamma! Reinie's havin' a fit! Connie pushed him down the stairs."

Ana pulled herself erect by the supporting post and went hastily inside.

As Hannah followed her mother indoors she thought: "And it'll be heaven to have some peace. No kids havin' fits."

It was long after midnight when Hannah heard Olinda tiptoe into the bedroom, undress and slip into their bed.

She don't want no one to know when she gets home, Hannah thought, but it's after midnight because I just heard the night passenger train. Her and Henry got it bad. Won't papa explode if they wanta get married! Them Goelzers! But she can't get married —not for a year anyway—'cause I'm going to high school. I'll get my books from school and I'll sure study. Only missed a week anyway —it's all review from now on—

"What's that?" Hannah held her breath, listening.

Olinda was crying, softly. Hannah could feel the covers quiver with her shaking body.

"Olinda," Hannah whispered, "what's the matter?"

The crying stopped. The very stillness of the room shouted. A mouse crawled in the wall.

"Nothing," Olinda finally answered.

"What you cryin' for, then?"

Silence.

"You and Henry had a fight?"

"No."

"You sick?"

Olinda cried harder.

"If you don't wanta talk, shut your face and let somebody else sleep!" Hannah bounced over in bed, gave the snoring Tabia a shove, straightened out her knees.

What on earth was the matter with Olinda? Ever since they had moved she had been going around with a sober face.

"Come on," Hannah forcibly turned Olinda and cradled her wet cheek against her own face. "Spill it," she commanded.

"Henry and me's gotta get married—right away."

Hannah's breath stuck in her throat. A coldness crept from her head to her feet. A dog howled beneath the window—a long mournful howl that sent prickles running over her body.

"Olinda! No!"

"Yes. I been scared for weeks." Olinda cried harder.

"O God. O God," Hannah whispered as her whole world tumbled about her. Gone was the future, gone everything but this terrible reality.

"Olinda, how could you? How could you?"

"I'll never be able to hold my head up again. Never, never, never."

Hannah, though stricken, tried to comfort her. "Don't worry, Olinda, I'll tell Mamma in the morning. You and Henry can get married right away. Quit cryin' and go to sleep."

But Hannah wept silent tears into her pillow for a long time. If Olinda got married, she'd have to stay. She couldn't leave her mother now. Tabia was too little and too lazy to help with a tiny baby. Her mind went over all the things that high school would have meant, all that staying at home next year would mean. Lugging water from the cistern. The pump handle frozen with ice, almost taking the skin from her fingers. Water slopping on her shoes with their run-over heels and broken laces. Dirty chicken coops to clean out and brush with oil to keep mites down. The setting of hens, and broken eggs in the nest all wet and yolky. There would be the tiny baby, its washing to be done, dirty diapers, and the ceaseless squalling. There would be the everlasting baking of bread, bedbugs and the dirt, and the dank smells from the barnyard, and the stinking beet pulp in the winter with the men carrying oodles of it in on their broad-toed rubber boots. There would be the beet-work, the bending, backbreaking work of thinning with the sun scorching down in the late spring. And in the fall they would top beets in the cold wind and spitting snow in order to get the beets out before freezing. In her bitterness she reviewed it in detail.

"You're tied," a still voice whispered. "You're here forever. You'll never get away. This is just the beginning. This will always be your life."

"No! No! I will get away! The devil himself can't keep me here!" Illogically, the words of confirmation came to her, "Do you renounce the devil and all his ways? All his ways?"

Her life verse stood before her, "Rejoicing in hope."

"I have no hope," she murmured.

"Patient in tribulation."

"I can't. I can't."

At last daylight came. Carrying her shoes, she slipped down to the kitchen. Quietly, she started the fire.

By Rosamund Dargan Thomson

AND WE CALL OUT

In the temperance of late September
At sundown, moment of no wind,
High over fields, bird-beautiful above woodlands—
Two of them in keenest flight:
Rehearsal in a proud American autumn.

Two of them over us suddenly, oh sombre!
(Remember dark eagles and all sad ancient omens)
In sturdy flight, injuring the quiet blue air,
Sharp and black, cruel and black,
Lording it over the eventide—bombers.

They dip, tilt at the veiling mountains,
Find a most innocent village to circle
And are flown, in sweetest light:
American weapons.

Quiet is augmented. Our pastures grow mysterious.
There comes to all the trees
A trembling—panic of small birds;
And to the white and voided sky there come
Night wind, a star.
Untenderly the red cock treads his hen.
Fruit is dark on the branch; the lightless flowers
Fail a little in the wind, die a little in the autumn wind.
And we call out to our cattle and our youngest sons
And turn us unto our peace.

THE CRADLE OF HISTORY

WE SAT ON Boone Helm's grave and looked over Virginia City, the cradle of Montana history, or so the signs said. It was a day of the present.

"Here is where all the big things happened, Walt," I said.

Walt grunted. A serious, sandy person, he squinted quizzical eyes, scanning the gulch that held the visible records of the past.

"The hell you say," he said.

If we had sat there in the 1860's, we would have seen a booming camp. We would have seen miners coming and going in the gulch; horsemen riding the trails; stagecoaches with painted ladies stepping out of them; bullwhackers with their wagon trains; prospectors. You know how it looks in the movies. We would have seen Henry Plummer stepping out of a log saloon, wiping his blond mustache with the back of his hand, hitching up his gunbelts, and striding down to the Wells Fargo office to see if the stage was ready to go out with a big shipment of dust that his boys would surely get.

"Does the past live, Walt?" I mused. "Do you hear the lost music of time, and the voices of forgotten men begging to be delivered out of history?"

"It looks like the place that God forgot," Walt grumbled. His gaze ranged up and down Alder Gulch. All you could see was ugly piles and ridges of gravel where the dredge had been.

I felt sad, looking over green hills where a May wind ruffled patches of blue flowers in the hollows. "It's here," I said. "A story that should mean more to us today than when it happened. The history that's here still lives, Walt. But I can't write it. Something stops me. What is it?"

"I wouldn't know," Walt said, grinning. "I'm just a Sunday tourist. I want to see all the relics and the historic spots, and get to hell home. Let's get going."

We made our tour. We drove up Alder Gulch to the big monument that marks the spot where Bill Fairweather discovered the richest placer diggings in the world. I could feel the epic events of history deploying about us, but Walt leered and made nasty remarks. We went through the museum, which was clean and orderly and hushed. There the testimonials of history glowed mutely in neat arrangement under glass. We saw a door from the stove that was used by Joe Slade. George Lane's club foot. The quitclaim deed by which Bill Fairweather and his partners sold their claims. Faded documents and old guns and Henry Plummer's boots. Photographs of the place and the time and of Mr. Laurin, the big fat Frenchman. And we stared at the Sunday visitors who were quizzically nosing even as we were.

Irrefutable testimony, preserved and enduring, electric still with the soul and spirit of a vanished time and circumstance. Or so I said to Walt, who made an unprintable statement.

We drove around town, up one hill and down another. We saw the livery stable that used to be a hotel, the place where Joe Slade was hanged. We saw the old newspaper office. We visited the place where the Vigilantes held their first meeting, and saw the gallows from which they hanged a slew of road agents.

"And if you write a historical novel about it, I'll personally see that you're hung with the same rope," Walt threatened.

"I guess I'm safe," I said. "But it should be done. God, Walt, the lives that moved here. You don't know this story. Nobody knows it. History doesn't tell it."

Anger was shaping the confusion that worked in me.

"What'll history say about you?" Walt jibed.

"Nothing," I said, staring bleakly at a faded cabin. "Romance," I said a trifle bitterly. "That was probably a hookshop."

"That's a safe guess," I said. "There were plenty of painted cats. The favorite sport of fellows like Bill Fairweather and Joe Slade when they were painting the town red was to burn one of these cabins down, after spending the night in it. I guess they liked to see the little gals flutter around in their nightgowns."

"Maybe that's why the Vigilantes hung Slade." Walt leered, "instead of for the reasons given in the books."

"Could be," I said.

We stopped in at a local bar for a sandwich.

"I thought this Pulitzer Prize novel of yours was going to be about Henry Plummer," Walt said.

"Yes, I guess so," I replied. "I had it all worked out once. Not the career of Plummer alone, any more than the career of Fairweather or Joe Slade or Wilbur Fisk Sanders or Boone Helm. Not the Vigilantes wiping out the road agents. Not the bringing of civilization to Montana. Not the great gold rush."

"OK," Walt said munching. "Now I know what your novel is *not* about."

"An interweaving of lives," I said. "I wish I knew what it *was* about."

The patterns of history began to form again in my mind, and I tried to tell Walt about them. How the miners took gold from Nature, and the Innocents took it from the miners. How Henry Plummer came and organized the road agents, got himself elected sheriff, married an Eastern girl and tried to reform, failed, stood finally on nothing and looked up a rope. How Bill Fairweather discovered the Alder Gulch diggings, threw gold away by the handfuls, wandered far, and returned to drink himself to death in his old haunts. How Boone Helm killed his partners and ate them. How George Ives rode into saloons and relieved the patrons of their dust. And the minor legends.

Before I was well started, Walt interrupted.

"Listen," he whispered.

The two girls who were tending the lunch counter next the bar were in a dispute with a couple of buckos who looked like service station boys.

"You never bought me that beer," one said. "You *owe* me one."

"Who owes who what?" the boy growled.

"He's tight," the other girl sneered.

"He wouldn't buy nothing for nobody. He wouldn't pay nothing for a crack at Sally Rand."

The second boy grinned, but the first boy considered this. "Well," he pondered, "she'd have to be good."

"Maybe you could put that in your novel," Walt said with malice.

We went out into the slumbering sunshine. "The road agents all got hung in the end, didn't they?" Walt demanded. "So what the hell? Let's get started home so we can listen to some foreign news broadcasts on the short wave. My radio doesn't work this far out in the country."

"One more thing," I insisted with weak stubbornness. "I want to find Dimsdale's grave."

Walt wanted to know who in hell, with emphasis on the hell, Dimsdale was.

"He was an English intellectual," I explained patiently, "who came out here for his health. He was the first schoolmarm in these parts. In fact, he was about the only literate gent in the camp."

We found his grave. He had a big steel sign, saying he was the author of *The Vigilantes of Montana*.

"He was a writer?" Walt said.

"Sure," I said. "He was the first feature writer in Montana, and the luckiest. He made one of the biggest scoops in the history of journalism inasmuch as he was the only writing gent that was in on the ground floor."

"OK," Walt declared. "That's the way history should be written— by those who are in on the ground floor. Can't you get in on the ground floor or something?"

I sat on Dimsdale's grave, and began to feel silly as hell. Alder Gulch lay asleep in wakeful sunshine. Mountains to the south and west were blue and glorious in their distance. The Passamari Valley lay northwestward, fat and secret. The land seemed smiling behind a mask of sunlight, smug in its refusal to share with men the secrets of its history.

I began to feel calmer. I would let history sleep with Dimsdale, and continue to write life while it was living, before it became history.

"OK, Walt," I said. "To hell with it. Let's go."

Walt gave her the gun going down the gulch. "That Pulitzer Prize is a lot of money," he said, mocking me.

"All right," I said. "Just for that we'll stop and see Robber's Roost. I was going to let you off."

"What's Robber's Roost?"

"You'll see."

We swung off the highway beside a faded two-story log building that sported a verandah along its entire length. There was the usual metal sign with enamel letters. An old guy shuffled out of his near-by cabin, eying us.

"May we look through the old building?" Walt inquired with exaggerated politeness.

Eagerness leaped in the old man's eyes. "I'll take you through."

We piled out. The old guy wore bib overalls, and his eyes were runny and his mustache was draggled and faded. He looked like something out of the 1860's. He started his lecture right off the bat.

"This here log house," he began, indicating with a possessive finger, "was put up by Pete Dailey in eighteen and sixteen-three."

The sign said that.

"Pete Dailey had a ranch here, and he put up this here road house to entertain the boys from the camps. Pete built this road house in eighteen and sixty-three—the same year I was born—and I'm seventy-seven years old, so this house is seventy-seven years old too. Now, lot's of people came down here to Pete Dailey's place to drink and dance, but mainly the road agents came here because Pete Dailey kept a lot of race horses down here. Down the valley a piece they had a race track where they tested them out, and they always had the fastest horses in the valley here. So when the road agents wanted to go some place in a hurry they come down here for a horse. Now, they was road agents in Virginia City, some in Bannack, some at Deer Lodge, some here. Some had a cabin in one of them draws you can see across the valley there. From that there cabin they could take field glasses and look right down into the streets of Virginia City, and when a coach was loading with treasure they'd know it and be on the lookout for it. Course it was always marked—George Lane he saw to that."

I grinned at Walt, and he glared at me. I was feeling very warm toward the old codger.

He had us going his way. "Come on, I'll take you through the house now. Mostly the road agents stayed here, but anybody could bunk here that had the price, and a lot of folks had the price in them days. Because the Alder Gulch diggings was going then and I think I may safely say that over a hundred millions of dollars in gold dust came out of them diggings." We entered a bare room. Plaster was crumbling from the old walls, but the room held a commanding silence and an air of spaciousness.

"This is the kitchen," the old guy said. "They had their meals here. Now, in this room—here is one of the chairs them road agents had in their cabin up in the mountains. 'Tain't much of a chair."

It was a log, split in two, smoothed, with four sticks stuck in the ends, like a sawhorse.

"And here's the barroom. Now, see this home-made bar. If you had all the gold dust that's been tossed over this here bar, you wouldn't have to work no more—neither of you."

The old man chuckled. He leaned against the bar as though he were about to order something.

"And if you had all the whiskey that went over it the other way, you wouldn't have to drink the rotgut you get now for a long time to come. Why, they had Old Crow and Four X that was fifteen and twenty years old. Yessir, this here's the bar them road agents leaned on, and sometimes they got pretty gay and shot up the place. Look here."

A stained and trembling finger indicated several holes in the walls and ceiling.

"Them holes was made by .45 slugs. From the cap-and-ball pistols too. They had no cartridges like they got now. . . .

"Well, in these little rooms off the barroom they had their secret meetings and made their plans. Plummer used to come here and meet with them. Course these little rooms was for gambling too."

We stuck our heads in the little rooms, and smelled rats and age.

"History stinks," Walt snickered.

The old man said, "Hey?"

"You say they had fast horses here?"

"You betcha. When George Ives made his run from Bivens Gulch, if he could of got here and got his favorite mare, they'd never of got to hung him. No sir. They captured him, and while they was bringing him over here he proposed a horse race, it was a cold morning and they took him up on it, and he got out ahead and stayed there. But they was pressing him too hard, and he didn't have time to stop and change."

"Did he get away?" Walt asked innocently.

"No, he got in the rocks, but they caught him when his powder ran out. Took him to Nevada and hung him."

Walt grinned foolishly and looked at his watch.

"Now you'll come upstairs," our guide said. "Here's where they had their dances."

We entered a long barren ballroom. Plaster all off the ceiling. Laths hanging in.

"This here house has lasted well," the old guy said. "Ceiling wouldn't have fallen in if the rain hadn't leaked on it."

Walt and the guide went out on the verandah. I lingered, scanning the names written on the walls, transient records.

"Where did people sleep?" I heard Walt ask, apparently determined to be as unpleasant as possible.

"Uh, they was a sort of annex with separate stairs. Tore down now."

We stumbled down the stairs and out into the sunshine again.

"They hung 'em all," the guide said, "all except Bill Hunter, and he got away by crawling down a ditch, but they finally caught up with him and hung him over near Bozeman. If you're interested, the tree where they hung Erastus Yeager and George Brown just at midnight in the dead of winter is still standing just south of the Laurin place up the road a piece."

"No," Walt said hastily, "we got to go."

"Wait, come back!" the guide called. "Want you to register. They been registering on the walls, but they'll fall off. Wait, I'll get a fresh bottle of ink."

The ink was dried up.

"Never mind," Walt said. "I have a pencil. It'll do for us to put our hentracks on the scroll of history."

"Hope to have five thousand names on that book this season," the guide said.

"How many do you usually have?"

" 'Bout four thousand."

Still he hated to have us leave.

"Come back again sometime—bring your friends. Maybe I should study up more so I could tell you more about it. Next time you come back, I will."

"Hell," I said, "you know the works. You're doing fine."

I nudged Walt. He stammered, and gave the old guy a quarter.

"That's good," the guide said bashfully. "Thanks. If everybody did that good, I'd get along fine."

"You should keep your hand out," Walt told him. "You don't even have your hand out."

We drove down the valley in the fine sunshine. With a contented sigh, Walt snapped on the radio.

"Now that we have the road agents and the Vigilantes forever disposed of, I hope, let's see what the war is doing."

Out of the radio came much crackling and strained rasping words. What we heard over the radio dates this story, but it is a historical story and has to be dated some way.

". . . desperate fighting continues around Dunkerque, while Nazi bombers ranged over the south of France and dropped a thousand bombs on the outskirts of Paris. . . . Almost miraculous evacuation of Allied forces from the Flanders pocket . . . Allies say the Nazis have lost over half a million men in the fighting. . . . German high command claims their losses were light in this greatest battle of all military history. . . ."

"Well, Walt," I said, "we've looked today into the seeds of time, into the very cradle of Montana history. What did you think of it?"

"Oh boy," Walt said softly. "Oh boy, oh boy, oh boy."

PAYDAY

A car passed by outside and the tires made a below-zero sound in the snow. Young Doc French took his pipe from his mouth and yawned luxuriously. "I hope," he said, "nobody breaks a leg or has a baby tonight."

"Listen, Johnny," said his red-haired wife, "you ought to take a nice, hot bath right now and go to bed."

"I'm too comfortable." He stretched his slippered feet toward the fireplace. "Suppose I ought to run over and see how Pop Phillips is getting along. If he ever turns into pneumonia he's gone."

"You had only three hours' sleep last night," observed Mrs. French, sewing at a patch on the knee of Johnny Junior's trousers. "If Pop Phillips needed you they'd phone."

"I suppose so."

"You can see him all right in the morning. And don't you go following in Dr. Bagley's footsteps. He's a broken-down invalid at fifty-two without a penny."

"Got hitting the liquor too hard," remarked Doc French evenly. "Suspect he'd shoot it in the arm, too, when there was an emergency or when he was too tired to sleep."

Mrs. French pursed her lips. The needle pricked her finger and she sucked the wound. "That may be," she said. "But he was too conscientious. Now, honey . . ."

She was interrupted by the telephone. Young Doc French counted the rings—three sharp ones, a pause, and another ring. He grinned at his wife and rose from his chair. "Somebody," he said, "has broken a leg or is having a baby. Hope it's not far away."

"Maybe it's the Phillipses," she said, as he walked to the phone and lifted the receiver. She listened to his conversation.

"Hello. . . . Yes, this is Dr. French. . . . Who? . . . At Cradle Rock? . . . Why, I couldn't get over there. Pass blocked for days. . . . Yes, I know where it is—and it's seventy-five miles from here. Dr. Durkin, in Enid, is on your side of the pass. Have you tried him? . . . Oh, I see. . . . Yes; I understand. . . . You're sure you can do that? . . . All right. Now, listen; I'll hold the phone and you go press your fingers on her abdomen. Have her relax. . . . Yes, loosen up, relax. You press in with your fingers and then come tell me whether her abdomen is soft or not. I'll hold the phone."

Mrs. French had laid Johnny Junior's knickers on the table and gone to the kitchen. Doc French cupped his hand over the transmitter and called to her from the hallway, "Girl over at Cradle Rock got a stomach ache. Probably appendicitis. Father's pretty excited."

"You can't drive over the pass," said his wife.

"I know it. I could just about make the twenty miles up to Humphreys. But Dr. Durkin is clear down in Denver and they can't reach him. This rancher Martin says he'll have a man named Joe Gilmer meet me at Humphreys with a sled and take me as far up the pass as horses can go. I could snowshoe it over the pass and he'd have another rancher meet me with a sled up the other side of the pass."

"You're not going to try snowshoeing over the pass this kind of weather, Johnny. Please listen, Johnny . . ."

"Wait a minute." He took his hand from the transmitter. "Yes," he said into the telephone. "It seems stiff? . . . All right. Have you taken her temperature? . . . I see. All right. I'll be starting right away. Don't know how long it'll take me, but this Joe Gilmer can phone you when he gets back with his sled, and you'll know I'm climbing the pass. He can tell you about the weather and snow and about how long it'll take me to get over the hump. Have the fellow with the sled on the other side build a big fire so I can find him. I probably won't be on the road. Probably can't find the road under the snow. . . . Yeah, I'll try to get some man to come with me and help carry. I have a man who can help me with cases like this. Sort of a lay brother, you might say. . . . Now, listen, Mr. Martin; have you got an ice bag? . . . No, get that hot-water bottle off her right now. Cold is what you need. Lots of it. Listen; fill that hot-water bottle with snow. You can do that. Fill it with snow and put that on her. . . . All right. I'll be starting right away. Good-bye."

Mrs. French called from the kitchen, "You can drink some hot coffee before you start."

"Yeah. And I'll take a vacuum bottle of it with me and some sandwiches. You can get 'em ready while I'm crawling into my fur-lined underwear and things. I'm going to phone Billy Huff. It'll be a tough drag and I'll need somebody to help me when I get over to Martin's."

His wife came from the kitchen and kissed him. "Another charity case, I suppose?" she said.

Young Doc French grinned. "Not this time. Daughter of Mansfield Martin. Big rancher over there. He's got lots of money."

Thirty minutes later Doc French was picking up Billy Huff at the outskirts of the village. Doc didn't risk pulling into the deep snow at the side of the road. He stopped his car in the street and struck the horn button softly three times. Immediately the front door of the Huff house opened and light streamed out on the snow-covered baby spruces in the front yard. Billy emerged carrying his snow-shoes and a bundle of lunch in one hand. With the other he was pushing a revolver into the pocket of his sheepskin jacket. Like Doc, he wore a stocking cap and short boots laced over his trouser legs.

"Hello, Doc," said Billy. "Awful cold."

"Yeah." Doc looked out at the glitter of frost in the moonlight. "Going to be a nice trip."

Billy dumped his snowshoes and lunch in the back of the car with Doc's snowshoes and two bags. He climbed in the front seat and slammed the door. "Is this girl bad?" Billy asked.

"Don't know for sure. She may be."

"Going to operate?"

"Possibly. Not if she can stand a sled trip to a train. If I have to operate I'll want you to give the ether. You can do it."

"Hm-m." Billy took off his mittens and dug out a pack of cigarettes. "Smoke?"

"Thanks."

Billy stuck a cigarette in Doc's mouth and struck a match for him.

Five miles from town Doc was in second gear, making an average of eight miles an hour—when he was traveling. Half a dozen times he was blocked temporarily by drifts, but managed to back and charge his way through. Then, in a cut ten miles from town, the snow packed under the crankcase so hard that the car was actually resting on its belly. Then the chained rear wheels spun impotently and he could go neither forward nor backward.

"I wish," said Doc irritably, "that they'd build a few cars with higher clearance for this country."

With a short-handled spade from the trunk and one of Billy's snowshoes they finally got the snow dug from under the car, and, with Billy Huff's thick shoulders pushing from behind, Doc wriggled the car through the cut.

"At this rate," said Billy, "we won't even get to Humphreys before morning."

But the road opened up for a way and Doc actually got the speed up to twenty miles an hour for five miles or so. Then he began to feel drowsy. That baby case last night. Only two or three hours' sleep. Doc blinked his eyes and shook his head violently, but the sleepiness persisted. He stretched his shoulder muscles and wished Billy were more communicative. The drowsiness became an agony. He stole a glance at Billy and saw his head was slumped over against the far door.

Doc felt resentful. Billy hadn't been up delivering a baby all the night before. "Billy!"

Billy paid no heed. The car hit a drift Doc hadn't seen and jerked violently. Doc straightened it out and went back into second gear. Then he looked again and saw Billy had slumped farther down in the seat when the car lurched. As he looked, a wave of dizziness swept over him, almost wiping out the snowy road ahead. "Billy!"

Doc jammed on brakes and pulled the lever out of gear. He turned the ignition key as the car slid to a stop. Another dizzy wave seized him as he struggled with the left door handle, and he had to use both hands to get the door open. Then he fell out of the car into the snow, landing on his hands and knees. But he took a long breath and struggled to his feet. He stumbled around the front of the car to the right-hand door and pulled it open, got hold of Billy's jacket, and hauled him floundering into the snow.

Billy sat up in the road, holding his head where it had bumped into the door jamb. "What the hell's coming off here?" he demanded.

"Something wrong with the car," said Doc. "Carbon monoxide. I nearly passed out. You were out and wouldn't wake up."

Billy stood up, still holding his head.

"What a headache!" he said.

"Me, too."

Doc got his big flashlight from the glove compartment and knelt at the rear of the car. He turned the flash on the exhaust pipe. "Yeah," he said. "The whole thing's filled with snow and ice. Jammed it full of snow backing up in the drifts."

"Too cold for the engine heat to melt it out," observed Billy.

While Billy trimmed off a half-inch limb from a cedar Doc opened one of his kits. First he took out a bottle of whiskey, and both he and Billy had a drink. Then he brought out a roll of bandage-gauze, which he wrapped around the end of the stick and dipped into the gasoline tank. This torch flamed fiercely when they touched a match to it, and Billy, squatting in the road, thawed the snow from the exhaust pipe. But they drove the rest of the way to Humphreys with both front windows down, continually rubbing their faces with woolen mittens to prevent freezing.

It was past two o'clock in the morning when they pulled into the village's single street, but Fred Hobart's general store was lighted and a bobsled stood in front.

Joe Gilmer, short and squat and dark, came out the door when he saw the lights of the car. "Where in tarnation you been?" he called. "Just getting ready to send out a searching party."

While Fred Hobart took a huge coffeepot from the heating stove in the center of the store and poured tin cups of scalding black coffee, Doc explained the delay.

"If it'd been anybody else but Doc we'd be out there in a ditch froze stiff," said Billy.

"Guess I better get hitched up," said Gilmer. "I was hitched up before midnight, but the horses was getting cold, and when you didn't show up I took 'em back in the barn."

Hobart sliced some cheese and piled some crackers on the counter. "You better put your car in the barn, Doc," he said.

Doc poured down some black coffee. "Yeah. No telling when we get back."

"No hurry, Doc," said Hobart. "I'll put it up for you when you go."

"Thanks." Doc nibbled on a cracker and a piece of cheese. "How's your head, Billy?" he asked.

"Not any too good."

Doc was feeling none too certain about himself, but he said nothing.

"Is that Martin girl pretty bad?" asked Hobart.

"Don't know until I see her," said Doc.

Then Joe Gilmer came back in the store, drank a hurried cup of coffee, and looked inquiringly at Doc.

"O.K.," said Doc. "Let's go."

The three men sat together on the wagon sled, wrapped themselves in blankets, and covered their feet with straw. Steam from the horses' breath came drifting clear back to the sled when they finally broke the runners loose and trotted up the street.

"Must be twenty-five below," said Billy.

"I know it," said Doc.

"Don't know how far I can take you. Snow's awful deep up the road. Doubt if the horses can get more than ten mile, and that'll be anyhow forty-five mile to Cradle Rock."

"Fellow's going to meet us on the other side of the hump," Billy explained.

"Well, even so," said Gilmer, "if there's as much snow over there as here and he doesn't get more than ten mile from Cradle Rock, you still got thirty-five mile of snowshoeing."

"We'll just hope there isn't as much snow," said Doc.

Two miles from Humphreys, where the tracks to Lazy Nine

Ranch branched off, the world lay in unbroken blue-whiteness before them. From now on they must break their own trail.

At four o'clock they had traveled a scant eight miles from
Humphreys and the horses were floundering and panting badly as
the snow increased in depth. Five minutes later the near horse
wallowed up to its belly in a drift and Gilmer had difficulty in
backing out. He tried again and both horses became so badly
bogged down he was obliged to climb off the sled and pull them
back out of the drift.

"No use, fellows," said Gilmer. "This is the end of the line."

Doc and Billy put on their snowshoes. Billy took the bigger med-
ical kit and slung the strap over his shoulder. Doc slung the other
over one shoulder and a canvas knapsack containing sandwiches, a
vacuum bottle of coffee, and the car flashlight over the other
shoulder.

"Put your lunch in the knapsack," invited Doc. "I can carry it just
as easy."

"O.K.," said Billy.

"Good luck," said Gilmer. "Hope you get over there in time,
Doc."

"Thanks," said Doc.

"Hope you have a nice walk, Billy."

"Go to hell," said Billy.

At dawn they had made six or seven miles. It was a slow, uphill
drag and they were still a very long way from the top. At eight
o'clock they found a sheltered place behind a cliff and sat down
briefly to rest and drink sparingly from the vacuum bottle of coffee.
It was bitterly cold yet, but not a breath of wind was stirring.

"How do you feel, Billy?" Doc asked.

"Not so good. That gas must have done something to me."

"Think you can make it?"

Billy looked off across the canyon. "Guess I can make it if I have
to," he said.

Doc himself felt sick.

"Suppose," said Billy, "that we turned back now to Humphreys."

"Well," said Doc, "I'd just be through here, that's all. I'd have to
move some other place and start over."

"Don't see why. That girl's not in your district. Nobody can expect a doctor to go seventy-five miles through this kind of country in this kind of weather."

"They do expect it, though. And if a mountain doctor turns down one emergency call he's all washed up."

"If you had died back in the car you couldn't have got back over there."

"But I didn't die back there in the car. I've got to go on, Billy, but that doesn't hold for you."

"If you can make it," said Billy, "so can I. Let's go."

It was after noon when they reached the crest of the divide and the cold, gray clouds were hanging around their ears. The Achilles tendons above Doc's ankles ached acutely. As he hobbled to a sheltered spot in the rocks and drew frozen sandwiches from the knapsack, he calculated their progress. "I figure," Doc said, "that we're within twenty-five miles of Cradle Rock."

"Twenty-five miles," said Billy bitterly.

"That fellow with the sled ought to make at least ten miles up our way."

"Gilmer didn't make more than eight."

"I know. But maybe there isn't as much snow on this side."

Doc bit into an icy beef sandwich. "I'd like to build a fire and rest here a while, but I'm afraid my leg muscles would tighten up and I wouldn't be able to travel at all."

"They'll probably find our bodies in the spring," said Billy cheerfully.

After the brief rest it was torture to Doc's Achilles tendons to start snowshoeing again. But traveling downhill brought another set of muscles into play and was somewhat easier.

At two o'clock Doc observed, "We're probably within ten miles of the sled."

"The sled," said Billy, "has got tired of waiting for us and gone back hours ago. The Martin girl has either died or got well. It's starting to snow. And they'll find our bodies next summer when the buzzards get going."

By four o'clock it was snowing so hard they could see no more than twenty-five feet ahead. They had no idea whether they might be on the road or miles from it.

Billy dragged himself to Doc's side. "Doc," he said huskily, "we're done. We can't travel in this storm. We'll fall and kill ourselves sure. We got to find some hole in the rocks or something and build a big fire and stay there until morning."

Doc nodded his head. "It's going to be pitch-dark in half an hour," he said. "We're lost. We've got to wait until morning."

At the foot of a cliff they found a crevice in the rock. They built a huge fire in front of this fissure. Years ago there had been a forest fire which left plenty of dead wood, but most of this was covered hopelessly with snow. There were, however, numerous white skeletons still standing and Doc and Billy managed to push down a couple of these. With the little ax Billy lopped off a pile of brittle limbs.

Huddling together in the rock crevice, with the fire scorching their faces and legs, Doc pulled out the whiskey bottle and both took warming drinks. Then they finished the sandwiches and coffee. Doc unlaced his boots and massaged his calves tenderly, noting definite swelling which might be crippling on the morrow. If neither Billy nor he could snowshoe, both would freeze to death. If one of them could travel, he could go for help and might get back with a sled in time. Well, he observed, at least it had stopped snowing.

Doc dozed in cat naps. Twice he awoke, to see Billy leaning against the rock and groaning in his sleep. He piled wood on the waning fire. He wound his watch, and was surprised to see it was ten o'clock. He wondered if the Martin girl were still alive. Well, he had done his best. He was sorry. Again he dozed off.

Billy woke him. "Just heard a couple of shots close together," he said.

"Maybe they've got a searching party out for us."

Billy pulled the revolver from his jacket pocket and fired two quick shots in the air. From off in the night came two answering reports. Doc piled wood on the fire and the flames leaped up.

At midnight four ranchers on skis and snowshoes reached them. They relieved Doc and Billy of the kits and knapsack and helped them stumble to the road a mile away and down five miles to their bobsled. It was two o'clock in the morning when they reached the Martin ranch, and Doc, haggard and hollow-eyed, hobbled into the house, warmed his hands on the big wood stove, and started to examine his patient.

"Marcella's some better now," said bearded Mansfield Martin, while Doc put the clinical thermometer between the lips of the wan girl. The pulse was inclined to flutter, but seemed strong enough.

Doc's hand shook disconcertingly as he held the thermometer to the light. His eyes blurred, but he finally caught the mercury at slightly above 101. Searching out the seat of infection, his fingers encountered boardlike rigidity in the abdomen. He knew the necessity for surgery was immediate, but he was so sick he didn't dare trust his hand with the scalpel.

"How's she, Doc?" demanded Martin.

"Considering everything, she's in good shape," said Doc.

"Don't have to cut her open, then?"

"I'm afraid we do."

Doc looked across the shadowy bedroom, at the Enid High School pennant on the wall, at the long-legged, limp doll sprawled on the dresser. He rubbed his forehead. "But we'll have to wait for daylight," he continued. He gave the girl a tenth of morphine in her thin left shoulder.

"If it ought to be done right away I could hold the lamp up like this. Could you see with the light up this way?"

"No. Couldn't use ether with that kerosene lamp near. It might even explode from that stove." This was partly true. But primarily Doc knew he must have a few hours' sleep before he dared undertake an appendectomy.

"You have somebody get a table in here. Dining table, kitchen table—anything she can lie on full length. And get some harness straps or something so we can strap her down after she has the ether. Have plenty of hot water."

"Table . . . straps . . . hot water."

"That's right. And now let me lie down some place so I can get two or three hours' sleep. I've got to have a little sleep. I'm bushed."

Martin woke up Doc at a quarter of six, and Doc, rolling from bed, winced with pain when he put his weight on his legs. His head ached throbbingly. The room swam before his dizzy eyes and his stomach contracted spastically.

The girl seemed weaker and apathetic when they lifted her to the dining table. Her fever was well above 102. Doc gave her a heavy jolt of morphine and she made no complaint when he placed over her face the cone he had improvised from a piece of heavy cardboard. Nor did she complain when Billy began to drop ether into the cotton filling. She breathed deeply and apparently confidently as Doc directed, and soon was unconscious.

Doc knew he must work fast, not only for the girl's sake but for his own. He assisted in strapping the girl's legs and in buckling a broad harness band across her narrow chest and under the table. The right wrist was strapped to this band.

"Will you," Doc asked Martin, "hold her left wrist and tell me if the pulse begins to weaken? And don't let her hand get way from you. You, Billy, any time she twitches drop in a little more ether."

Before he shaved the fine hair from the surgical area Doc loaded a hypo with a precautionary strychnine dose. He gave his hands and wrists a perfunctory wash, slipped rubber gloves from their sterile case, and donned them. His instruments were steaming in a dishpan on a near-by chair. He took a scalpel from the pan and deftly slit through the skin. With surgical scissors Doc snipped through the wall of muscle. He clamped hemostats on blood vessels and inserted gauze sponges into the wound. He went through the peritoneum with a scalpel. He seized tweezers and changed sponges.

Then he set a retractor into the aperture to hold it open and his rubber-clad forefinger explored for the appendix. His tortured legs brought a sigh from him as Doc found the appendix adhering to the colon. . . .There was the telltale odor of a rupture. Doc had hoped against that.

Doc cautiously applied a little pressure, and the appendix came loose and up. It was badly infected and split for a quarter-inch near the end. With catgut Doc made a suture at the base and severed the appendix with a new scalpel. He put sponges into the cavity and rapidly changed them, trying to clean out the infection as well as possible, but in his heart he was sick. In a modern hospital, perhaps. But what chance here?

He cauterized the appendix stub with pure phenol and neutralized the phenol with alcohol. Now what? A hundred miles of snowdrifts between the girl and a hospital. That wound must be drained. If not now actually present, peritonitis was very near.

"Doc," said Martin hoarsely, "I can't feel her pulse."

Seizing his stethoscope with reddened gloves, Doc listened at the girl's flat chest. There was neither respiration nor heart. He motioned Billy away with the ether cone, stripped off his gloves and gave the girl the strychnine hypodermic. But the stimulant had no effect.

While Doc removed sponges and the retractor from the wound and sewed up the incision, Martin still sat beside the table holding the girl's hand. Tears were running down his cheeks into his whiskers.

Billy unfastened the harness straps, and Doc and he carried the girl's frail body back to her bed. The father followed. Doc placed his hand consolingly on Martin's shoulder. "Anything I can do for you?"

Martin pulled his shoulder away. "Nothing you can do now," he said gruffly. "Guess there was nothing *you* could do at any time."

Doc blinked. "I did everything I could do," he said. "But it was too late."

Martin ignored him. "John," he said to one of the men, "will you call Reverend Seebass in Enid? And you better call up that undertaker Hauser, too." Then to Doc he drawled, "If you want to sleep and you *can* sleep at a time like this, you can go back in that room, you two."

"Thanks," said Doc. He and Billy slept until after noon.

When Doc came out, the Presbyterian minister was there talking to Martin.

"Excuse me, Reverend," said Martin, rising. Then curtly to Doc, "How much do I owe you?"

"No use of talking about that now."

"Yes there is. I want to get everything straightened out."

Doc calculated to himself. Martin was well-to-do, but one couldn't charge city prices out here. Besides, he had lost his patient.

"Fifty dollars," said Doc.

Martin's eyes narrowed. He nodded his head, smiling bitterly. "Fifty dollars . . . well, I'm not surprised at you. Over at Bramer's ranch two years ago young Tommy Bramer had his appendix out by Doc Bagley—a real doctor. Tommy Bramer lived, and Doc Bagley charged twenty-five dollars. You cut into my girl and she died— maybe you killed her; I'll never know. And you got the guts to ask fifty dollars. Well, think again, Mister."

"I'm awfully sorry, Mr. Martin."

"Yes, you're *sorry!*"

"I'm sorry enough to say you can pay what you like when you like—or nothing."

"I'm not trying to beat you down. I'm willing to pay you what you're worth—and more." Martin pulled a fat billfold from his pocket and drew forth two ten-dollar bills, which he handed Doc.

"Thanks," said Doc. "Want a receipt?"

"Yes."

So Doc wrote out a receipt, paid in full. . . .

Two days later Doc and Billy Huff pulled into Humphreys on a bobsled, got Doc's car and drove back home. It was about nine-thirty in the evening when they stopped in front of Billy's house.

"Well, Billy," said Doc, still hollow-eyed and haggard, "we've been gone about ninety-six hours. I figure you were working about seventy of those hours and I pay you thirty cents an hour. That would be twenty-one dollars, wouldn't it?"

"Make it twenty and we'll call it square."

So Doc took out his lean purse and drew forth Mansfield Martin's two ten-dollar bills and handed them to Billy.

Billy grinned. "Want a receipt?"

"No, thanks," said Doc, and drove toward home. He was very weary. "I hope," he said to himself, "nobody breaks a leg or has a baby tonight."

By Norman A. Brittin

SPRING WIND

Buffeting boxer, whirligig flail of fists,
The wind drives at the land, beating, assailing, encircling.

Its deep pour streams from the cold-brimmed canyon,
Swoops in a smooth, declivitous volplane down on the sun-bright
    roofs;
With whirl and pounce captures the flying wash on the line,
Clips and laughs it into a foolish, loose-jointed jig;
Teeters the brown bundle of branches the poplar balances;
Pummels the door in a tantrum, races and rumples the scooting dog.

This is the brawny day-wind, a rowdy with shining teeth.

But at night the wind is a sneak, is a facelessness at the window,
A wistful, uneasy migrant, sifting through street and alley.
What man-work above ground, what citadel stony can stand,
    unheeding
His tentative finger, his whisper under the sills?

SMOKE ON THE SNOW

I

HAM WARDLE poked the logs in the grate and watched the shower-
ing wood sparks bloom and fly into the black maw of the chimney.
He threw a fresh pine log on the embers and jockeyed it into position with the poker. Then he stood up to his full height and
stretched. He turned and winked at his wife, who sat sewing in
the rocker before the fireplace.

"Sure is comfortable inside on a night like this," he said. She
nodded gravely and smiled at him.

Ham flexed his muscles by bending his thick-palmed hands at the
wrists, working his arms at the elbows and breathing deeply. The
fire blazing up with little reports seemed to impart its own cheer
to him, and he danced a little clumsy jig.

"How you do go on for a man of your age," his wife said. Her
gray eyes regarded him tolerantly; she earnestly believed that, except for Ham's unpredictable impulses and enthusiasms, he was
the finest man she knew.

"I can't help it, can I," he said, "if I feel good? Believe me, I'm
glad I don't have to be out on a night like this."

"Is it still snowing?"

"Nope, it's cleared off, and the moon's shining and it's pretty out,
like—well, I'll tell you what it reminds me of. Remember those
old movies we used to see years ago, how they'd have everything
green when they wanted to indicate it was night? Well, that's how

the snow looks tonight—everything clearcut and distinct, but a different strange color."

"If I wasn't so comfortable I'd get up and look."

Ham shrugged and reached for his pipe on the mantel. As he filled it, he looked about the room, and his solid face, the color of an Indian's to just above his eyebrows and from there to his strong short gray hair as white as a woman's arm, assumed a wholly contented expression. He thought of his sons, both of them married and doing well, and of his daughter who had gone to work in the town, and of his wife who certainly gave him as much as he was entitled to. She kept his feet solidly on the earth, and that's where a farmer's feet belong. His eyes turned and contemplated her with a quiet and admiring glance, and she looked up from her sewing and saw it.

"What are you thinking about, Ham?" Miranda asked.

"Nothing," he said, tamping the heel of hot ash deeper into the pipe's bowl with a thick forefinger. "I was just thinking that it's mighty comfortable inside tonight."

"Yes, it is," she said.

Her words left the room silent save for the hissing of the log and the occasional report of a bursting resin pocket. But before Ham's pipe was a third smoked down both of them turned an ear toward the door: the crunch of heavy footsteps, screeching in the frozen snow, announced a visitor, and Ham arose regretfully and went to the door.

He admitted Jack Vowle, their nearest neighbor, and invited him to stand up to the fire and thaw out. Jack was a reedy-thin man, tall and spare, and one of his eyes was permanently closed from an accident with a hayfork years ago.

"Ham," he said as he put out his hands to the hearth and fixed his good eye strangely on his friend, "you been listenin' to the radio?"

Ham shook his head. "Miranda and me have been sitting here just enjoying our own company. Why, what's on the radio?"

"You ain't heard about the plane crash then?"

"No!"

"Well, a plane crashed right near here, Ham."

Miranda put down her sewing. She looked intently at Jack Vowle.

"Go on," Ham said.

"That's right," Jack said. "I heard it on the radio. They claim it's up on the Peak or somewheres near it."

"When did it happen?"

"This morning, I guess. They've seen flares tonight on the Peak. That's what I heard on the radio."

"They aren't all dead then," said Ham.

"Figure some of 'em must be alive, and why I come over, Ham: they said they had reports Captain Veritt was aboard."

"No!"

Ham went quickly to the set that had a sweet potato plant in a bowl on the top and flicked the switch. "The poor devil," he said. "That's terrible."

"My, that's too bad," Miranda said. She had dropped the sewing in her lap.

"You see, they was flying too low is the only way they can figure it out, and pancaked onto the Peak somehow," Jack said. "I knew you'd wanta hear, Ham. You always paid particular attention to what this Captain Veritt was doin'."

Ham fussed with the dial until the music of an orchestra blared into the room.

"I guess they'll give more reports," Jack said. "What do you think of it, Ham; we never had a plane crack up this near."

"What kind of a plane was it?" Ham asked.

"One them big transports."

"Are you sure about Veritt, Jack?" Ham asked. "I wouldn't doubt it, he's always flying. I suppose he was a passenger."

"I suppose. They said there was nine people aboard."

"They'll freeze to death if any of them are alive," Miranda said.

Ham looked at her with remote eyes. "Did you say flares?" he said to Jack.

Jack nodded.

Ham began to button the loose sweater he was wearing. He looked at Jack with the same remote expression. Miranda watched with dread as Ham buttoned his sweater tightly about his neck.

"I'm going out a minute," he said. "Jack, let's take a look at the Peak."

Jack didn't answer; he glanced uneasily at Miranda and was afraid to speak. Ham avoided his wife's eyes.

"Well, are you coming?" he said, and went to get his hat and coat.

"I—I just thought I'd come over and tell you folks," Jack said lamely. "I——"

Miranda started to sew again and she did not speak.

"Come on, Jack," Ham said, heaving into his mackinaw.

They walked away from the house with ringing footsteps in the hard snow until they could see the high shoulder of Granite Peak standing up in relief forty miles away. The night was moonless now and sharp with a clean wind blowing that was like a knife in the face. They looked up to the Peak of massive craggy granite and snow limned against the blue night haze, and stood still for a moment.

"My God, Jack," Ham said. He gazed steadfastly as if he expected to see a flare rise from off that bold white face.

They watched for some time but nothing happened. At the uttermost top the wind blew the snow off the Peak in a constant spume that looked like cloud. The darker bases on riven rock, black ravines in the ribbed face, were shadowed in mystery. Timbered slopes and lower-lying farms at the foot of the Peak also were bleakly remote in the night, veiled in distance and zero cold.

Jack flapped his arms and stomped his feet. "Ain't much hope for 'em, Ham."

"Nephi Larsen once climbed Granite Peak," Ham said.

"Don't I know it! Not in the dead a winter, though."

"It's always winter up there," Ham said. "Well, let's go in and see what the radio says."

II

A few hours later, about five in the morning, Ham made up his mind. The night-long reports showed there was hope. He backed the car out of the garage and drove to Nephi Larsen's shack on

Bitter Creek. Nephi was drying muskrat skins in the odorous warmth of his cabin, and not even exhibiting surprise at the early call, the man as always was pleased to see him and awkwardly hospitable; but Ham put all that aside. He said, "Nephi, could you climb Granite Peak?"

"Ay did," the Swede answered steadily. "Ay might could again."

Ham explained the circumstances that led him to ask, adding, "Would you go with me if I asked you?"

"Ay would go," Nephi Larsen said simply.

They began to talk about Nephi's traps and discussed the winter's catch. Again Ham was humble before this good man's unseeking devotion to him. The small matter of having lent a little money hardly justified the request of risking life; but without some sense of dedication the search could not be undertaken.

As he drove home he wondered if, in some less articulately realized way, Nephi's feeling paralleled his for Jim Veritt, if on their different levels the loyalties and aspirations of men did not generally coincide. Yet that was hardly the situation; it approximated more nearly the condition in which envy and self-seeking have fallen away and love alone remains. Ham marveled to think that Nephi might regard him in such a way as to justify these lofty suppositions. As he drove along the highway hardpacked with snow in the gray morning he considered what he would need for the journey.

III

"It's foolhardy nonsense," Miranda said. She went right on making the food packs.

"I can't help it," Ham said. "This is something a man has to do."

His wife went ahead with the preparations, and Ham avoided further discussion. He was uncomfortable in her disapproval, but he knew that nothing she could say would dissuade him. She evidently knew it too because she said nothing more.

"Well," Ham said, "take care of the place. I won't be gone any more than if it was a fishing trip."

"All right," Miranda said. Ham got into the car and drove off quickly without looking back.

Nephi Larsen was ready. He gathered up his pack and climbed in beside Ham. They spoke little; but Ham felt a strange exhilaration. He did not even think of what he might find but instead turned to old intimations of the real Jim Veritt, the shining figure out of his youth. He did not think of Jim as a man of his own age at all. The years were stripped from this image of incorruptible young manhood. Jim (or the memory of him) recalled his own blameless youth again, for they had been fresh in the world together, at school and later in the close brotherhood and personal revelation under fire in France. To him, Jim Veritt had been incomparably the newly-minted coin of young manhood in those days. He had always accomplished what he had set out to do; the man was a living epitome of integrity. The miracle of Veritt was that he had already become a legend, known by the world for his exploits of daring and for his inviolate honesty. There had been something about an airman which took its quality from the medium of the air itself and was lonely, austere and unalterably faithful.

Yet in reality little was known of Veritt as an individual. He was personally ubiquitous at the same time that he appeared to be inaccessible. He tried to keep his whereabouts unknown, and perhaps for that reason received more than his share of publicity.

Of all the men he had ever met, Ham loved Veritt best, bound in the memory of a youthful friendship stronger than most men know. The man was a wonder, and besides having become legendary for the feats he had accomplished was personally an enigma to all. Those who had come to know him in the days since he had achieved fame could not claim to understand him; their knowledge was superficial or even false. The only way you knew a man like Veritt was by the good fortune of meeting under circumstances that come seldom in a lifetime. When he read accounts of Veritt's life and peculiarities, Ham always smiled. How foolish it was to suppose that a few encounters with such a man could expose his real being. That that being could be extinguished was unthinkable; Ham could not believe in such a negation of the faith he had in the man or his legend.

Ham stopped the car in a familiar recess among pines at the Upper Forks of Bitter Creek. Nephi Larsen pointed to the mountain. "That's where ve go," he said.

And now, from where they stood, the Peak was no longer simply a distant immensity; Ham regarded the vast jagged mountain before them with a quailing heart, for now that he was close it seemed less accessible than ever. He could see that enormous tiers of riven rock piled one upon another composed this giant peak and that each stage upward would constitute the equivalent of an Alpine climb. From a distance the Peak seemed one fabulous rugged mass; the nearer view showed it to be a heaping of minor masses each towering like Himalayas until the final upflung tier seemed to sweep the ceiling of the sky itself.

Ham wetted his lips, and his eyes stung with cold as he remarked, "Up there, there won't be any secrets. If they are there, nothing on earth can hide them."

The morning was sunless. Larsen found green boughs to lay the base for a fire, and he observed cryptically that the day would be very cold. "But ve warm up," he added, preparing to make coffee from melted snow in his canteen.

IV

Conviction and the contemplative habit of mind do not often go hand in hand, Ham thought, as about noon when the sun was a dull eye in the center of the gray heavens he and Larsen sat facing each other across the fire. He regarded the Swede contemplatively; the man was iron or he was stone with its eternal insentience. Whatever he was, he inspired in Ham chiefly a wondering awe. Yet this rocklike stability was no good at all uninformed with intent.

"Let's get started," he said.

"Yep, ve ban get on now," Nephi agreed.

They kicked out the fire. Larsen shouldered the duffle and would not relinquish any part of it, saying that he was used to this kind of work and that Ham should conserve his strength for the tough going ahead. They set their snowshoes to the soft snow with splaying feet outward to climb the hill.

The snowy incline seemed intent upon vanquishing them, for their progress was continually retarded by small avalanches of snow. Soft and powdery the snow would rush down upon them from two or three yards ahead in a flurry that buried them to their knees. Floundering out of the slide, another swooping fleecy torrent would descend upon them. In two hours they had gone only a few dozen rods, and the exertion brought sweat steaming to their faces, soaking their underclothing so that Larsen shook his head and looked grave.

"No good ve sweat," he said. "Better slow down some."

Ham realized that with the approach of evening and sub-zero temperatures, wet clothing would be dangerous. "We've got to climb. What can we do?"

"Better slow down some," Nephi said.

As Ham toiled along in Larsen's wake he was amazed at the man's indefatigability. He began to think of Nephi as an individual too. Most people saw in him the possessor of no worthy attributes whatever. Ham's memory of Nephi's final falling out with society was fresh; and it was through his good offices alone that Nephi now walked the land a free man. If he hadn't paid Nephi's debts, land-grabbing swindlers would have had him behind bars. That slow-witted trustful Swede had no attributes that would be advantageous in society.

Ham climbed slowly behind the tireless man, until it seemed that he had been doing nothing else all his life. The snow surrounding them created a hushed world inimically external. A hundred times Ham cursed the sifting powdery slides, and he cried out to the Swede against the snow, but the man only grunted and kept on silently digging his way upward.

"If you don't let me carry some of that duffle," Ham shouted, "I'm not coming any farther."

Larsen then let some of the pack come sliding down, and Ham shouldered it without speaking.

As darkness spread on the mountains Ham noticed a different quality in Nephi's methodical upward movement. The man's exertions were less sure; several times Larsen slipped and came swooping back upon Ham, tearing through the trajectory of snow like a bullet and stopping short. They saw a promontory of ice-encrusted rock and toiled slowly to it. Leveling off a harboring ridge, they were able to forage a few twisted faggots of scrub brush under the sheltered side of the rock. Ham built a fire, taking half an hour at the task so that no scrap of wood was wasted. They settled down to rest and eat and drink smoking hot coffee.

It was always difficult to make conversation with the Swede; but Ham felt no real need to talk. In this hour of exhaustion no words could amplify the creature identity he felt with Nephi. They nodded by the fire, wrapped in every inch of bedding they had.

The fire lasted only an hour, and before the heat was entirely dissipated Ham noticed the growing cold. He spoke of it to Nephi, but the Swede only shrugged and grunted. Ham looked down into the valley and saw a few winking lights, dim and wavering as fireflies. He could not tell whether they came from his ranch.

As soon as the fire went out they got to their feet and started moving. The cold was so intense that inaction had already numbed their hands and feet. It was then about midnight and Nephi said they were probably one-third of the way up. Ham asked about Nephi's former climb, but the Swede did not seem to want to talk about it. So Ham's mind reverted to what might be above. Jim Veritt is alive, he thought, that's all that is important. I've got to get him out. Other thoughts took shape in his mind; he wondered what Miranda was doing; but strangely all his past life, at this moment, seemed remote and unimportant. He knew that he might not return to it, and somehow his apprehension of it seemed anaesthetized. He wondered what was passing in Nephi's brain. Nephi was a good man; he would come much nearer to attaining grace than most. His faith, if it was not founded on reliable precepts, was buttressed by works. The simple soul, Ham thought as he struggled wearily along, may find the answer where more complex minds become lost and discouraged and fail when the real trial is set.

V

The character of the snow changed quite abruptly. Instead of the powdery fine and maddeningly unstable texture underfoot it became crusted and firm where the wind had molded it in shards and sculptured hummocks against the granite outcroppings. The going was suddenly easier and they made better time.

The night cold increased. The prickling sensation of frozen moisture in his nose caused Ham continually to snort and break away the ice. Soon however that slight pressure was insufficient, and presently a muzzle of ice was attached to his nostrils. In attempting to break off the encrustation he brushed the skin of his nose and found that there was no sensation in his face.

They clambered over jutting crags and around forms of hardened snow. The wind's keen edge cut through the layers of clothing. Ham shivered and at the same time felt small rivulets of perspiration trickle from his armpits. Looking up now, he could see the grand turrets of the Peak swimming in the moonless misty sky.

Nephi Larsen was toiling ahead of him. Ham heard a cracking report, sharp and smart as a pistol shot. He glanced ahead and his eyes widened in horror as the whole icy side of the mountain began to slip with a tearing savage thunder slowly, and with increasing speed avalanched upon Nephi Larsen.

He stared stupidly; he could not believe his eyes; what was on their retina had been wiped off. The world whirled in darkness. He began to call Nephi's name. He moved ahead in the hampering snow, shouting. He flailed the snow with his duffle bag and yelled until he was hoarse.

The man was gone. He was snuffed out. It was Ham's responsibility alone. He was to blame. He had sent the Swede hurtling to his death as surely as if the plot had arisen in his brain. He slumped to a sitting position, supported by the waistdeep snow. And Larsen had climbed the Peak once in his life. He had climbed it once, and perhaps once was all that was permitted.

After a while Ham began to move on. The rousing of his blood awakened the faculty of reason again. He had to move, he knew, or the thread of the whole fabric might unravel and whip away into space. He clutched frantically at that fraying thread. Without glancing into the jumbled tomb of snow, he began to circle the slide and struggle stubbornly, zigzagging a course up the face of the mountain.

VI

At first his mind refused to understand the significance of what his eyes saw. In the fury of his climb his memory and his thoughts were welded in an invincible confusion: there was no path in the maze. Then he saw the smoke like a veil across the snow. He looked into the issuing wind and attacked the final immense area above with redoubled energy, flogging himself to action, tearing at the ledges of granite and ice, flinging off his mittens in impatient frenzy to make his grip more effective, and finding too late that the moment his hands made contact with air they lost sensation and were as wood. He retraced his steps thirty feet where the mittens had lodged. He beat his hands until circulation was re-established and began the ascent again.

Immemorially he had been flinging himself against this granite face. The cold and the eternal upward struggle were a blind antagonist that he had fought forever. He attacked the broad cliff unaware of time or danger, inching up the barrier of infinite ice.

And then, with a suddenness that wrenched reason, he stumbled over the last ridge and half dead plunged to his knees, his eyes staring up an incline to a V-shaped embrasure of rock. In the recess of this blind debris-strewn alley, like a miracle past belief, lay the shining aluminum hulk of the lost plane. Out of a hole in the crumpled cabin, smoke drifted into the early morning air.

Ham staggered to his feet, shaking with a violence that made standing unthinkable effort. He glanced back along his path and saw incalculably down, across miles of hardship, the valley as remote as another planet. He took a few steps. His legs buckled and threw him into the snow. Then he began to crawl on all fours toward the plane.

Through his exhausted brain passed a swift procession of images; he could see Veritt the man in a thousand old attitudes; he began to call Veritt's name. He pawed the snow with desperation and imagined that he was winging toward the aluminum shell with splendid haste. But he only crept forward by inches, his eyes half shut and encrusted with ice.

In time he scrabbled himself by brute movement to the plane. His voice had failed and though he imagined himself to be uttering words of salvation, he managed only to croak hoarsely and snuffle against the frozen wall of metal. That, however, was enough; in a moment the door swung out with frail hesitancy, as if a vagrant wind had blown it open.

His eyes beheld a face in the aperture, and he mumbled through the fringe of frozen spittle stuck to his mouth. He spoke Veritt's name with a vast urbanity no shock could surprise. The face withdrew, and as if in a dream Ham found himself inside the smoke-filled compartment. He could take in only by degrees the unimaginable litter, the several bodies reclining in stricken postures about the cabin, some dead for days. He fought to pierce the shadows that oppressed his mind, and he looked for Jim Veritt.

He crawled near the stove made from a ripped oil tin and shut his eyes tiredly.

"You're too late," a voice cackled. Ham looked into the mad face he had seen at the door.

"Where is Captain Veritt?" Ham croaked.

The man did not answer but slumped into a cocoon of blankets.

"Where is Jim Veritt?" Ham asked more firmly.

The eyes of the survivor opened. "Are you alone?" the sepulchral voice asked.

Ham said, "Is he dead?"

"They're all dead. You're too late."

Ham rubbed his frozen cheeks and they burned like fire. That was serious, he thought, but that thought was only a faint contrapuntal theme against the torrent of feeling that began to mount in him.

"You dirty bastard!" he said. "What have you done with him? Where is he? Damn you, tell me!"

The wretch turned bulging eyes on him. "Who?"

"Jim Veritt, you son of a bitch."

"I don't know him," the man said without interest.

Ham felt the rage within him mount like upheaving lava, and the heat seemed to burst out like flame through the pores of his beating face as he pawed his cheeks to quench the blaze. He had been betrayed by these scoundrels; there was no goal; and the world had dissolved behind him. He cursed the dying man, and the fire spread to his feet and hands until he could not bear it.

The voice from the blankets said weakly, "Veritt? That's funny! What did you come here for? You can't help us; you can't help yourself."

Ham looked dully at the man. He sat quietly, and his eyes grew dim and indifferent. Sun entered the smoky cabin, but its light made no impression on Ham's mind. Outside the bright free wind blew cold, silent with snow spume on Granite Peak.

SHERREL

I DO NOT know whether I can do this thing or not. Maybe it is just a thought, maybe I just think it is necessary to do it. I mean about the name. I have thought about it a lot though and it keeps urging at me. It is not easy to understand. But I must try to understand and explain it.

You see, I actually did have a brother. People sometimes asked me, Are you the only boy in the family? and I've said, Yes. This wasn't a lie wholly. I was the first born in my family. But there were others, two others. One died in long clothes. We have his picture at home. The other was named Sherrel.

It is easy to remember him. My mother had us photographed together, for instance. And one especial print was transferred onto little smooth discs the size of a saucer. The discs fit into small twisted wire easels and my brother and I used to sit on the easel like that on my mother's bureau in the bedroom. He was, as I said, younger than I. This is important. The neighbors used to say, It's the difference in their ages. They tried to explain in that way why I was so mean. And you can see the difference clearly enough on the picture discs. We both stood by the photographer's chair, a plush chair. But I was up to the top of it. My brother's hand rested on the arm. It looks pretty small to me now because I'm twice as old as I was then. We both wore black velvet tam-o'-shanters and dark red velvet coats and pants. My mouth was a little open, too, looking at the photographer. I did not touch my brother. He had

362

one hand, which was very small, on the chair, and the other one had hold of me. His hair was lighter than mine and softer and his eyes wider and bluer. He had a small mouth like a flower and it was smiling. He was a beautiful child. This was the brother I killed.

I am not telling you about a melodrama. I won't be arrested and hanged. I did not kill him yesterday. It was a long time ago, in fact, and I do not remember it all the time, only sometimes when something suggests the way I was then or when some one asks, Have you any other brothers? And I say, No. And here too in this other town at this school except for a girl I know I am quite alone in certain ways and in the winter as now I have seen any number of things to remind me. There is, for example, an epidemic of smallpox here and instead of smooth fast automobile hearses they still have funeral carriages that drag along slowly through the streets. Only once have I ridden in such a carriage. And that was then.

There are some things difficult to remember out of childhood. I do not remember when my brother was born. There was not so much difference then. Only four years before, I had been born. But I remember clearly when I was nine. My brother then was five. And we were two in the family. But I was the first.

Do you know how this is? Nine and five? Well, nine is somebody. Five is still curls. At nine I have seen something of the world. What have you seen at five? Go on, you can't come with us! Go on back to the house! We're going down to the store. You'll get run over. Go on, you can't play with us. You ain't big enough. Go on, grow up some before you come tagging around after us. Who asked you along? Beat it! I know how that is. I said all that, more brutally even. He didn't say anything. He didn't cry or whine or crab. I probably would have. He stopped following simply and stood there. And then we ran off. He stood alone. Sometimes I found him other places alone, sitting still in a corner thinking quietly about something. I am always a little puzzled now I am older. I have talked it over with others. He would have been important. . . . But at nine one is a weed, growing wild. Five is still in the hothouse.

We lived near the sandhills. It wasn't until several years later that I really got into the hills exploring them with a cousin of my own age. Sherrel never did get there. And there was a great liking in both of us for the hills, his maybe different from mine. I often found him sitting dreaming, looking at them. But one day late in the spring the hills in a way came down to our house. A cloudburst drenched them, rolling down soft sand, cutting great ditches in the road in front of our place. We weren't long in discovering that, I'll tell you. When Sherrel wandered out of the kitchen the ditch was full of us kids. It was a peach of a ditch as high as our heads, gnawed with caves and dangers.

I started the discoveries. There's some hole, I yelled. And down I had gone, doing what the others wanted to do, the first to absorb their wishes. Then they followed, yelling too. Sherrel, I suppose, could hear my voice coming up out of the ground. He came over to the ditch and looked down, standing alone above us. Go on back, I shouted, you'll fall in. He moved away. I paid no more attention then to him and the rest of us ran racing, hiding, searching, together in the wash.

And then, separated from the others for a moment or so, I noticed something odd about my hands. Hey, kids, I cried, lookee! Look at my hands! They looked. They stood back in wonderment. They looked at their own hands. No, they couldn't, they said. It was something funny. Look what Martin can do! Lookee, he can peel off his hands! It was true, something had happened to my hands. I took hold and pulled off long shreds of skin. I amazed them all. They stood astounded.

Let me see, said somebody. It was Sherrel.

Say, I yelled, didn't I say not to come down here? You ain't big enough to be in this here ditch. Let me see your hands, he said. The kids were all looking at me. I'll let you see, all right! I said. He stood his ground and didn't go. That makes me mad, I felt. No, I said. I took him by the shoulder and talked straight in his face, hard. How many times do I have to tell you to get out of this ditch! He turned around and walked up the gorge to a shallower spot and climbed slowly out.

A day or so later Sherrel stayed in bed. There's something the matter with him, my mother said. She didn't know what. Then he took a high fever, they said, and was delirious. I thought it was strange about delirious. Sherrel's eyes were shut and he looked as if he was sleeping but he was talking without any sense. We'll have to have a doctor, my mother said. And that afternoon the doctor came to our house, wiping his feet at the door and entering with a serious look. Let's see the other young fellow, he said. Anything wrong with him? He had a little sore throat, my mother said, but he's all right. He looked down my throat. Look at my hands, I said, ain't they funny?

What I thought, he said.

The same afternoon a man from down town came and nailed up a yellow flag. It was a cloth sign saying, black on orange, Scarlet Fever. I couldn't go out of the yard. That's sure tough, the kids said, peering through the pickets. I even had to keep back from the fence, too. It was catching.

I sat on the steps fronting north from our bare two-room brick house and looked at the hills. I had had the Scarlet Fever and hadn't even known it. Why, my mother said, he was playing around all the time. Why, he was out there playing in the ditch with all those children. That's bad, said the doctor. But my brother was worse. He had it good.

I remember the windows in the front room were darkened and my mother never went to bed. She never took her clothes off. And my father didn't go to work. My aunt came to the fence with a bag of oranges and bananas. How is he? she asked. If he isn't any better Dr. Anderson says he'd better have a consultation, said my mother. How is Dr. Anderson? asked my aunt. He is the best doctor in town, my mother said.

I sat in the sun all tired now and weak. But I wasn't sick. I was big and nine.

I remember the consultation. There were four doctors in the kitchen standing around and talking low and sitting down and getting up. I could see in from outside. My mother was nervous and walking around too and sat down and then got up. They were waiting for something definite they spoke of that I could not understand. It was the Crisis. I asked what it was, and my mother had said, Sherrel will get better then. I didn't know what a Crisis would be like and I opened the door slowly and got into the house quietly past the doctors.

My father and mother were in the front room by the bed where Sherrel lay. He was still and wasn't talking deliriously. And then my mother, who was standing by him with my father waiting, suddenly cried terribly for a minute or so, and then she took hold of my father and pulled him down by the bed to the floor. I didn't know what was happening. I was frightened, too. Pray, she sobbed. Pray, if you never prayed before. Oh, God, she began . . . and she was crying more and more. My father was kneeling heavily and strangely in a big dark bulk. He put his arm around my mother. There, there, he said. I never saw them like that before. My father is English, my mother is German. I did not think about that though then. I thought, I am scared; this is all different, and dark. I stood in the doorway, too frightened to move.

Come in, Martin, my mother suddenly cried out to me. Come in to your brother. Come here with us. I came over, and there we were all kneeling down together.

Do you want your brother to die? she asked. No, I said. I was frightened at her, at the strange heavy silence on my father, and my brother even. Go and look at him, she told me.

I got up and looked at my brother's white face. It was like a face of ivory with pale lips. I looked hard. He was different too. My mother is looking at me terribly. Kiss him. I bent over and touched his face. His lips opened with a quiet breath, like a little flower bursting on my cheek.

The Crisis came and passed. It came while we were in the room there. My mother could not wait. She went to the bed, trying to wake my brother. Look, Sherrel, she whispered, we are going to get you the nice pearl-handled pocketknife tomorrow. You won't have to wait till Christmas. Tomorrow. You just get well, now. Sherrel! Do you hear me, Sherrel?

Or, he can have mine, I thought.

But he didn't hear us. He didn't hear anybody. Then my mother went to sleep suddenly, it seemed, and drooped down by the bed and they put her in the other room on a couch.

I stood in the dark by a curtain when the doctors came in. Too bad, said Dr. Anderson. He leaned over my brother. Remarkable head, said one of the others. Isn't it! spoke up another one. Artist's

head, said the one with the beard. Yes . . . Then the doctors
walked out together into the room where my mother was and in a
little while they all left the house.

A few days later there were the strange preparations for the
funeral. I don't want to dwell on the funeral. That is not the point.
But we rode in a carriage shut in by ourselves, still quarantined,
the others following slowly behind us. I remember we passed the
Watsons' place. They were standing at the gate, the family, staring
stupidly at the procession as the horse carriages jogged down the
hilly street rolling off to the cemetery.

That is all strange, I thought, riding along past the Watsons'
house in a carriage like this. My mother and my father and myself.
I was taken up with the thought and looked back out of the carriage
window now and then at the carriages behind me. My mother
pulled me back to sit up straight. My mother's face was drawn and
tired and she was crying. My father's eyes had tears in them too.
I could not cry. I thought, I ought to cry. How can I cry? I am not
hurt in any place where I can feel. I squeezed into the corner of the
carriage opposite them, pressing up against one hand hard to make
it hurt. It turned numb and pained, but not in a crying way. You
cry easy differently, I thought. Onions, for instance, make you cry.
Would it have been a trick, I thought, or right and honest if I had
put an onion in my handkerchief, no one seeing me, and then
smelt it now and then in the curtained shadows of the carriage. I
would have cried then. I wanted to cry. But all I could think was,
Sherrel was a queer kid. Were we brothers sure enough? Am I
anybody's brother? Why don't I cry? . . .

You see, he would sit in a corner quiet and fraily beautiful. I
was nine and active. It's the difference in their ages. Maybe so.
There were the Elwell brothers, now. They were twins. They had a
carpenter's shop. It was a peach of a shop down in the cellar and
they worked together great, making book-ends and rabbit hutches
and things like that.

I gave him that sickness. I knew that. That killed him. That is
why my brother is dead. But I am trying to remember, to clear
things up. I am trying to remember if I thought that then. I remember I thought, It's funny just he got it. Why not Leona Eads, Ed

or Billy Simons? They touched my hands. I wondered if I hadn't forced my sickness on my brother out of hatred for him, out of my own peculiar older-brother hatred. Did I slap him, maybe strike him in the face with my peeling hand? Perhaps I did. I wondered over this for many weeks now and then. I'm not even sure now. I might have. It's funny how mean, you see, a person can be. I've thought of that. I've got a girl. I've talked things over with her, not everything, but generally you know. She doesn't like meanness either. I remember when I was about twelve my sister was just coming along then. She was about two and I had to tend her occasionally. I didn't like it. Once my mother said to me, Do you want your little sister to die too? Well, no, I said. She might even have said, Do you want to kill your little sister too? Maybe this was it, because I asked myself that a lot later, trying to be better. I said, Do you want to kill your sister too? No, I said.

I didn't either. But I remembered what I'd said when she was born. I said, There's enough in this family already. But I didn't want to kill her. Still I had killed my brother. I had killed Sherrel. Not only by giving him sickness. But by meanness.

This is how I figure it now. I killed my brother by meanness. And it is too bad. I wouldn't do it now. I am not that way. I could have got him a job here in this other town where I am now after he got out of school. I'll be out of school here pretty soon. I'm eighteen next week. Then I'll go on a paper where I've got a stand-in. I'd have said, Now you keep on at school and read a lot of good things, good books, you know, poetry and good things and learning how to write. You've got good stuff in you, I can tell. You're going to be an artist. So am I. We'll be two artists, brothers, maybe different, but we can help each other. You've got poetic style, and I've got a stronger style. I see things more as they are. I'm a little tougher. I can digest more. But that's all right. When I get going, I'll help you. You've got fine things in you. I'll help you bring them out.

That's the kind of person he would have been. He would have been an artist. There's nothing any bigger than that. Nothing finer. It's the best, in a holy way. It has to be in you first. It hides sometimes and doesn't get a chance to come out where people are.

I've talked that over with people, with that girl I spoke of. I want to be an artist. A writer. I can see back from where I am, though. I've been pretty mean, pretty contemptible. It's funny to look back like that and see yourself in old pictures and things. It's hard to think you had the same name, even.

And that's what I'm puzzling over now. There's nothing wrong with my name, actually. Mark. Mark Stowe. It was first Martin. It was even Martin Tilton Stowe. It made me feel surer, quicker, stronger.

But even that doesn't quite go. It doesn't all fit. I'm not all blunt, like that. Mark. Mark Stowe. I've got other things. I've written poems, even, and I wouldn't kiss a girl hard. I know how my brother was. He would have been like that too, only a lot more.

And, you know, about the name . . . My folks are getting along now. Sisters don't count, the way I mean, that is. I'm the only boy in the family. And I've been thinking, what if I should write a poem, a long, good one—here I am, alive and everything—and sign it not Mark Stowe but well, Sherrel Stowe? Do you see what I mean? And then by and by there would be another poem, and after awhile I would just go ahead and use it right along. Can you understand that? How I would be more him too, then—Sherrel?

CONCLUSIONS

Did you know, now these long nights are coming,
That we're picking up our talks where they stopped **last year**
When you went East and I stayed on at the drumming
Village, hoping next fall would find you here?

Your knock just after sunset was as natural as some
Before, almost expected, like a thing you've waited
For and then forgotten until suddenly it's come
Without excitement, as if that's what it had hated.

I thought you'd know that by now no distance counts.
You remember our autumn walks through the seeding mallow,
And how by the river you made the flat rocks bounce
While I waded for shells in the ford where the water was shallow?

And once how we climbed too far over hills unnumbered
And darkness sank, rose-gray from above and below
The warm brown met it from the plain that the sun had summered?
We stretched by a fern that scarcely had room to grow:

But it clung to its lifetime niche in the shallow soil,
And we wondered at its contentment with tired minds.
You said that the striving for goals brings only toil—
It's the thing one is looking for that he never finds.

I thought, as these memories tottered like loosening rocks,
If you helped we might find some stronger brace
Against a landslide than this shale of a past that mocks
The both of us building our paths from this slippery place.

So it's not for your love that you come now. Nor proximity, sure;
Settled for sure: you're there and I'm here. And to show
How little distance and time mean, this minute from more
Time than is measured is all time for what I must know.

And for space: well, you're here and it's night—for my purpose.
You're really a continent off though. And once when you were here
I even wondered if you were, the way a nervous
Distance crept in your eyes at the sound of a bird near.

But whether you've thought these things or know what I mean
Is something I can hardly tell. That's why these September
Conversations appear suddenly like a scene
From an old play whose end I can't remember.

And that's proof that space means nothing, the way you always
Get here when the questions come. Still, to be wary,
The paradox is that the thousand or so miles raised
The questions, rather, they made answers necessary.

That's the reason for our talks now. Thoughts may be timeless,
But in the endurance of a year like last, one must abandon
The eternal for a single speckle of real in the rimeless
Stretch: all heaven for a little space to stand in.

I can imagine people crushing through the streets, and you
To your room with no one in it, and hurrying weeks
Untasted except in a dreaming that's only true
At times like this when an almost-lost voice speaks.

You wouldn't have noticed the newsboy at the office entrance,
Nor talked to the children playing from door to door,

But watched the lighted houses for some token of acceptance,
Remembering someone waited once before.

The house that we both remember was a patched-up thing.
In the mellow settling, of twilight, as we passed, I asked:
Will our house be kept pretty like this newer wing?
And you knew at once the meaning I had masked.

I don't know what part of us lasts or what dies,
Or what part of you is gone through the door
That you threw wide open on our love, but I surmise
It's something that tears or apologies can't restore.

So your talk about necessity has no more use
Than to say that you tried to catch quicksilver in a net.
You didn't love her? Well, that's no excuse.
And still love me? Then how did you forget?

Because it's midnight now you'd better go.
We needed to settle these things. Now we'll have no worry
Like people who go on hoping and never know
That they're living their feelings on past the end of the story.

By Ray B. West Jr.

THE BLUE SPRING

HE STOOD for a moment looking down over the tops of the willows into the cool blue of the water. He could see the silver shadows of the sunfish darting like arrows through the shallows near the bank. He arced a bright, wild-rose berry into the pool, saw one of the fish streak toward it, hold it for a moment in his mouth, and then like a surprised child spit it out again. The berry descended slowly as the fish slipped quietly into deep water. The ripples faded, and the surface became smooth and unbroken as glass.

He stood back and surveyed the willow cave. That was what he had named it during the beet-thinning season when he had lain in its shade at noon. He remembered its cool dampness against his muscles. He had lain here during midsummer too, when he had come down to help his uncle get in the hay. He had been too young to use a fork—that is, regularly to pitch the hay—but he had tromped and so had learned to build a load, forming it gradually away from the top of the rack.

There was a little fear with the pleasure he felt now in surveying the cave. The place was nothing but a niche his uncle had cut into the rows of willows in such a way that the bowed stalks formed an umbrella from the sun. There were still scraps of waxed paper scattered about the edges, and when he bent over to pick them up, he saw that there were even a few hardened scraps of breadcrust that the birds had missed.

When he had cleaned up, tidied as carefully as a housewife, he
walked out into the alfalfa patch and pulled several armfuls. He
spread them evenly over the hardpacked dirt until the whole space
was covered. Then he lay down and tested it. The stalks were soft
and leafy—even though the hay was in its third crop—and he
sniffed the bitter fragrance of the juices as his body pressed them.
His limbs were like water as he imagined Jamie with him. He remembered what Harry and Stew Pendleton had told him.

"She likes you, Kit. You could do it easy. Just ask her to go bike
riding. I done it with Megs Brodie."

He thought of the things Harry had told him about Megs, and
he tasted the thought of it, a bitter pleasure, full of the knowledge
of what his father and mother would say if they knew. What his
uncle would say, or his teacher. He was tempted to give it up, but
the idea had taken hold of him, and he knew he couldn't. He'd
already asked her to go riding with him on Saturday, and she had
said she would. She would have her mother fix a lunch for them,
she had said, and he had told her, almost afraid to look her in the
face, that he would call by at ten-thirty.

Mrs. Merriwether came to the door when he jangled the bell on
his handlebars.

"Jamie's not quite ready yet," she said, standing in the door and
wiping her hands on her apron. "Won't you come in?"

Kit said, no, he'd wait there. Mrs. Merriwether looked at him
closely, and he was afraid for a moment that he had spoiled everything. He leaned his bike against the fence and stepped inside the
picket gate.

"I'll sit here," he said.

There was just a dirt path leading from the gate to Jamie's front
door, and it had a little irrigation ditch running down the side of it
and around to the vegetable garden. He sat with his feet in the
dry ditch and poked between his knees at a pile of dry mud that
had been used for a dam.

"Looks like a hot day," Mrs. Merriwether commented. "I hope
Jamie don't get burnt."

He pretended to look at the sky. It was hot, probably the last
hot day of the summer. He didn't care about Jamie's being late. He

had worried about getting there too early, before his uncle had left to do the Saturday shopping.

"She burns awful easy."

Kit looked at her, hoping to reassure her, but no sensible words would come. The concern in her voice made him wonder if Harry had been right about Jamie. If her mother worried so much about her—

"You're Doctor Lowes' boy, up at the college, ain't you?" Mrs. Merriwether asked.

He acknowledged that he was. He saw that it would make it all right—Jamie's going bike riding with him.

"You'll be careful. See that she don't do nothing foolish?"

"Yes, ma'am," he managed to say.

She smiled at him then and went away. In a moment Jamie came out.

"Hello," she said.

She was wearing a white dress with a wide-ribbon sash about the waist. She had a straw hat hung over her arm.

"Now, Jamie. Don't you forget. Keep that hat on."

Mrs. Merriwether's voice came from the dark interior of the house. Jamie smiled at Kit.

"All right, Ma. I won't."

She had dark curls that hung to her shoulders, and that was one reason she had become so popular with the boys since coming to town. This was her first year. Kit didn't know what her father did, but he was a carpenter or painter or something like that. Some of the girls didn't like her, because they said her father was a working man.

"I'll get my bike."

She disappeared around the side of the house, the big bow on the back of her dress bouncing as she ran. She came back in a minute pushing a new bike, a girl's model, one which Kit could see was much more expensive than his own. It seemed strange that she should have such a good bike.

"Where are we going?" she asked when they were ready to start.

"I'll show you. It's a keen place," he said, throwing his leg over his seat almost as though he were mounting a horse. "You follow. I'll show you."

She was carrying the lunch in a wire basket on her handlebars. He felt that he should have strapped it on his rear-mudguard carrier, but she had said nothing about it, and he didn't know how to offer without seeming sissy. He slowed down until she was almost up to him, and then he speeded up again, knowing she would cry after him.

"Please, Kit! Wait for me! I can't go so fast."

It made him feel good, knowing he could ride faster than she could. He turned around and pulled a face at her, and she pretended to be angry. He could tell by her eyes that she wasn't. One thing though. He didn't want anyone else to see them. It wasn't quite the way he had imagined it, Jamie in the clean white dress, the new bike. He remembered when Harry had told about taking Megs Brodie, she had worn overalls and had ridden on his bar.

There was something wrong about the way he was doing it, Kit thought. Too much like going on a Sunday picnic up the canyon with his family. More than that—it was almost like going to a birthday party at one of the girls' houses. He didn't have on his best clothes, but Jamie did, and that wasn't the way he had imagined it.

"Where we going? Please tell me," Jamie said again when they turned west toward the fields.

Her hair was blown out now, and the hat had come off and was trailing by the ribbon around her throat. Kit thought again how she was the best-looking girl in their grade at school. He knew Harry would like to be him, even if he wouldn't admit it. He thought maybe Jamie wouldn't even go with Harry, because lots of the girls wouldn't. Only a certain kind of girls liked him, and Kit hadn't decided yet whether Jamie was that kind or not.

"How would you like to see them make bricks?" he asked.

He was sorry at once. He had decided not to go by way of the brickyard, because that was the way his uncle would be coming back from the fields.

"Maybe we can come back that way," he told her.

"Where are we going?"

He told her finally: the Blue Spring.

"It's a keen place. You'll see. The spring's so deep, no one ever touched bottom. A man dropped a plow in once, and he got the longest rope he could find. He put a hook on it and tried to find the plow, but he never could get a long enough rope to touch the bottom."

He was relieved when they got to the top of the lane and he couldn't see his uncle on it. The road was clear all the way to the cut-off. Across the valley he vould see the 11:45 just coming through the narrows, and he slowed down and pointed it out to her.

"Look!" he said. "There's the 11:45. See it?"

The train wound like a black snake over the foothills. He knew it was almost eleven o'clock because the train had to go all around the valley before it arrived in the station at 11:45. He told her how when they were thinning beets they would watch for it, and when it pulled into the station they would know it was only fifteen minutes to lunch time.

Jamie was interested, and she had him tell her what it was like working on his uncle's farm in the summertime. When he opened the barbed-wire gate at the head of the beet-patch, they pushed their bikes a little way out into the field and he showed her the beets, explaining that they would be ready for topping soon. They lay the bikes in the tall grass along the irrigation ditch, and he offered to carry the basket. He showed her the place where they had fed a frog to a water-snake. He told her how they had cut the snake open and the frog had hopped out.

"Just as lively as you please," he said. "A little damp, that's all."

"How could you?" she asked.

That made him feel strong and grown-up again. It was nothing, he replied, forgetting how his stomach had almost turned when they had first cut the snake in two with their beet-hoes. Course, he told her, we don't kill water-snakes. They're good. But frogs are valuable too. They eat insects. It was just an experiment, he told her.

He set the basket down in the shade of the willows. His heart beat faster when he saw that no one had molested the green covering. The alfalfa leaves were wilted now, but otherwise the cave was

just as he had left it. Jamie threw her straw hat down beside the
lunch, and they crossed to where he could show her the spring. He
was afraid she might have noticed something strange about the
cave, but she didn't seem to. He wished he had the nerve to hold
her hand. That would help, he thought. When she saw the spring
she gasped.

"Oh!" she said. "It *is* blue, isn't it?"

He laughed and tried to pretend that it was nothing. But he
couldn't help noticing that it was as blue today as he had ever seen
it. It was bluer even than the color of the water his mother used to
rinse clothes in when she washed, deeper and more natural, and
two small white clouds were mirrored in the center of it.

He told her how cold the water was, how they filled their jugs
from it when they worked in the hay. It was just like mountain
water.

"But I go swimming in it," he boasted. "I've swum all the way
across it."

"Have you?" she said. "It must be fun. Oh, don't you wish we
had bathing suits with us?"

He must have looked at her kind of funny, because she blushed
and turned away. Then she changed the subject.

"I want to go down and feel it," she said.

He took hold of her hand then, because he had to help her down
the narrow path. There were only two places to get to the water;
that is, unless you went further down and waded up the slough. He
told her that. You went down and waded up the slough when
you went swimming, he told her, because the water in the slough
was warmer. That way the cold water came upon you gradually.
Sometimes they took gigs. She didn't know what a gig was, so he
told her it was like a small pitchfork, only it had barbs on the end,
like fishhooks. There were carp and suckers in the slough and you
could spear them. His uncle had planted trout in the spring once,
but the carp all came up and ate the trout. He told about the time
they had planted the trout. His uncle put dynamite in the spring
and blew it up. Some of the fish, he said, were blown clear out into
the fields. The rest of them just came floating to the surface. His
uncle put a screen in then, and planted the trout, but the screen

broke before the trout had grown big enough to get away from the carp that came up from the slough.

He felt a particular pride in telling about the Blue Spring, though he was simply reflecting his uncle's pride. His uncle wouldn't let anyone come near it unless they promised not to throw trash into it. He kept the bushes trimmed just as though they were growing in his front yard in town. Being here alone with Jamie, Kit felt almost as though the spring belonged to him instead of to his uncle. He could almost imagine it.

Jamie felt the water and said it didn't feel as cold as he had said it was.

"Say!" he said. "You just want to try going swimming in it."

She laughed at him this time. He could feel the red flowing up his neck until his ears burned.

"Why," she said, squealing with delight, "you're blushing."

He looked away from her, glad that Harry and Stew couldn't see him now. What would they say if they knew Jamie had made him blush. Then he saw that she was taking off her shoes and stockings.

"I just want to put my feet in and see how cold it is," she said.

He took his own shoes off too. He kicked about in the water, feeling the chill creep into his ankles. In a moment Jamie put one toe cautiously over the surface. He reached with his foot and pushed it under water.

"Don't!" she cried.

But she didn't try to pull it out again. He felt his excitement mount at the feel of her bare flesh against his feet. He kicked again, running the sole of his foot down her leg. She pulled her feet onto the bank and tucked them under her, and he caught a quick glimpse of her underthings—a pink petticoat and white bloomers. He pulled his feet from the water and stood up.

"Let's go," he said. "I got another place I want to show you."

He led her back up the bank to the cave.

"This is where we eat lunch," he said. "When we work, I mean."

He hadn't meant to suggest that they eat now. He wasn't hungry, and besides she had brought the lunch, so it was her place to say that. He had carried her shoes back with his own, and he lay them at the edge of the willows.

"Isn't this a nice place?" he asked.

She didn't reply, and this surprised him. But she did come into the cave and sit down beside him. He glanced at her, and she was chewing a grass stalk. Her forehead was puckered thoughtfully.

"You know," he said, attempting to speak lightly. "You know what the hired man told me?"

She shook her head, but she still didn't look at him. He wondered, now he had gone so far, just how to continue.

"He said—he said he played poker once. You know what poker is?"

She nodded.

"He said he played once where—" He seemed almost choked for breath now. It was like the time he went in Woolworth's to swipe a watchfob when Harry bet him he didn't dare. "—where each time anybody lost they took off some of their clothes."

He looked at her, wondering what she would say, but she said nothing.

"Shall we play that?" he asked. "Course we can't play poker, but something like it?"

"I don't care."

Her voice was low and sounded a little frightened. He felt suddenly very happy, the way he had when he came out of the store with the watchfob and Harry and Stew were waiting for him. His legs and arms were weak and trembling.

"Look!" he said, but she didn't look. "I'll pick up these two little rocks. See? You guess how many I got in my hands—either one or two. If you guess right—then I got to. If you don't— That all right? Well—how many I got?"

She waited so long he was afraid she wasn't going to say. He had to repeat it.

"How many?"

"Two," she said.

"Two," he repeated, confused. "That's right."

He hadn't thought about what would happen if he lost. He had made up the game on the spur of the moment. He debated what to take off, then decided on his shirt.

"How many this time?"

"One," she said.

He had known she would do that, and he had saved two, the same as before.

"It's your turn," he told her.

She hesitated, then reached slowly around her back and loosened her bow. The dress had a wide neck, and she just pulled it over her head. He was disappointed. She didn't look any different except for her bare arms. The petticoat was just like a dress.

The next time he lost again, and there was nothing he could do except take off his trousers. That left only his underwear and he would be stark naked. He wondered how many things she had left. Two that he knew of. She lost the next time, and he was afraid for a minute that she was going to back out.

"Turn your head," she said finally, so low he could scarcely hear.

He had already turned partly away from her, because he was ashamed of how he looked in his underwear. He squirmed a little more, but he could still see from the corners of his eyes. She wore nothing below the petticoat but her bloomers. It took him longer to decide now how many stones to keep. He didn't want to be the first. He thought how easy it would be to cheat. She never looked at the stones when he told her. He decided to try two again.

"How many?" he asked.

"One," she said.

She had lost—fair and square. She didn't say anything and she didn't move. He wasn't even looking at her now, but he could remember her body. The thing that struck him was its whiteness. He wondered if all girls had skin that white. Aside from that her body didn't look any different than his. The skin was softer maybe, but her chest was flat and hard. He wondered if Harry had been lying when he had told him about Megs Brodie. He bet Megs didn't have skin as white as Jamie.

He turned his head a little and saw that she had not yet moved. He wondered what he would do if she should take the bloomers off. He knew that she would if he asked her. She was kneeling, her head turned away from him as though she were simply staring out over the fields, and her dark black curls fell over her white shoulders. She reminded him of a picture he'd seen somewhere, he couldn't remember where, but it might have been in church. Suddenly he knew he didn't want to see any more of her body. He didn't feel the way he had before, and he knew she didn't want to go on with it either. She would if he told her to, but she didn't want to.

He threw the rocks out into the alfalfa patch.

"Let's not play any more," he said.

She looked at him then, and it was he who turned away. When he looked back in a moment she was still staring at him, and there was a peculiar look in her face that he had never seen before. She put her hands to her face, and he was afraid she was going to cry. He didn't know what to do, so he began suddenly to get back into his clothes. He wished he had never suggested the game. They were really having a good time until he had suggested taking their things off. He wished now that she would be the way she had been when he rubbed his feet against her legs down by the spring.

She didn't cry, and he saw in a moment that she had begun to dress. When he had got his shirt on, he stood up and walked away from the cave to button it. Then he walked back. She was just tying her bow and putting her hat back on when he got there.

"Let's not stay here," he said. "Let's go someplace else."

She didn't reply for a moment. Then she looked up at him.

"Kit?"

"Yeh?"

"It's a lovely place, really it is."

"Oh—"

He kicked his toe into the dirt, loosening a clod that sprayed out from his shoe.

"Kit?"

He looked at her again. He wished she wouldn't talk. He had liked it better the other way.

"Kit, are we engaged now? Does that make us engaged?"

He hadn't thought of that. He wondered if it did. The idea pleased him in a way, but he wondered what Harry would say.

"Ye-ah, maybe," he said slowly.

She picked up the lunch and scrambled out from beneath the bushes.

RAY B. WEST JR. [383

"Where is it you want to go, Kit?"

"Oh, I don't know," he said. "I just thought maybe we could go up the brickyard and watch them make bricks."

He couldn't tell whether she really wanted to or not. She seemed to, though. She set out ahead of him, running, even carrying the lunch basket.

"Come on," she called. "I'll race you to the bikes."

He pretended to try to catch her, but he really didn't. Somehow he got to wondering about the Blue Spring, if it was really so deep no one had ever been able to find the bottom. When he was grown up, he thought, he would come out here sometime with all the rope they had in all the stores in town. He would tie a big weight on it, and he would really see if he couldn't find the bottom of it then.

When he caught up with her and they were picking up their bikes he told her about it. She seemed pleased and excited at the idea.

"You do that, Kit," she told him. "I'll bet you could do it too. I'll bet you could really find the bottom."

WINTER WHEAT

SOME folks begin their spring plowing when the county agent tells them to, some folks watch their neighbors, but we always wait till there's life in the ground. There was life in the ground by the last week in March that year. Some years it didn't come till later, as late as May, one year. After the hard dead look of frozen gumbo the earth changes, shows cracks around the roots of the windbreak, looks darker. Ground sparrows dart up from the stubble, ants crawl across the bare ground, and green shows bright in the winter wheat and up the side of the coulee. It's a thing you can feel. Then you know it's time to plow.

It was good to be out working in the fields again with nothing between me and the sky. It was still cold early and late, but the sun was warm on my head and the back of my neck by midmorning. I was glad I wasn't in the library at the university or in the teacherage at Prairie Butte. I was glad I was back here riding the tractor across the fields.

There's one thing about plowing: trying to keep a straight line with the tractor, you forget other things. A ground sparrow will fly up from the furrow ahead of you or a Chinese cock pheasant will flaunt his colors against the plain dirt and take your mind off what you were thinking.

But I thought often of Anna Petrovna and Ben Webb plowing this same dirt their first spring in Montana. I thought of them hardly speaking all day. I knew so well how Anna Petrovna's face could look when it closed all her feelings inside, and I knew how Ben Webb could look when he was discouraged and tired and sick. I thought of them going up to that unpainted house under the coulee and eating in silence and lying down beside each other at night. That they could plow under their hate and bitterness and grow any love for each other seemed a greater miracle than the spring. Sometimes it was hard to believe, I had believed in their hate so long, but I could look over and see the green of the winter wheat. Because of what Mom had said, I took it as kind of proof.

One day, the first week of April, we had a turn of cold. The wind blew so hard it lifted the fresh dirt I had plowed. By afternoon, a thin snow came down and covered the fields an inch deep, but the wheat stuck up through it as green as life. It gave me a good feeling all day.

I thought of Gil as I went back and forth over the field, and I tried to plan out my life and think what I would do after the harvest. I turned the tractor at the corner and felt the extra pull of the moist spring earth, then I faced across the field to the east again.

Some days I forgot everything but the good feeling of the spring day and the soft cool air and the wideness of the field. When I stepped down off the tractor I liked even the stiff, sticky squish of the gumbo furrows under my feet. I was glad it was an early spring; the winter had been long enough.

The sun stayed longer each week. We could work later in the fields. Mom seemed to know I wanted to be outdoors. She was the one who always went up ahead to tend to meals and she and Dad did the chores while I was still riding the tractor. They left me a lot to myself. I felt a sense of understanding between Mom and me, without any words. It seemed to grow with the green that spread up the coulee.

I remembered how impatient I used to be with Mom because she never seemed to be excited or to look ahead; she just worked through the day as it came. But I knew that there were times when you couldn't look ahead. It hurt too much if you tried to think what came after spring and what after summer. It was easier to go along and work so hard in the day that you were tired at night. It came to me one morning, going back and forth over the field, that maybe so much had happened to Mom back in Russia that work out here had seemed peaceful. Maybe it had seemed good to Dad, after being sick so long, just to be out here in the sun. I began to understand how they had stood that first year here. Maybe it hadn't seemed like being exiled to Dad, after all.

It was after eight o'clock when I stopped some nights. Leslie often came down to wait for me by the fence and I would let him drive the tractor a few rods across the field. The wild flowers were out, but I didn't have time to climb the rimrock these days—maybe I didn't want to. But Leslie would try to bring me something new he had found: the first pale lavender crocus, some little bright pink flower, no bigger than an ice crystal on a frozen windowpane, or a bluebonnet as bright a shade as the Thorson children's eyes. And in my mind I would show each one to Gil.

Once Leslie took a flower home to press and send to Warren in a letter.

"Maybe, by now, he's lost the feather I gave him," he told me.

Leslie and I walked back up to the house together, leaving the tractor in the field for the next day. Oh, yes, Warren, the spring hurt. Sometimes it hurt most on these walks back up to the house at the end of the day. I thought of writing that to Warren in one of Leslie's letters, because Warren must know for himself how spring could hurt. But I didn't write.

"Bailey says up on the high line they've lost half their winter wheat crop; they're going to have to reseed to spring," Dad said one night at supper.

"How, Uncle Ben?" Leslie asked.

"Winter-killed," Dad said. "So many hard freezes after warm spells this last winter. A freeze on the bare ground does it."

"You know how that water stood in places, Ben, an' then froze solid!" Mom's face was as solemn as wood.

"That's what does it," Dad said.

"The ground heave up," Mom added, showing Leslie with her rough red hands.

"You see, it tears the wheat loose from the roots, Leslie," Dad explained. He could make sentences out of Mom's phrases when I couldn't get the meaning at all.

"You mean that could happen to our wheat?" Leslie asked, his eyes bigger with sudden alarm.

"Sure," Mom said darkly.

"But it's green now. Ellen said it could stand cold and snow!" His voice was like a cry of protest. I knew what he felt. It was more than wheat to him. It was more to me, too. I got up to fill Leslie's glass with milk.

"I was looking at the wheat today," Dad said. "I pulled up some stalks here and there that weren't really rooted. But you can't tell how much of it's that way."

"You mean, we might have to plow it up and reseed the whole thing?" I asked.

"Sure! All that seed an' gas an' time gone for nothing!" Mom said. "You won't get that money paid back on your combine this year, Ben Webb. An' I don't see you've heard anything from your sister yet about what you send her!"

I held my hands tight together under the table. There was that sharp, almost taunting note in Mom's voice that went through me. "Don't do that! How can you?" My mind cried out as it used to when I was a child. I couldn't look at Dad. I wished Leslie didn't have to hear them.

"Well, maybe I won't, but we won't lose the combine, either," Dad said, setting himself against her taunt so firmly I was suddenly all on his side. "We'll pay off half anyway." Dad had a different kind of strength from Mom. I could feel it.

"No, we just go on dragging a mortgage after us. Work so many years to be free an' then go out and ask for more!" Mom was so angry her face blotched with red, her eyes flashed, and her voice was heavier.

"The combine isn't the biggest thing in the world to me, Anna." The coldness of Dad's voice separated the two of them as far as Russia was from Vermont, I thought.

I started to clear the dishes. Here I was again, as I had always been, pulled this way and that by their attitudes. I was glad when Dad went into the front room with his magazine and Mom went

out to the chicken house. Leslie came to stand by the sink to dry
the dishes. I didn't quite meet his eyes.

"But, Ellen, I thought you said *for sure* that the wheat could
stand the cold?" he insisted.

"It does mostly," I told him. "It isn't the cold that hurts it. It's
these warm spells that melt all the snow and leave the wheat exposed, and then the cold strikes." But my voice trailed off. I felt
there was nothing you could say "for sure." I dumped my dishwater
outside and hung the pan against the house. I stood there by myself in the dark. The house was too full of feeling and tension.

"Oh, God!" I said, as I had that night in the blizzard, and only
the snow had blown in my face.

"When you feel it, you will pray," Mom had said.

"Oh, God, don't let the wheat all die," I prayed with my whole
heart.

That night I made up my bed again on the glider on the porch.
It was still cold at night, but I couldn't have stood the house.

I woke next morning to an all-day rain. I helped Dad in the shed
all morning, but in the afternoon there was nothing more to do.

"It won't hurt you to take time to fix yourself up," Mom said.
"Put on that white dress, for once."

But when I dressed up in the white piqué dress I could only
think how I had worn it to town last spring with Gil. I looked at
my hands and they were red and rough against my skirt, like
Mom's. My nails were dry and worked down close to my fingertips.
Gil would wince to see them now. I felt such a longing to see Gil's
hands again, to feel them against my face, that it was like a pain.
"I know he was coming back to me," I said out loud in my room to
the icon and the peach walls and the mirror that Gil had looked
on. That was what the little color meant. That was why he sent it.

All that next week we watched the wheat without saying much
about it. I saw Leslie on his way to school stop by one of the long
strips of wheat. He pulled up a single stalk. I couldn't see from
where I was how it looked, but it seemed to come out easy. Then
he walked slowly away before he began to run.

The second week of April came off warm. The grass around the house was green, the aspens in the coulee shivered in their pale green leaves. The box elders that sprang up wild against the bank held out tight-furled green torches at the tips of their bare branches.

"Well, let's go down and look at the wheat again," Dad said one morning, as though we hadn't been watching it every day.

"How do you think it look, Ben?" Mom asked.

"I don't think it did any harm to wait," Dad said. "Some folks have plowed up and reseeded already, but there's too much good wheat left there."

Once again, the three of us sat on the seat of the truck while we went to see the wheat. I was driving and I went the long way around.

"The road's muddy the other way," I said. I came around the first strip of stubble and parked. We made a procession across from the road. The stubble creaked like an old basket as we walked over it.

"There's some brown, all right," Mom said, pointing.

We each studied every strip with our own eyes. Through the green wheat that stood already four inches high there were spots where the blades had turned brown and lay along the ground or drooped with a sick whitish-green, and here and there were bare moth-eaten places. I walked up a row and pulled up one of the brown withered stalks and felt it come away in my hand. I looked out over this strip and the one beyond. The brown stalks were only scattered. There were places where the wheat was deep green and thick. I pulled at a green stalk beside my foot, but it clung to the earth as though its root reached two feet deep.

I looked at Dad. His face was thin and already burned by the wind. He had a stick or a match in his mouth and his lips gathered up around it as he considered. I could feel his impatience, that was still part of him even after all these years out here, in the way he took off his hat and put it on again and then felt for his package of cigarettes and lighted one with so much attention he hardly seemed interested in the wheat. When he got it lighted he turned back to the field. Mom had tramped ahead of us to look for herself.

"How about it, Dad?" I couldn't wait any longer.

"Well," he said slowly, "it's spotty. There's places where it winter-killed, but some of those spots were just wind-blown. It came through better than I thought it could. There's enough good wheat there for you to ride to school next fall on a first-class ticket, girl! All that through there has been slowed down a little because of the rain and cold these last weeks, but it'll blaze now. Anna!" he shouted.

"Ben!" Mom's voice across the strip had a warm excited sound to it. "Look over here! It's good here. She done better than she look last week!" Mom came back to stand by Dad.

"I thought you said I'd lose the combine!" Dad had a laugh in his voice.

"Well, you might yet with hail or grasshoppers. Watch out!" Mom looked up at him with her eyes sparkling the way they did over a joke.

I went back over to the truck. This afternoon I would bring Leslie down here to see the wheat that didn't winter-kill.

"See," I would say, "it didn't die out. Oh, in a few places, but look here—try to pull it up. See how strong and green it is?" Leslie would know what I meant. His eyes would shine.

I slid in on the seat of the truck to wait for Mom and Dad. They had walked a little way along the strip. Now they were standing together. They looked smaller under the too-wide sky, Mom so thick and peasant-looking with her bandanna tied around her head, Dad spare and angular and a little round-shouldered.

Why had I worried about them? I had been as blind in this world as Mom had said. They had love that was deep-rooted and stronger than love that grows easily. It gave me faith for my own life.

"You can't pick up faith at the cut-rate drugstore," Warren had said. I must tell him sometime that faith had to grow like wheat, winter wheat. Love was like that, too.

I thought how I had sat in Dunya's cold stall and wished I could stop feeling and thinking and remembering after I knew Gil was dead. How had I ever felt that way? I didn't feel that way any more. Now I wanted to live my life with the strength of the winter wheat, through drought and rain and snow and sun.

I honked the horn. It grated noisily on the bright spring day.
"Come on!" I yelled. "It won't grow while you watch it!"
Mom waved.
"Hold your horses!" Dad yelled back. They came up the field
together.
I had not always been glad that I was their child, but today I
had a kind of pride in being born to them.

Appendix

WRITING IN THE ROCKIES

By Thomas Hornsby Ferril

ROCKY MOUNTAIN literature is devitalized by a low-grade mysticism dictated by landscape. Mysticism is a nebulous word. I use it simply as a blanket concept covering a wide field of emotional response to magnificent landscape. The imagination, transported by enormous mountains, deserts, and canyons, endeavors to answer landscape directly and tends to disregard, or curiously modify, what might otherwise be normal considerations of human experience.

Indeed Oscar Wilde may have been talking sense when he said that our West could never produce literature because, as in Switzerland, the mountains were too high. He visited the Rockies in 1882. Lloyd Lewis and Henry Justin Smith in "Oscar Wilde Discovers America" quote Wilde:

> There are subjects for the artist, but it is universally true that the only scenery which inspires utterance is that which man feels himself master of. The mountains . . . are so gigantic that they are not favorable to art or poetry. There are good poets in England and none in Switzerland.

It comes as a shock to an imaginative person to realize for the first time that landscape as such has no particular meaning and he may reject for years—costly years in the life of an artist—the human experience which gives it meaning.

But in our region poets, novelists, and—though they would be

the last to have an inkling of it—writers of pulp adventure fiction
are at heart rudimentary metaphysicians trying to fit some system
of thought or action to the demands of pictorial nature. It is an in-
verted Romantic movement because no conscious philosophy ac-
companies it. Tom Mix in the Wild West movies is really a hang-
over of Rousseau.

The case for landscape mysticism is clearer in poetry than in
prose. Yet I believe that the same emotional influence which, in the
presence of vast mountains, causes the poet to say: "This is all so
big, only God could have caused it" is responsible for the notion of
prose writers: "This is all so big, only supermen can cope with it."
The ancestor conveniently becomes a tribal god and here, I think,
in the hero convention of prose, we have a clue to the specious
perpetuation of the pioneer legend as a contemporary presence.

Underlying all our imaginative writing is a religious impulse,
nature worship in its simplest terms. Perhaps the Rockies are the
last stronghold of animism in process, the recognition of something
divine in the inanimate forms of nature. Our folkways are full of
incipient nature myths and hero myths which have been arrested
by the shift of our credulity to the myths of economics.

Let me illustrate how this religious impulse, or mysticism excited
by landscape, thwarts the poet and causes him to waste time. Since
the clinical evidence is clearer in poetry, I prefer to emphasize that
aspect before indicating a direction for studying the problem in
prose.

First: most people, beholding Nature in large and unfamiliar
scale, think about what caused it and answer: God! Critically, we
may have ignored a profound platitude and all that it implies, the
designation of the West as *God's Country*. Discovery of God in
scenery tapers off as the arroyos flatten into the Corn Belt, but in
the high country the naming of a group of rocks "The Garden of the
Gods" is not fortuitous; it answers a primitive impulse.

God-finding is widely distributed, in prose, poetry, postcards, ad-
vertisements. Willa Cather refers to "the Genius of the Divide, the
Great Free Spirit that breaths across it." The Billings Advertising
Company quotes Chief Plenty Coups: "The mountains are still as
God made them," and the Colorado Association assures us that

Colorado is "a land where the Creator has stamped his Eternal Monogram." Harriet Monroe, late editor of *Poetry*, told us from the rim of the Grand Canyon: "In these warm and glowing purple spaces disembodied spirits must range and soar, souls purged and purified and infinitely daring." William Winter, dramatic critic, at the Grand Canyon could only quote Coleridge on "The Invisible." "Out in Arizona where God is all the time," writes the Hon. David Kincheloe of Kentucky in the *Congressional Record*.

I might endlessly elaborate supporting data on the pandemic prevalence of God-finding and causation ideas, also simple mountain worship such as we find in the poem which Helen Hunt Jackson, author of *Ramona*, wrote in the presence of Cheyenne Mountain overlooking Colorado Springs: "Beloved Mountain, I Thy Worshipper . . ." As a rule, these poems attempt to give a verbal facsimile of the appearance of a mountain by piling up too many desperate adjectives, with hints of fear and wonder coupled with the God idea, stated as an abstraction. Stripped of applied decoration, the organic verbs and nouns say very little. The contest of literally hundreds of Rocky Mountain poems is represented by Walt Whitman's "Spirit That Form'd This Scene," written in Platte Canyon, Colorado. I agree with Irene Pettit McKeehan of the University of Colorado that this poem sums up "the underlying idea" of Colorado literature, but I am disappointed in her belief that it expresses "its hope, its intention," because the Whitman who wrote this verse was moving away from the function of poetry:

Spirit that form'd this scene,
These tumbled rock-piles grim and red,
These reckless heaven-ambitious peaks,
These gorges, turbulent-clear streams,
     this naked freshness,
These formless wild arrays, for reasons of their own,
I know thee, savage spirit—we have communed together. . . .

Compare Whitman's Colorado lines with a similar idea in a God-finding poem by Coleridge under the spell of Mont Blanc, "Hymn before Sunrise in the Vale of Chamouni":

O dread and silent Mount! I gaze upon thee
Till thou, still present to my bodily sense,
Did'st vanish from my thought: entranced in prayer,
I worshipped The Invisible alone.

Observe that Whitman is talking about an abstract spirit. Coleridge's "The Invisible" is an abstraction. Harriet Monroe gave us abstractions in the "disembodied spirits" hovering over the Grand Canyon. Willa Cather's "Genius of the Divide" is an abstraction. Unfortunately, anything which drives a poet to abstractions, drives him away from poetry. Poetry is concrete. Poetry is a passionate apprehension of experience based on the magical statement of how things sound, smell, taste, look, and feel. Poetry can work from concrete specification to abstract implication, but never, without leaning on some external context for a crutch, can it work from the abstract back to the concrete. Preponderantly is this true of religious poetry. The bewildering richness of Revelation or Genesis, or Blake, Dante, Hopkins, or Milton, leaps like flame from the concrete image.

So it appears that the mountains demand religious utterance yet deny the poet plausible symbols for implementing such ideas concretely. He may exhibit some skill in remanipulating established symbols, but somehow our mores are out of step with the revelations of Pisgah. It bores us to be asked to supply a context for these abstractions; they exert too futile a draft on our recessive faith. True, we still thirst for concrete specification in our gods, but reject it as absurd unless taken vicariously and, I think, snobbishly through what we regard as some simpler culture, Negro culture being the handiest. It answered something deep in our hearts to see God smoking a cigar in *The Green Pastures*.

The Indians were the last to write successful religious poetry in this region. Had Coleridge or Whitman lived long ago in Walpi, their God need not have been "The Invisible." On the mountain top they could have described the Sun-God Ahul wearing turkey feathers, corn husks, a reddish fox skin, leggings netted with bean sprouts, and tinkling anklets terraced into rain. In this direction lies poetry.

But if mountain mysticism leads to the dilemmas of abstraction, let it not be inferred that specification is not attempted. Yet I feel that Colorado's poet laureate, Nellie Burget Miller, is using a doubtful method when she tries to make us see Galahad and Percival in mountain clouds, and Maude Freeman Osborne has not quite convinced me of the immortality of Mount Evans which has sisters and blesses lambs. In this field of specification of the supernatural, my favorite is T. O. Bigney who observed in 1875 that:

> The thorax and the pelvic space
> Of the grand old Rocky Range,
> Are the vasty, ever beauteous parks,
> Features fair and strange,
> Peculiar to this giant chain
> Which holds the continent's vast brain.

You can paste that in your memory book along with Byron's "Mont Blanc is the Monarch of Mountains."

But landscape such as ours cannot be ignored. It is an integral part of our emotional experience. A mountain range is forever a blue wall behind which something is happening. Being an emotional person, it is difficult for me to turn from those glorious ranges and say to myself: more water, better tilth, more straw needed for bedding, earlier decomposition of manure, higher yields of grain, alfalfa, sugar beets, yet this is the road to poetry: men in action, the transitoriness of life, memory, desire, agony, ecstasy.

If landscape cannot be used directly as subject matter, its beauty can be employed vividly in symbols of instrumentation. Pictorially, mountain snows are meaningless, but meaningful if the poet feels the mountain waters moving up through the grasses and the beasts into the metabolism of men with power to dream beyond the wasting of the glaciers and the granite. It is safer for the poet to be impressed by the erosion of the mountains than their enduring qualities, or any attitude which gives him the whip hand. It was good to hear Robert Frost say at George Cranmer's ranch that the mountains were pitched just right for his convenience: he could read the ferns like a book. Early in February Carl Sandburg was working in Denver on a nostalgic rough-and-tumble poem about "the God-damned Wasatch Mountains" which left no doubt as to who was boss. And in lieu of the pathetic fallacy—a familiar pitfall where landscape is compelling—a disciplined poet can take the direction of empathy, projecting his own imagination into external nature as a springboard for human implication, but always keeping control.

Referring briefly to fiction, the same forces of mountain mysticism are at work. In abandoning the play for the setting, the fiction writer feels under pressure to fit his characters to the vast panorama his eyes behold. He becomes oblivious of the complexities of natural experience and naively rationalizes history to select the most active behavior appropriate to the scene. This results in a simplification of life into rather pure and tight patterns, rigidly conventionalized. He contrives heroes and heroines capable of meeting an apparent nature on its most elemental terms. I say apparent nature because actual Western experience in conflict with actual nature is as complex as elsewhere. Our economic and moral adjustment to the physical facts of climate, water, soil, mineral resources, etc., is infinitely involved and does not lend itself to the simplification the apparent landscape suggests.

It is not drawing too long a bow to regard the galloping heroes of popular fiction as vestigial tribal gods. They have emerged through about the same process which once produced centaurs and titans, but their development has been arrested at a rudimentary plane. They are supernatural in the sense that they tend toward caricature only dimly related to human life. They are clearly creatures of landscape commingled with ancestor worship, the apotheosis of the glorified pioneer. Moreover, they possess another god attribute, timelessness; they are immune to anachronism.

Note some of the foregoing points in the ritual of the pulp paper magazines. *Thrilling Ranch Stories* wants material in which "the background of the Old West is used—no radios, automobiles, etc., —but make the characters *modern* in spirit." Observe that satisfying landscape gives the illusion of reality: "Colorful terrain and a clear working knowledge of the vegetation and countryside bring a quality of reality," advises the editor of *Thrilling Western,* but as for life itself "we prefer the flavor of the Old West with the impression that the happenings are of today. If the setting is in the West today [again the setting dictates the play] it must be idealized. The people must be modern in spirit with boundless courage and endless endurance. Western dialect must be used and the slang of today should not be allowed to creep in." Being naive, the pulp formula may be more significant than other evidence bearing on our literary folkways.

One further observation on fiction of different quality: the case of Hamlin Garland. He wrote well on the prairie, badly in the mountains, and well on the prairie again. Possibly he illustrates my earlier point: that the inspiration of scenery works at cross-purposes with the inspiration which produces literature. If anyone ever repudiated extravagant pioneer romance, it was the Garland who wrote *Main-Travelled Roads* in 1891. This was followed by other works conceived with such savage integrity that even Howells, who admired him, felt obliged to apologize for such unconventional realism. Then Garland came to the high lands and wrote a basketful of Rocky Mountain novels in which he capitulated completely to the conventions of scenery. But back on the prairie in 1917 he gave us *A Son of the Middle Border* with the old integrity.

Carl and Mark Van Doren attribute Garland's mountain lapse to "errors of enthusiasm." This is correct. Perhaps "errors of enthusiasm" covers the field I designate "landscape mysticism." But regardless of what we call it, it is equivalent to a physical force which destroys the uncontrolled artist and delays orientation of the controlled artist. Garland, a man of considerable control, was drugged by the same lotos Whitman had tasted when Whitman wrote this nonsense:

> Talk as you like, a typical Rocky Mountain Canyon or limitless sea-like stretch of the great Kansas or Colorado plains, under favoring circumstances, tallies, perhaps expresses, certainly awakes, those grandest and subtlest emotions of the human soul, that all marble temples and sculptures from Phideas to Thorwaldsen—all paintings, poems, reminiscences or even music—probably never can.

It isn't true, and to believe it causes the artist to waste time and effort, winding himself into cocoons of futile metaphysics. Art, as we have come to know it, does not exist in external nature, nor can external nature, powerful as it is, move us as we are moved by Shakespeare or Brahms. Landscape was irrelevant to Greek and Elizabethan dramatists. "Scenery is fine," wrote Keats, "but human nature is finer—the sward is richer for the tread of a . . . nervous English foot."

Having indicated the difficulties of poets and one novelist whose case I believe to be representative, I might close by suggesting that our most competent writing, with richest overtones, has always come from reporters: scribes with Coronado—after 1573 all Spanish expeditions were required to keep journals; from the scientists accompanying trappers up the Missouri and down the Columbia; the diarists of the wagon trails; the geologists; the topographers; the reporters, like Villard and Richardson who described the Pike's Peak gold rush. True, many a Parson Weems crept into the picture, but on the whole the reporting was well done and the perspectives are very deep: reporters were on the scene long before Shakespeare dipped his pen.

The dominance of the conscious literary artist characterized the last half of the nineteenth century. No sooner was the first goose-quill filled with Cherry Creek gold than the artists-with-a-purpose began their spiritual exploitation. But these conscious artists, enthralled by the demands of landscape for the pure and picturesque —seeking a western type, so to speak—rejected what was complex. Meanwhile the reporter, when he was not too busy drinking or preaching, was making a naive record of these complexities.

Take, for example, the ethnic, moral, and psychic complexities in one episode of the Meeker massacre in 1879. Here we had a full-blooded Ute chief with a British name getting drunk on Kentucky whiskey and singing a Negro spiritual to a captive American girl, then asking her, like Sigmund Spaeth, if she knew what it meant, while her murdered father lay over the hill with a log chain around his neck and a barrel stave down his throat. A sound novelist, like H. L. Davis, author of *Honey in the Horn,* would be interested, I believe, in developing the influences bearing on such a situation, but to the rank and file these confusing compressions of experience are outside the code. These compressions are taboo unless idealized. My father, who is considerably older than the city of Denver, spent a recent week trying to figure out how his office boy was affected by social security legislation. This was immoral: he should spend his time lamenting the passing of the bison.

It is in the summarization of reporting that the region now is becoming articulate. I refer to such books as *Here They Dug the Gold,* by George Willison, whose fine work on Leadville and the Tabors was followed by a number of others; the material, if not the treatment, of *The Forty-Niners* by Archer Butler Hulbert; and *Timberline,* Gene Fowler's colorful but incomplete story of Bonfils and Tammen. Haniel Long's new volume *Interlinear to Cabeza de Vaca,* is a by-product of reporting. The *Colorado Magazine,* edited by Leroy R. Hafen of the State Historical Society, is doing a competent job of revealing the past through the reporting method. The field, however, is large and I shall not attempt to give an inventory.

There has lately been an inordinate regional consciousness, tremendous eagerness to do something about the various art forms. Equipment is not lacking: the Fine Arts Center in Colorado Springs with Boardman Robinson; the Central City Play Festival directed largely by Anne Evans and Robert Edmond Jones; the Writers' Conference in the Rocky Mountains, well organized by Edward Davison, the poet. These activities have at least focused attention on our spiritual confusion by engendering marvelous cat-and-dog fights. The row over the $100,000 Speer Memorial has made every Denver wardheeler a critic, and it is a dull barber who cannot regale you with focal points and plastic organization. Yet all this rationalization usually winds up in esthetics rather than art. None of our literary work compares in quality with what Burnham Hoyt is doing in architecture, and I prefer the workaday output of such newspaper craftsmen as Lee Taylor Casey and Larry Martin to that of the interpretive artists. Indeed few of the upland bards have as vivid a sense of poetry as appears naively in the cadenced captions, dynamic and concrete, which Martin turns out daily for *The Denver Post.*

MORMON STORYTELLERS

By Dale L. Morgan

EVEN THREE YEARS ago it would have seemed that the columns of the *Rocky Mountain Review* could be occupied to better advantage than by an article on this subject. The whole Mormon story, one of the richest, most variously faceted, and altogether extraordinary American history affords, awaited discovery like another Comstock Lode. Placer miners down the gulch had panned day wages from these riches, but the lode itself was inviolate, shrouded in sage and sand and piñon. The Mormon lode differed from the Comstock, however, in that everybody could see the proportions of the wealth, and it was not ignorance of its existence but the lack of a technology to mine it which prevented its exploitation. A prospector's eye and the drunken aberrations of an Old Virginny might suffice to open the Comstock, but the writing of an adequate Mormon novel required a glowing vision, an integrity of purpose, and above all a technical equipment which, in 1939, was nowhere in evidence. Three years ago, the Mormon riches were untouched and therefore inexhaustible.

In the autumn of 1942, however, we can number nine novels that have proceeded from the presses since *Children of God*, in 1939, ushered in the new dispensation. These nine novels represent the individual response of an astonishing variety of authors to an anomalous literary vacuum, and will have their weight in all further writing on the Mormon theme—if not as a direct impact upon the literary consciousness of individual novelists, then as a limiting

404

factor in the willingness of publishers to accept books written out of the Mormon experience.

Some attention must be directed to Mormon fiction published before the fall of 1939. To the turn of the century, one hunts almost in vain for fiction concerned with Mormons. This is not altogether surprising. The violence of Mormon group relations was not conducive to the encouragement of fiction. For their part, quite aside from the fact that their society was notably a frontier culture for which fiction, under any circumstances, constituted a luxury expensive and suspect, the Mormons had more pressing uses for the literary talent of the Church. Polemical writing, aside from its social utility, had also an affirmative value in advancing a man's stature in the priesthood. Polemical writing and the expounding of the Gospel, as compared to the writing of fiction, brought greater social rewards and answered to a greater social need. Under these circumstances, it would be extraordinary if any Mormon writer to 1900 had produced a novel of distinction. Edward W. Tullidge, who may possibly have been capable of portraying Mormon society, chose to occupy himself with heavy historical plays at such times as he concerned himself with other than journalism and expository history. There were a few other native writers who now and then tried their hands at playwriting, the drama enjoying a certain social acceptance in Utah, but Mormon literature remained barren.

Mormon materials fared hardly better in non-Mormon hands. Except, perhaps, for Lily Dougall's The Mormon Prophet (1899), a novel centering upon Joseph Smith's life which is chiefly important (to history, not to literature) for its psychological explanation of Smith's puzzling character, there is not a single work of fiction dealing with the Mormons worth anyone's attention. Joaquin Miller's The Danites in the Sierras, published in its final form in 1881, vaguely incorporates Mormon materials, but is worthless from any point of view. Most non-Mormons who felt impelled to write about the Mormons did so out of an urge to attack the hydra-headed monster, and fiction was just another instrumentality; the anonymous and typical Apples of Sodom (1883) frankly closes with the pious hope that the book "may serve as a drop to overflow the bucket of popular prejudice against polygamy."

The quarter century after 1900 did hardly better by the Mormons, although the assimilation of the Mormons by American society, following upon the Woodruff Manifesto and the granting of statehood to Utah, permitted a more stimulating contact of artists with Mormon experience on the American frontier. That there was no important Mormon novel written is, in part, of course an accident of time and place. Another Mark Twain could have been born in Utah. But he wasn't. Books about the Mormons, during this quarter century, were pedestrian endeavors.

Alfred H. Henry's *By Order of the Prophet* (1902) somewhat anticipates Susan Ertz' *The Proselyte*, written thirty-one years later; but this is not a novel of distinction, or even of much interest. Harry Leon Wilson published in 1903 *The Lions of the Lord*, but this was what today we would call "slick fiction," stock characters expertly manipulated in a never-never land. In 1909 Susa Young Gates published *John Stevens' Courtship*, a romance of the "Echo Canyon War" serving much the same purpose as the autobiographical narratives of the "Faith-Promoting Series" written nearly a generation earlier. Pierre Benoit's *Le Lac Sal*, published in France in 1921 and printed next year by Knopf in English translation as *Salt Lake, A Romance*, is by long odds the most astonishing production of the period. This novel of intrigue after the Utah or Echo Canyon War reads like greased lightning (in pleasant contrast to most other novels here mentioned) but Benoit's conception of Utah as a more singular Graustark is almost absurd. *Salt Lake*, like *The Lions of the Lord*, has nothing to do with the realities of Mormon life; it is a projection of the writer's interior fantasy into the Mormon environment.

There are, however, two books out of this second period that may be read with interest and pleasure, a pair of juvenile adventure novels by Walter Nichols, *Trust a Boy* and *The Measure of a Boy*. While these books, published in 1923 and 1925, respectively, have no pretensions as literature, as a picture of boy life near and upon Great Salt Lake in the eighties they are unique, and possessed of considerable charm.

Bernard DeVoto's *The Chariot of Fire* (1926) announced the imminent assault of responsible artists upon the Mormon story. This novel, which was followed in two years by Mr. DeVoto's novels of a West in which the Mormons were conspicuous by their absence, used the Mormon story by complete conversion; essentially, *The Chariot of Fire* is a study of a phenomenon: frontier religion. It drew upon Mormon materials sufficiently that members of the Church heartily disliked it as a caricature of Mormon beginnings, but it did not come directly to grips with what writers were now beginning to see as "the Mormon epic."

In 1928 Vardis Fisher, with *Toilers of the Hills,* published his first novel, an account of farm life in the Snake country which only incidentally was concerned with Mormon society, but which was important as marking the first realistic use of native materials by a native artist. In later books that preceded *Children of God,* primarily his autobiographical tetralogy, Mr. Fisher occupied himself to some extent with contemporary Mormon society, but he was engaged in exorcism, and Mormonism and the Mormon environment were only incidental in that.

Norton S. Parker's *Hell and Hallelujah!* (1931), laid principally in Nauvoo during the strenuous years, 1844–46, inaugurated in modern Mormon fiction a kind of novel that has since been seen with increasing frequency. The exterior violence of Mormon history has much to attract tale-tellers; history itself is already an involute plot, and it is only necessary to lash the chief characters to the mast and let them run before the wind. *The Rocky Road to Jericho* (1935), by Frank Chester Field (Frank C. Robertson), has many points of similarity to Parker's novel, as have also Jeremiah Stokes' *The Soul's Fire* (1936) (one of the few novels of orthodox Mormon viewpoint) and several of the new crop, though Mr. Robertson's book exhibits a greater earnestness in trying to resolve the contradictions of Mormon history than is expected of this type of work.

In popular consciousness, Susan Ertz, with *The Proselyte* (1933) was first to discover the Mormons. More weight has attached to *The Proselyte* than it deserves on its merits as a novel, primarily because Miss Ertz was already known as a writer of distinction. Although Miss Ertz brought sympathy and discernment to her theme, and was first to exemplify the dignity and integrity of Mormon social life, her novel peers out upon Mormonism from the shuttered window of an English parlor. It misconceives the vigorous Mormon story at vital points, its detail sometimes falls strange on the ear, and altogether it gives somewhat the effect of having been written at the tea table.

Rather more significant than *The Proselyte* were George Snell's *The Great Adam* (1934) and *Root, Hog and Die* (1936). The former, concerned with the rise and fall of a banker in a small town of southern Idaho, is, despite the impression it gives of the arbitrary imposition of a classical pattern, a novel rather more richly conceived and well-rounded than the book which followed it. *Root, Hog and Die*, a realistic picture of Mormon life over three generations, is an exciting exploration into the possibilities of the Mormon theme, but it seems more the outline of the story Snell wanted to write than the story itself. More important than the actual achievement, in the case of either novel, was Snell's evident consciousness of the literary potentialities of a life to which he is native.

Although I have not attempted a complete catalogue of writing by and about the Mormons to 1939, the authors and books mentioned represent most of what could be called significant in this writing, and this catalogue roughly indicates the status of Mormon fiction in 1939. A very few novels, distinguished for one reason or another, stood out in a wasteland, and none of these novels was possessed of such force and individuality as to inhibit any writer from making any use he chose of Mormon materials. It is important now to consider the change in this state of affairs produced by the nine novels already mentioned.

I should begin by listing these specifically: They are Vardis Fisher's *Children of God* (1939), Jean Woodman's *Glory Spent* (1940), Paul Bailey's *For This My Glory* (1940), Rhoda Nelson's *This Is Freedom* (1940), Maurine Whipple's *The Giant Joshua* (1940), Lorene Pearson's *The Harvest Waits* (1941), Hoffman Birney's *Ann Carmeny* (1941), Elinor Pryor's *And Never Yield* (1942), and Virginia Sorenson's *A Little Lower than the Angels* (1942). Of these novels the first, fifth, sixth, and ninth may be regarded, for various reasons, as important. *This Is Freedom* is a treatment of the Mormon theme for adolescent readers, and not strictly of a kind with the others here mentioned; while *Ann Carmeny*, a tale of glittering derring-do in the Salt Lake basin in 1860, is more particularly of the genus of historical novels of adventure currently in vogue.

Fisher's novel, because most ambitious, is most important among these nine books. Subtitled "An American Epic," *Children of God* endeavored to swallow the Mormon story whole. Although the degree of success that attended the effort is illustrated by the fact that the book was the Harper prize novel in its year, that it sold well, and that it attracted a considerable measure of critical acclaim, *Children of God* is by no means a front-rank novel. Mr. Fisher has reached directly into Mormon history for the majority of his characters, and his Joseph Smith, Emma Smith, Lyman Wight, and Brigham Young, for example, are warm with life—within the limitations of his intention. The panoplied movement of Mormon history itself was sufficient to give this novel a magnificent color and direction, granted an initial success in the recreation of the book's basic historical characters. *Children of God* was not, however, the successful epic it aimed to be.

Although he adopted orthodox Mormon views for the greater part of his novel, Mr. Fisher's sympathy and understanding were something less than whole-hearted, and this emerges in the impact of the book as a whole. Perhaps a kind of lifelessness about the novel is a consequence of the fact that Mr. Fisher clothed the bones of history with Mormon flesh of the kind he knew in the Snake River Valley. Dock Hunter and his tribe are the legitimate offspring of the Mormons who saw glories in the sky and praised God for a latter-day prophet, but Dock Hunter is the product of the interaction of Mormon society with the desert environment; in peopling his pageant with a congregation of Dock Hunters, Mr. Fisher achieved a flavor of the frontier but lost qualities of personal fulfillment and deep spirituality that were profoundly important in the inception and growth of Mormonism.

With all its merits, and it should be understood that they are many, *Children of God* does not emerge as a finally important treatment of the Mormon story as an epic in itself, history immediately invaded by fiction. There is still room for such a novel. But *Children of God* will remain as a formidable barrier in its field to anything except a really front-rank novel. To that extent limitations have been imposed upon exploitation of the Mormon literary wealth.

Maurine Whipple's *The Giant Joshua* derives its strength from its warm humanity and from Miss Whipple's delighted absorption in the sensual splendor of Clory MacIntyre's world. Nowhere in Mr. Fisher's book, despite his greater technical competence, is there a comparable abundance of life; perhaps this reflects the greater nearness of Miss Whipple to the people of whom she writes, and the exactitude of her frame of reference. In the magnitude of its intention and the extent of its accomplishment, *The Giant Joshua* has claims to be considered the best of the Mormon novels so far published, though its character as a first novel is clearly evidenced in a technical incapacity; the book, structurally, seems to run in circles; it is repetitious and its feeling for romance sometimes flounders in sentimentality.

A novel of the type of *The Giant Joshua* tends to be a law unto itself. Any writer on the Mormon theme whose book overflows with life may be assured a hearing, for such a novel is richly rewarding to the reader who would find, in fiction, a renewed and deepened apprehension of his own life and all human living. Mormonism and Mormon materials theoretically need not intervene upon this function of literature. Practically speaking, however, writing is hardly to be divorced from its social context, and anyone, writing out of the Mormon theme, who can feel so deeply and write so eloquently will probably have something to say that will be of interest and importance first of all to the people in the Mormon country. Apart from such considerations, Miss Whipple's novel must be said to have laid these restrictions upon use of Mormon materials: On the romantic plane it got very nearly all that is to be gotten out of the problems of matured polygamy (especially, from the woman's viewpoint), and of warfare with the desert by the Mormon community. Additionally, the abundance of Miss Whipple's local color, which gives her novel at times a lushness almost overwhelming, will require of new Mormon writing that it stand upon its feet without

the props and crutches of quaintness and mere novelty of background.

Lorene Pearson's *The Harvest Waits* is radically dissimilar in
point of view and choice of materials to any other among the Mormon novels. Although "realism" has been employed to a greater or
lesser extent in half a dozen of the novels about the Mormons, Mrs.
Pearson's book most nearly approaches the classical ideal. Her
realism is a cumulative effect of her detached and broken viewpoint, of her deliberate emphasis, and of her choice of subject
matter and detail. It cannot be said that Mrs. Pearson's novel of the
struggles of Mormons to live together during and after the period
of the United Order, is altogether successful, but it is perhaps most
thought-provoking of any of the Mormon novels. *The Harvest
Waits* attempts to come to grips with its people without the marching and countermarching of mobs and armies, the passage of glittering personalities, and all the lovely violences. This novel does
not suggest itself for best-sellerdom, and it is probable that neither
author nor publisher had any illusions upon this score, but its
solidity, its quality of detail, its dignity, and its unexcited earnestness are rare qualities in a Mormon novel. Writers projecting
Mormon novels would do well to review Mrs. Pearson's book for
the wide bases of its approach to a Mormon community, and its
ease of manner in the utilization of distinctive Mormon detail,
though also, negatively, they may find instruction in observing its
defects in its confusing progression of viewpoint, its insistent
ellipses, and its determined repression of emotion at times when
sustained emotion is not only valid but essential to the book. *The
Harvest Waits* is a constructive performance that need not be in-
hibitory in further writing on the Mormon theme.

The fourth of the new novels that I have called significant is
Virginia Sorenson's *A Little Lower than the Angels*. Mrs. Sorenson's
excellent novel of life in Nauvoo exhibits several fundamental differences from its fellows. The growth of a society, and the relationships of people, one with another, in this developing society, occupy
her less than the age-old questions that are always new, on what
terms a man and a woman may live together, what they can possess
of life, and what life can do to their possession of each other. Al-

though it would be misleading to say that the Mormon background and the events of Mormon history woven into the fabric of this novel are inessential to its development, it seems clear that Mrs. Sorenson could have adapted her characters to, and worked out their problems in, another environment. Miss Whipple's characters, by contrast, are clearly the direct product of their time and environment; Abijah and Sheba and Clorinda MacIntyre, in the very stuff of their life, are inseparable from the Mormon frontier. We shall probably see more books of the general type of *A Little Lower than the Angels*. I would guess, however, that such novels are likely to be important to Mormon fiction primarily for their contributions to technique.

Attention must be directed, finally, to the other novels that have appeared since 1939. Jean Woodman's *Glory Spent* must be praised for the honesty of its intention, and Mrs. Woodman remains the only writer who has had the courage or the insight to attempt a depiction of Mormon society as it is today. Unfortunately, *Glory Spent* is primarily an essay in ideas, and the novel, as a work of fiction, is something less than adequate. *Glory Spent* has, for this discussion, the importance that it has brought into the open Mormonism's problems in a modern world; it relieves other authors of the responsibility of stating those problems for the record, and imposes upon them the responsibility of creating from this material a deep humanity, a richly felt life. There is no question of the need for a good novel of contemporary Mormonism, and Mrs. Woodman must be commended for her discernment of the need, whatever is said of her book itself.

Comment was made earlier on a type of adventure novel that has appeared in the Mormon fiction. Paul Bailey's *For This My Glory* is one of the more unfortunate efforts in this field; the novel is harnessed to various Mormon experiences of violent interests—the Missouri and Illinois persecutions, the march of the Mormon Battalion, the discovery of gold, the Utah War, the "polyg hunts"— and this flow of events, rather than the characters concerned, gives the book such interest as it commands. Elinor Pryor's *And Never Yield* has certain points of similarity, but it is written in the tradition of *Anthony Adverse,* a now familiar kind of pageantry. Miss

Pryor's book, once more to adopt the viewpoint of this discussion, is chiefly important because it makes further inroads upon Mormon history conceived as an epic. Mrs. Nelson's book, and Mr. Birney's, may here be regarded as primarily important because their bulk weighs in the possible exhaustion of the Mormon theme.

The broad outlines of what has been accomplished with Mormon materials should be fairly clear. A long period in which novelists more or less neglected the Mormon story has ended with a series of novels which, with varying success, has attempted to translate this story into a fiction of integrity and depth. It will be observed that the ambition to write on the epic plane has forcefully influenced the majority of these books. It is inevitable that the Mormon story should commend itself first of all as an epic, for it possesses historical continuity, spectacular violence, cross-grained social texture, and tragic content. Epics, however, feed voraciously upon their own being, and the measure of preoccupation with the Mormon theme that we have seen in the last three years establishes a probability that Mormon fiction will now be given over to writers less opportunistic and more serious in their purpose.

REGIONALISM

By Wilson O. Clough

We have heard a good deal of late about "regional" literature. Does it exist, should it exist, how can we stimulate it? With the vanishing of the frontier and the decrease in national nomadism, we are said to be developing more regional homogeneity and character. The theory is that such homogeneous areas will be or should be articulate in some special way; and if they are not, stimulants should be applied in the form of regional magazines, classes in creative writing, and hortatory articles and speeches. Even publishing houses can be shown that there is sales appeal in the term "regional."

Let us assert dogmatically that no genuinely enduring regional literature can be produced by exhortation, manifesto, wishful writing, or precarious magazine ventures. All of these, especially the last, render real service in the encouragement of timid creative talent seeking expression; but all are more symptomatic than causal. They may water the roots, but they are not the plant. This is only to suggest that the term "regional" has taken on connotations that are, to say the least, tangential to the problem of the production of literature of abiding value.

We are familiar with the parallel between regional development and that of our own early colonial—the initial concentration on survival with the premium on the non-literary; the slow acquisition of a living and some leisure; the gradual appearance of records, journals, newspapers, political papers; and finally the timid ex-

cursions into *belles lettres,* imitative, yet aggressive and self-asser-
tive. These are normal beginnings, but they may still have advanced little beyond crudity and provincial bumptiousness. This is
the stage Cooper satirized in the early republic.

Again, the process might be compared with the acquisition of a
language: the first surface contact and sorting out of bewildering
impressions; the period of conscious attention to form and matter;
the fluency of maturity, rooted in habit and become spontaneous
expression. The adult rarely acquires a new language with more
than superficial fluency. So, too, the truly regional writer is not a
transplanted adult, a Bret Harte or a Bill Nye, but one to the country born, of the second or third generation, if not further delayed.
Authentic regional expression is a matter of living and of absorbing
landscape and character into the unconscious. It is natural, even
inevitable and it can be neither forced nor faked.

But we are considering enduring literature that is at the same
time regional. We must distinguish between regional and provincial.
The provincial is narrow, unreflective, even unself-conscious, because it lacks external criteria for comparisons. The provincial sub-
stitutes local habit for reflection, or is animated by a stubborn im-
perviousness to what the rest of the world may offer. The regional
takes in more territory, geographical and intellectual. Its mental
processes have advanced to self-awareness, because it has gained
perspective. It is provincial, of course, in so far as it has been
molded by environment, but it is saved from blindness by intel-
ligence and sympathetic insight. Its preference for the native scene
is not ignorance or suspicion, but both preference and understanding. Probably our original hesitation over the word "regional" was
really over the element of provincialism implicit in its too urgent
use.

We must further distinguish the regional from the outsider's
description, however sharp and true. The old term "local color" included a good deal of this "visitor's sketchbook" approach. But
the truly regional is more than description of natives and local
customs. Struthers Burt's use of Jackson Hole, Wyoming, is thus
not truly regional, however excellent. But Vardis Fisher, whatever
the final opinion on his intense volumes, must be conceded an

authentic regional note. This is not to deny other values to his novels.

It is instructive to note how often good regional literature has been the product of writers exiled either by fate or choice from the native soil. In absentia, they write with a nostalgic verity that the untraveled provincial could never attain. Mark Twain's *Life on the Mississippi* was written after a fair amount of living and traveling had intervened, and it is psychologically truer than a host of newspaper clippings written on the spot in local pride. Even his *Innocents Abroad,* not intended for regional writing, is full of the overtones of the western United States, almost as much so as his later deliberate efforts at local color.

Has the Rocky Mountain area a special regional character? The answer still awaits the appearance of great writers. But there is a unique quality to this area. It is the most inland of all, a thousand miles from the Pacific or Gulf or Great Lakes. It is mountainous and arid, imposing on its inhabitants a certain isolation. Its social origins were in mining camp and cattle raising and the Mormon settlement, the latter affecting the western half. Thomas Hornsby Ferril of Denver wrote recently that such a landscape encourages a myth-making literature. Man, diminished by the vast scenery, feels the need to create men to match it. The point is sound; and it is possible that for a long time to come this region will remain a symbol of our frontier tradition, the individual man rising to heroic proportions to meet a none too pliant nature. It will forever be different from either the great urban centers of the rich agricultural areas, though its cities, Denver, Salt Lake, resting economically on remote mining camps and far-flung ranches, will link themselves increasingly with major urban currents in the land. Until Western scenery bites deeper into its men and women we shall have little more than myths, cinema bad men and "westerns." But the truth lies deeper. Perhaps great literature doesn't come out of natural scenery so much as from the mental scenery. In that case, our emphasis will not be so much on the region as on the society in it.

So far, this region has produced a few ballads, often imitative rather than indigenous, a few "westerns," mostly written by non-natives, and a few uses of the setting by outsiders. Native poets like Ted Olson and Ferril are more hopeful signs, as are a group of younger aspirants in poetry and the novel. But the point here is that there is a certain danger in a too great insistence on the regional, for the best writing will always be found to contain universal notes as well. The too conscious effort to be regional is apt to distract the younger writer into artificiality, or into straining for what are, after all, secondary effects. The important thing is character, truth to men and women, wherever they live. Egdon Heath, for example, is a region and Hardy's folk are regional. But the power of the novel is not that it is regional, but that it sets off man against nature in terms of a universal conflict. The regional element is, in one sense, little more than stage setting, the concentration of a cosmic problem into a narrowed focus, for the sake of heightened intensity. The region gains its importance from the greater issues.

The point, finally, is that the term "regional" should be used sparingly. The sensitive, intelligent writer, honestly endeavoring to say what he has to say, will reveal his origins, even against his intention. The regional will take care of itself, for if it is genuine, it will be at least half unconscious, unplanned. It will be present in its proportion by virtue of the laws of creative maturation. As the single writer will speak as an individual if he have something worthwhile to say, so the literature of a given area will be regional in the best sense if it has come from the deepest springs of creative life in the men and women who write first of all as human beings.

TWO ROCKY MOUNTAIN POETS

By Alan Swallow

ONE GOOD practice in criticizing poetry is to discover the poet's intention, the problem he has set for his own work. This practice is, of course, not a method for appraising the value of the finished poem, but it is a means to fuller appreciation of the poem; and perhaps in the end will be of some importance in any final judgments attempted.

Thomas Hornsby Ferril's interest has been exceptionally regional. He lives in Denver, Colorado, in the center of the pioneer West and in the twilight shadow of the Rocky Mountains. And even a casual reading of his poems will demonstrate that one of his primary concerns has been the influence of such a regional geography upon the creation of poetry.

This interest is made explicit in a valuable essay on "Rocky Mountain Metaphysics" which Ferril contributed to *Folk-Say*, 1930, edited by B. A. Botkin of the University of Oklahoma. However much I should like to do so, I cannot in the short space of this criticism give an abstract of this essay. But a few of the arguments are particularly pertinent. Ferril says that "in the mountains we feel that everything is very big and we are impotent," and further, "the mountains suggest, more often dictate, speculation on the supernatural." "Some form of god-finding seems necessary in the West, it appears." Now for the modern man, with his long forceful tradition of scientific thinking, this god-finding is virtually impossible (that is, the concrete god-finding necessary for poetry). As Ferril puts it, "You experience the supernatural, but you express it as an abstraction. Your intellect won't let you be specific as were the Greeks and Navajos."

Western writers have met the problem by making gods or supermen of the pioneers who explored and settled the area. That is also true of the popular fiction of the two-gun Western. As Ferril says, "Wild West fiction does not deal with humanity at all. It deals with supermen designed to cope with a savage region." The almost universal theme of the Western writer has been man's relations with man, which Ferril calls "the great theme of literature."

Ferril insists that this answer to the problem of the Western writer must be exchanged for a more adequate one. "The Western artist must rediscover humanity. It is simple enough. Willa Cather has done it. Miss Cather merely insists that her people be more important than their background. Doubly interesting then does Nature become through her eyes. . . . Nature unrevised perpetuates the pioneer legend. The ancestor slowly becomes a god, and I think he lives in the same Valhalla where the Creator of the Mountain lives. The plow is His enemy."

Has Ferril followed this intention in his own poetry? He has published two books of poetry, the first being *High Passage* (Yale University Press, 1926), a volume that, however, gives no indication of the direction he took later. The second, *Westering* (Yale University Press, 1934), is a highly mature and valuable volume.[1]

But most, and the best, poems in this volume are concerned with the general theme of man and nature. "Time of Mountains," "Blue-stemmed Grass," "Fort Laramie," "High-Line Ditch," "Lodgepole Creek," and "Something Starting Over" are poems of this type, and they are certainly among the best poems in the group. "Jim Bridger" and "This Foreman," poems closer to the "great" theme, are less successful. The former becomes immediate and concise only in the last part. While a dramatic structure is necessary to "This Foreman," which won *The Nation* poetry prize in 1927, the structure seems not completely successful. It is used mainly for the purpose

[1] A third volume appeared in 1944—ed.

of introducing material. By comparison with the dramatic structure of poems by Donne and Shakespeare, a structure used by them to give the intellectual and emotional firmness of qualifications and ironies, "This Foreman" seems a naive and somewhat unsatisfying poem. On the whole, the least successful poems are those with historical settings. They often commit the fault of the pioneer legend as Ferril has outlined it in his essay on "Rocky Mountain Metaphysics." Further, the materials are not always assimilated; certainly the poems do not become firm and immediate. They remain interesting experiments more than full-bodied poems.

In composition, these poems are in the American Tradition, if there is any predominant tradition in American poetry. The structure is usually the ruminating monologue characteristic of Poe at his best, of Bryant, of the New England school, of Whitman and of Lanier. This method is not often found in the very best poetry. But the French Symbolists and our contemporary American and English poets have added to this structure some of the exciting devices of the Elizabethans, to give an added richness, vitality, and depth to our poetry. Ferril, however, mostly leaves those devices alone, or uses them quietly and unimportantly.

The result of this method is that most of the poems are much longer than the usual lyric, and they are wisely so. In fact, the short poems, of which there are only a few in this volume, are not important, with the exceptions of "Blue-Stemmed Grass" and "Elegy —New Mexico." "Blue-Stemmed Grass" is given here because it is short enough to be quoted in this essay. It is similar to the most successful poems in the volume, and belongs with them.

> There's blue-stemmed grass as far as I can see.
> But when I take the blue-stemmed grass in hand,
> And pull the grass apart, and speak the word
> For every part, I do not understand
> More than I understood of grass before.
> "This part," I say, "is the straight untwisted awn,"
> And "Here's the fourth glume of the sessile spikelet,"
> And then I laugh out loud at what I've done.

I speak with reason to the blue-stemmed grass:
"This grass moves up through meadow beasts to men."
I weigh mechanical economies
Of meadow into flesh and back again.
I let the morning sun shine through my hand,
I trace the substance bloom and beast have given,
But I ask if phosphorus or nitrogen
Can make air through my lips mean hell or heaven.

All that the grass can make for any beast
Is here within my luminous hand of bone
And flesh and blood against the morning sun;
But I must listen alone, and you, alone,
Far children to be woven from green looms;
We move forever across meadows blowing,
But like no beast, we choke and cannot cry
When the grasses come, and when the grass is going.

This poem also has a touch of Ferril's concern with science, always a recurrent theme in *Westering*.

A final judgment on the work is not possible now, nor is it desirable. We may expect much more of Ferril. But on the basis of this one volume alone he has earned a position as perhaps the best poet of his immediate region, and a place among the few dozen best poets writing in America today.

The work of Ted Olson, a Wyoming poet, has been considerably slighter than Ferril's. It has in the main been less successful, but its temper is no less individual.

Olson has published only one volume, *A Stranger and Afraid* (Yale University Press, 1928). Since that date subsequent poems have appeared in a number of magazines, but a second volume has not as yet been published.[2]

Since the title of the volume is taken from some verses by Housman, it invites a comparison with Housman's work. The comparison, however, will prove of little value. A note of pessimism is characteristic of Olson's work, but it has less of the poise, and cer-

[2] A second volume appeared in 1941—ed.

tainly less smoothness, than Housman's. His pessimistic mood is more urgent, more impulsive, less tempered. This is to say that Olson, in his philosophy, is more contemporary than Housman, the scholar (the scholar, as W. H. Auden notes in a recent essay, whose scholarship represented his Angel face, and whose poetry represented his Devil face). Olson is immersed in the multifarious conflicts of the day.

It is this philosophy (together with his images, which are derived from the Rocky Mountain area) which is the most regional aspect of Olson's work. He has met the problem suggested by Ferril by a philosophy natural to the Rocky Mountain region and the pioneer tradition. The poet has noted the impotence of man before the bigness, and the occasional cruelty, of nature. But he has also noted, as Ferril puts it, the "The plow is His enemy." Such a philosophy, or any philosophy for that matter, cannot of course solve the specific poetic problem. But it can provide the materials and the temper of a distinctive regional poetry.

But his philosophy plays another important function in Olson's work. It has been pointed out by the better Marxist critics, and also by Dewey and a number of modern philosophers and psychologists, that a person's philosophy enters even his perceptions, determining in a large measure what the person actually sees, or is aware of. In Olson we are always aware of what his viewpoint is. We are continually aware of it because he often uses explicit, prosy statement containing the attitude, which is not a good thing in poetry; because almost every adjective is freighted with it, and is often well able to carry the load; because a liberal use of two-syllable, yet clipped and impulsive, rhymes seems to convey it (these will be noted in two examples below); and because the expression in the poems is itself impulsive, almost phrasal. Two passages (out of their context) from the first section of *A Stranger and Afraid* will demonstrate these points.

> Fools, I have died these decades past, and I
> Am ash in tombs unnumbered and unknown,
> Spoil of the seas, prey to the wind's dissection,
> Scattered too far for any resurrection.

Who have no faith, and cringe, naked and lonely,
Fueling flesh to dull the wind of reason. . . .
Flesh will requite us well, and in good season.

One of Olson's most successful poems is "Ski," first published in
1933. It was reprinted in Thomas Moult's anthology.

We need not envy anything
Climbing on miraculous wing,
Now we too have learned to write
Our shining autograph in flight.

Here where never falcon lifts
His arrogant wings above the drifts
That bloom and burgeon, swell in swell,
The shape of wind made visible.

We take the falcon's highroad, dare
The glittering canyons of the air—
Swooping, wheeling, hovering shod
Like the sandaled courier god.

What wingless thing could dream to win
This world of frost and porcelain?
It would splinter under feet
A shade less insolent and fleet.

And even we sometimes look back
Along our carven crystal track,
Incredulous it should endure
Beauty's very signature:

As if the hawk should leave his trail
Printed on the fluid gale;
As if the sky should keep the proud
Sculpture of the chiseled cloud.

Miraculous beyond belief
The way of wings; and fierce and brief.
The ripening year will soon erase
A very shining arrowy trace.

And none will know again, or guess,
The way we went in happiness.
None will mark if one should stand
Alone where two sped hand in hand,

Or paused a little, breast to breast. . . .
April's wind will take the rest.
And that is best. And that is best.

This is a good lyric, with the basic metaphor good in itself and well-handled. However, a few faults mar the poem. A few lines, such as "A very shining arrowy trace," are too easy and do not carry their proper load. And the last line is not satisfying as an ending. It does not participate in the poem before it. With another stanza for preparation, it might function with complete satisfaction.

The characteristics of Olson's poetry add up to an individual style. The reader will perhaps have caught an indication of its flavor from the examples given. It is a style as individual as Ferril's, but the poems are usually not as good as Ferril's. A partial explanation may be that Olson has apparently given less consistent effort to his poetry. But he is a poet of no mean importance, and those who have followed his work would like to see the publication of a second volume.

VARDIS FISHER

By George Snell

IN THE WHOLE range of contemporary fiction there is not another career that parallels Vardis Fisher's. After publishing nearly twenty novels, he is still the least read of the major American literary artists. After winning one of the country's fattest novel prizes that assured him at least one appearance at the top of best-seller lists, he went on to write books that had meager sales. His name is seldom seen in popular critical surveys though he has been hailed time and again as a great novelist. He has his zealous partisans and his equally outspoken enemies. But the reviewers and critics, by and large, have been content to dismiss him with faint praise.

There are various reasons for all this. Like Faulkner, Fisher has shunned the *soirées* and refused to help grease the machinery of publicity and "connections" that manufactures book sales. His flat refusal to compromise any of his convictions, and his intransigeant stand regarding the treatment of sex in his novels, have probably cost him some favor with publishers who might have made his works more viable. But we can have nothing but admiration for a writer whose serious regard for his work counsels him to spurn glittering Hollywood offers and to hold tenaciously to a high purpose through years of toil and begrudged public attention and relatively small emolument.

Fisher has been difficult to catalogue; his novels have fitted into no neat category; just as one believed Fisher had emerged as a novelist of the recent frontier (*Toilers of the Hills*), he became a Wolfean autobiographer (the tetralogy); or he had just fixed himself as a psychoanalytical writer *(Forgive Us Our Virtues)* when he exfoliated as an historical novelist *(Children of God)*. No writer can be so Protean and still be first rate, might be the dictum of Fisher's exasperated critics. And then, there is an extremism in Fisher's work which tends to alienate the average susceptibility. Like Wolfe, he has until recently seemed to make a fetish of force and power and hence to exaggerate and distort. With him a point had not been made until it had been doubly made. Wolfe's gigantism and Fisher's extremism sprang from the same power-fetish, but while in Wolfe one glimpsed an occasional sunny vista and an intermittent balance, in Fisher there is never a moment of equanimity; the conflicts and tortures of his protagonists are exhausting, as they are unresolved. The resulting over-balanced picture and the "life's not like that" effect it has upon the average reader is another reason for Fisher's lack of popular acceptance.

It might be profitable, in this connection, to make a comparison between Fisher and another writer of not altogether dissimilar nature, Erskine Caldwell. At first glance there would seem to be many correspondences. Both deal with bucolic subjects, both approach their material realistically, both depend heavily on colloquialisms in dialogue and narrative style, both have a "message," both are concerned with aspects of modern life that are brutal and raw, both are vigorously and uncompromisingly outspoken, and finally both render a report on life that is, to say the least, unencouraging. But the divergences are equally marked. Caldwell maintains a rigidly objective attitude toward his characters and keeps himself out of his fictions. Fisher, as the creator, is always in attendance upon his portrayals; one feels his presence even though there are no overt author's asides. Caldwell is the mouthpiece for a philosophy of social amelioration and leans toward the political left; Fisher has a system of corrective psychology with which to save the human race and is a conservative in politics. Caldwell's debt to predecessors outside the realistic stream seems greatest to Faulkner; Fisher's perhaps to Wolfe. Of the two men, one feels that Fisher is the more versatile and still growing, while Caldwell has been the finer artist.

Caldwell, dealing with characters as near the animal level as any of Fisher's, and choosing them with as little regard for their representative norm as Americans, has always had a large audience. His people, starved and dull as they are, lewd and lusty as goats (whose sexual affairs are reported with a humorous leer) appeal to us as being somehow human. We can laugh comfortably at them, since they are far enough removed from the conception we have of ourselves as civilized beings. We can feel sorry for them and even become militantly aroused by the injustice they suffer. But in Fisher's case we have none of this sense of removal; he insists that we identify ourselves with his people. His characters' ignoble patterns of thought and pretences of superiority are presented as the norm for humanity. Our self-love is affronted, and we read insults into these books. That is exactly the trouble: we feel that this is precisely how Fisher wants us to react. It is as if he has a perverse wish to outrage us, as if in his desire to publish discoveries of our common frailty he stands in the position of prosecutor and accuses us of crimes.

For it is evident that Fisher's novels have sometimes cloaked a resurgent tractician, and that the message has often gotten in the way of the story. The argument underlying several of his novels is that modern man can find salvation only when he knows himself and is willing to act on that knowledge. When we admit that we have animal impulses, and are not ashamed to act according to them, we will have gone a long way toward self-knowledge. When we realize that we live largely by false moral standards and act out a lifelong drama of deceit and subterfuge by evading our ego-drives, we shall be in a position to develop our true humanity. The co-existent urges toward self-love and selflessness must find a happy balance before we can be delivered. "We are betrayed by what is false within," is the theme of the tetralogy and of other novels; it even appears to be the central idea toward which the "ascent of man" series is shaping. To illustrate this argument seems to have been the principal intention of such novels as *No Villain Need Be* and *Forgive Us Our Virtues*. Even *April*, a delightful satire and parable, is not without the didactic element. And this is undoubtedly another reason why Fisher is not as widely read as some of his contemporaries.

Regardless of these handicaps, and they are serious ones, Fisher's position as novelist is certainly equal to that of Caldwell. For what he may lack in finesse and in artistic craftsmanship he easily makes up in scope and depth. As Caldwell is the spokesman for the Negro and the sharecropper of Georgia (less in his novels perhaps than in his documentary and travel books), so Fisher is the delineator of the Idaho farmer. Caldwell's few writings with a New England background and his one lamentable excursion into a portrayal of Russian life do not compare in any way with the extended scope that is Fisher's. Besides the Idaho mountain man and his hard-bitten ways of life, Fisher made the American western hegira his province in one of the great historical novels of our day. Unlike others of our modern primitives, he has not hesitated to write "intellectual" novels; and finally he has embarked on the most dangerous of all novelistic seas, that of recreating Mankind—a task that has been tried before with dire results. Thus his scope is indubitable; whether he has "found himself" in any field is a question that concerns only his detractors. He has done distinguished work in all of these fields; and to the present time, he has made his greatest contributions in the realistic tradition in *Children of God* and *In Tragic Life*.

His two earliest novels, by themselves, would have been enough to make the reputation of an average novelist, who would have gone on repeating the formula until, by dint of sheer repetition, he had made his weight felt. *Toilers of the Hills* (1928) and *Dark Bridwell* (1931) are poignant, deeply beautiful novels of the Idaho soil in which Fisher paid tribute to the people and the acres of his youth. They are probably the most objective of his novels (before *Children of God*), and they have a freshness and a nascent power that is lacking in the later books. Opal and Dock Hunter, the indomitable couple who cleared sagebrush and planted wheat on an Idaho homestead fifty years ago, are fine, original people. Charley Bridwell whose dark destiny it was to play the role of a Lear when he was so obviously meant for a life of lazy philosophizing—his story is alternately tender and brutal. These novels are all story-telling; the preacher in Fisher never shows his zealot's face. Their characters are, like Caldwell's, childlike people in whom myth and lore are strong, since they live in a world tenanted by vast interrogations. Their knowledge is so limited and their animal power so great that, like Jeeter Lester and his family, they exist almost on a level of intuitive awareness. We pity them and are moved by the elemental sufferings they endure, but we do not closely identify ourselves with them and their misfortunes. There is seldom anything humorous about them; Charley Bridwell finds it comical to teach his three-year-old son Hamlin to chew tobacco and swear. ". . . he would stand up and curse with such deadly earnestness that his father would nearly fall off his rock with laughter. 'The God-damn trees!' Ham would shout, in his small enraged voice. 'Who put them there, I'd like to know! Christ and Jesus on them, the sons-of-bitches!'" Jeeter's profanity ultimately becomes funny, but not so Ham's. That Fisher can write comedy is admitted; the second novel of the tetralogy, *Passions Spin the Plot,* rises to heights of high comedy. Fisher believes that irony is the only source of humor,[1] and it is true that "Forenoon" McClintock's escapades, Vridar Hunter's first experiences with drunkenness, are hilariously funny; but in a different sense than Jeeter Lester's actions are funny. There is something wry in the response Vridar's peccadilloes wring from us, because we have a recognition of ourselves in him; we laugh at Jeeter largely because he is, to our sense, grotesque; we do not delight in his misery so much as find joy in his unusual reactions to environment. There is too much that is relevantly personal in Vridar's and "Forenoon's" reactions. On the whole there is not much humor in Fisher; his work is for the most part deadly earnest, extraordinarily "serious," and informed with an almost Calvinistic fervor to be truthful according to its own lights.

Only the short novel *April* (1937) besides *Passions Spin the Plot* has this lighter touch, the humor of irony, and it differs widely in tone and spirit from the Caldwellian comedy. In poking fun at the homely heroine April, which was June Weeg's pet name for that lovely woman she knew her unseen inner self to be, Fisher far too much intellectualizes the situation, and what was evidently planned

[1] "All genuine humor is ironic. It is not possible to conceive of any other kind."—*The Neurotic Nightingale.*

as comedy (and sometimes written in a style ponderously "comic" [2])
turns finally to a dubious pathos. The novel remains an indeter-
minate entity, but it provides an interesting contrast to staple
American humorous fiction as represented in Caldwell. June is not
really funny; she is an interesting case of megalomania; perhaps
with some justice a similar view could be taken of the mountebanks
in *God's Little Acre* who are not really funny but absorbing cases
of erotomania.

Though it is probable that Fisher regards himself as a comic
writer in the Meredithian sense, it is more likely that he will be
remembered as an Ecclesiastes of modern life. He will be remembered also as a chronicler of the Mormon story, and perhaps as a
fictioneering champion of philosophic Naturalism. It is in these
three aspects that one may most profitably consider his work
through the most successful novels in each kind: *In Tragic Life* for
the first; *Children of God* for the second; and the early panels of
his anthropological series for the third. They are the summits of his
achievement. The lesser novels have interest and some of them
easily exceed in value books far better known. In a sense it may be
unfortunate that *In Tragic Life* was the first section of the tetralogy
which included *Passions Spin the Plot, We Are Betrayed,* and *No
Villain Need Be,* since it so clearly overshadowed them. They were
anti-climactic, but any of them, by itself, was a respectable performance. Furthermore, the series did not add up to the excellence
of its parts. In this respect the Vridar Hunter tetralogy does not
compare with *Studs Lonigan,* though the two epics are in other
ways comparable. Among the historical novels *Children of God* is
easily superior to *City of Illusion* and *The Mothers. April* and *Forgive Us Our Virtues* were two excursions into abnormal psychology
and succeeded least as fiction. Finally we arrive at *Darkness and the
Deep* and *The Golden Rooms,* where again one can only feel that

---

[2] June had a thigh "as large as the waist of many girls; . . . she measured her
hips and then upon the earth she drew the circumference and stood within.
'As big as a washtub or a sofa or a well. Just the size of a barrel,' she said. Her
calf and her neck, they were the same size: two feet anybody might say and
she would not say no, three feet or six feet, or half a mile. The distance around
her was just about equal to that of the equator; and how could a man be expected to love that?"—*April.*

Fisher is blazing a perilous trail but that he might with luck arrive at a safe destination.

Among autobiographical studies of adolescence in fictional form, *In Tragic Life* stands in a small and elect company. *Look Home-ward, Angel, Young Lonigan,* the early volumes of *Jean Chris-tophe*—it is with works only like these that it can be compared. This searing evocation of childhood is charged with a passion for truth, for the anatomical exposure of every hidden event in Vridar Hunter's formative years, told as if for cathartic value, as if to exor-cise. This accounts for the Dreiserian doggedness in tracking down realistic detail and for the enormous and single-minded concentra-tion on the harsh aspects of life as they impinge on the conscious-ness of a hyper-sensitive youth. Vridar's early years were filled with loneliness and terror. "He gathered from them a morbid fear of blood and death; he never looked back upon them without pain. He learned to hate, with intensity that shook him, all the brutal and ruthless forces of life. . . . When looking back, across a great surface of time, he felt most deeply the agony and fright. . . . It was the seared and blinded hours that rose out of darkness and lived again." Given this attitude, the recounting of childhood's experiences was bound to be a horrific tale, but it was equally certain to be an honest one, for Vridar not only hated brutality but despised all falsity and sham and regarded even the ordinary small pretenses, like the myth of Santa Claus, as betrayals. His reactions to these betrayals are always extraordinarily violent; he retches, weeps, turns into the dark, or seeks escape in the hills. Upon the occasion when he learned the facts of birth, he "rose, feeling violently sick, and went into the bedroom. He lay on the bed and retched; and when his mother heard him and came, he turned from her and strove to hide his face." These remarkably strong reactions are those of an almost insanely sensitive individual; and the rendering of that in-dividual's experience is done in like terms. Less highly organized beings, the rest of us may tend to feel that all these reactions are overwrought, that no childhood could be so harrowing, no environ-ment so inimical as that of the black canyon of the Snake River in which Vridar grew up.

Joe and Prudence Hunter, his parents, were stern, puritanical

Mormons, and they knew nothing of child psychology. Their lack
of understanding helped warp and distort Vridar's view of life;
every natural discovery and inclination of his youth and young
manhood was blighted by parental indifference or proscription; his
native environs, and the playmates of his childhood were both of
them primitive or savage; life became a nightmare to be endured.
The burgeoning of sexual instinct and interests in the boy, more
powerful than in most, received preternatural repressions. When
Vridar persuaded his little sister to expose herself before him, and
his mother discovered what he had done, she spoke quietly first,
then flogged him with a chokeberry limb, and "it wrought upon his
soul a violent distortion; it laid a lonely estrangement between
mother and son. Because from every burning stroke, he took into
his heart, not a clear sense of error, but a ghastly dread of the
beautiful, the sweet, and the unexplained. Nothing was right, nothing was godly, except pain and solitude and hard ways. That was
the meaning, that was the lesson, of the chokeberry limb. The soft,
the alluring, and all the tenderness of rapture: these were of the
devil, these were to be cast out. There was sin in the world, there
was guilt, and it was decoyed in everything of loveliness and light;
and virtue, upon which God alone smiled, was to be found in the
stern and the austere."

There were few interludes in which life took on any brighter
raiment. On the whole "when he looked back . . . his adolescence
seemed to have been a dreary autumn, with little in it of light and
hope. It was a gray time, a time of despair." He believed that all
the world was bad, but curiously, that "nearly all the people in the
world were honest, wise, and brave." Only he was vile. Yet at times
even he felt stirrings of greatness, and from determining to be a
prophet, he resolved to be a great poet or a teacher. His brother,
Mertyl, a couple of years younger, reacted more equably to this
harsh life; and we are never in any doubt as to the really exceptional quality of Vridar or of his exceptional response to life. The
boy is by no means average; he is a genius. It is only when we
understand this fundamental circumstance that we can account for
the agony and terror with which Vridar's story is filled. It is Vridar's

agony we are meant to feel; life is "tragic" for him; it is much less so for everyone else in his world.

And yet the picture we get of the two little boys, lost like waifs in this cruel outpost of the Idaho hills, is a moving one; we cannot help suffering with them, and we feel pity and tenderness as they creep through this amazingly brutal scene, each with such infinite potential capacity for absorbing love and beauty and a little understanding, yet condemned to wander, strangers and afraid, beneath the dark sky of a benighted childhood.

In its technical aspects *In Tragic Life* shows flaws, but the novel triumphs over them by the sheer power and intensity of its manner. Fisher is constantly holding bait up before our eyes: he prefixes each scene with signal. "The first crucial period of Vridar's life fell between the April and the October of his ninth year. Twice, during this while, his spirit was desolated by his father's wrath. . . . Joe's first rage fell in the month of June. It came about this way." These stage-settings are superfluous when they do not detract from the effectiveness of the drama. In scene after scene Vridar is shown as reacting with almost identical outward effect, as mentioned above. These repetitions are annoying; but they cannot materially harm the novel. It sweeps through and beyond such flaws in the mighty tide of its vigor, thoroughness and passionate honesty.

Certain scenes are unsurpassed for raw outspoken power, as that of the disemboweled horse, or of Vridar in the flume, or of the innumerable bloody fights. The Fisher style, tending to nervous effects and a Wolfean rhetoric, is fully adequate although there is often a feeling of language being pushed to its extremes. And there are passages of remarkable beauty, as when Vridar responds to the burgeoning year. "He walked in fancy, and beauty clothed him. Beauty gave him golden trousers of sunlight, hats of cloudscarf, and shoes of odorous soil. In a later time he traveled far on land and sea; he awaited spring in many places; but he never saw it shower such wealth, such mammoth armfuls of loveliness, as it bestowed with blind extravagance upon this sunken bottomland, this well of winter that was his home. Summer he had learned to fear because of its murmuring flies, the passionless aloofness of its zenith, the quiet fixed insanity of its heat; autumn because of its carpets of desolate frost, the naked bones of its trees, and its loneliness; winter because of its white deserts and screaming winds. But spring was all tenderness and faith. Its great pulse gushed and ran and out of everything came beauty. The sky was a blue allegory, each tree was a green parable; the sun was a warm legend out of Palestine. He loved it. He trusted it. April and violet and bluebird: it was a time to smell and breathe and feel. Ah, Spring! Spring!"

Stylistically *Children of God* (1939) is in all respects on a par with the tetralogy, but it is worlds removed in tone, spirit, and method. The often tortured and neurotic self-obsession of the Vridar Hunter books led some to believe that Fisher was a novelist with but one story to tell. *Children of God* prodigally proved them wrong. It is wholly objective in its dramatization of the Mormon movement, a saga that encompasses scores of characters, literally hundreds of fantastic events, and nearly a century of time. It adheres faithfully to the historic facts; one of Fisher's boasts is that in his historical fiction he has never imagined a basic fact or event; and still *Children of God* is selective and, in its mass, a balanced artistic whole. Its three sections center attention first upon Joseph Smith, founder of the religion, then upon Brigham Young, its consolidator, and lastly upon a group of fictional third generation Mormons who are symptomatic of the spiritual decay and ultimate disintegration of the church. If the first two sections seem more vivid and better realized than the concluding one, it is upon history and not the novelist's handiwork that the blame must be laid. No historical novelist ever built more closely upon the records; it may be a limiting factor in Fisher's case that his conception of such fiction excludes the license Tolstoy allowed himself in *War and Peace* and fixed his boundaries so straitly in the tradition of *Henry Esmond.* However that may be, *Children of God* is all drama and has the pace and color of its epoch, a straightforward chronology, and it eschews authorial asides. Its Esmond is Brigham Young, who breathes with sturdy life in an interpretation that is more satisfactory than any biographer's; its Beatrix is Amelia, the only one of more than twenty wives who fathomed the heart of that desert statesman. Numerous others are limned with nearly equal insight.

Caldwell's use of colloquialism is one of his more distinguishing practices; Fisher too has a remarkably accurate ear for speech, and he has produced the racy Rocky Mountain argot in all of his books. *Children of God* is especially rich in them, though one sometimes wonders if they were all current during Joseph Smith's time. Mormon lore because of its Western pioneer associations is replete with wonderfully expressive epithets and figures of speech; Fisher dug into a mine of them in his researches for this novel. "Mouth-almighty," "hog-in-togs," "pack up your daisy kickers," "send you to hell across lots," "devil-dodgers," and scores more, besides the insane rhetoric of a Parley Pratt or a Sidney Rigdon, strengthen the picturesque realism of a historical novel planted firmly in a great tradition.

For the present, at least, Fisher has given up historical fiction as it is usually defined; but he has launched upon an undertaking of literally unlimited scope: a novelized reconstruction of man's growth from the pre-human stage to his present degree of civilization. *Darkness and the Deep* (1943), the first volume, established the cosmic beginnings, described our universe according to Jeans and Whitehead, and traced the slow ascent of life from protoplasm to the first prehistoric man who learned to use a club. *The Golden Rooms* (1944) continued the evolutionary epic. At the outset having the aspect of a *tour de force,* the series as it progresses promises to shape toward a successful achievement, but it is still too early to prophesy. One feels that, so far, an incredible amount of ingenuity and steady stratagem was required to make the sub-human figures and their poor, beastlike reactions to environment sufficiently dramatic to hold attention. With material such as this a novelist, whose business is to portray human beings in conflict, with their retinue of ideas and customs and morals, is very nearly hamstrung. Yet *The Golden Rooms* manages the feat of dramatizing the discoveries and awakenings of these insapient beings in a striking degree. We see Harg, the Stone Age man, surrounded by his females and children, learning almost by chance, yet with some vestige of intelligent direction, to make a fire with sticks. We follow him as he discovers that with fire he can hold off the terrors of night and the cold. We enter with him into the "golden rooms" of firelight in those long prehistoric nights when the world was young and infinitely terrible for ignorant, animal-like men. We see him strut and become a tyrant through his superior claims as a fire-maker. It cannot be said that we identify ourselves with him, but we cannot help feeling sympathy and some vicarious terror as this ancient life impinges on the imagination.

We have had similar experiments in fiction before, from Jack London's lamentable *Before Adam* to Johannes V. Jensen's trilogy *The Long Journey*. I doubt if any novelist, working in the realistic tradition, and positing a naturalistic view of the universe, will ever have done as thorough a job as Fisher's when his series is completed. The project promises to be a multiple-volumed series; it may telescope eons and it may lavish details in the life of a single figure, Christ, let us say. This is historical fiction on a vaulting scale, and that is the measure of Vardis Fisher's ambition. It is a talisman of his scope and resources; and it is doubtful if any other naturalist, literary or philosophic, among his contemporaries, will hew more closely to the naturalistic line, and work with more patience and fortitude. The series, at this late date in his development, shows a continuing improvement in technique. In the marshaling of narrative, in sheer story-telling, *The Golden Rooms* is superior even to *Children of God;* and in style it is more direct, simple, and effective than any writing he has so far done. From these facts one might easily see an augury of greater work to come. If, as can hardly be doubted, it is the duty and the glory of the novelist to illumine life's meanings by dealing with our common humanity, then Fisher must soon turn his attention not to man the puppet of history, but to man the social being who suffers and rhapsodizes in his full stature upon the summit of all his inheritance. That he is equipped to do this, *In Tragic Life* showed. The answer, whether he will do it again, and with universal meaning, waits upon the completion of his experiment-in-progress.

Here She is!

THE STORY OF TOPSY

LITTLE LONELY OF CENTRAL ASIA

BY

Mildred Cable and Francesca French

HODDER AND STOUGHTON
ST. PAUL'S HOUSE, LONDON, E.C.4

First printed 1937

PRINTED AND BOUND IN GREAT BRITAIN FOR HODDER & STOUGHTON, LIMITED
BY RICHARD CLAY & SONS, LIMITED, BUNGAY, SUFFOLK.

SCENE

THE Chinese town called Spring-of-Wine which is situated at the western extremity of the Great Wall. To the north lies Mongolia and on the south is Tibet. The town is at the foot of the snow-clad Richthofen Mountain Range.

In one corner of the town is a courtyard where three missionaries live. In this story they are called the Grey Lady, the Blue Lady and the Brown Lady, because they wear Chinese dress of these colours.

LIST OF ILLUSTRATIONS

Facing page

CHAPTER ONE

TAP, tap, tap; tap, tap, tap, went the little
stick on the uneven stone outside the courtyard door. It was certainly a beggar asking
for food, but which of them could it be?
This house was on the calling list of most, and
the people who lived in it knew well the special
sign by which each one clamoured for attention.

Again tap, tap, but no other sound. It

9

could not be old " Ragbags," for he always yelled furiously if not attended to at once, nor " Grannie Bless and Curse," for her whine was unmistakable, nor could it be " Mother Hubbard " with a brood of borrowed babies trained to weep in chorus round the courtyard door. All these beggars called frequently, for they had noted the address as that of a house where no dog was kept and where food was always given to the hungry.

Tap, tap, tap, once more, and the lady in blue walked to the door to see who it might be.

" I have never seen this little girl before," she called out; then she spoke in Chinese : " Where do you come from, my child ? "

The little girl who stood there was about seven years old, and was dressed in a few dirty rags tied on to her anyhow. As soon as she saw the lady, she pointed to her legs, which were bleeding from dog-bites; then she held out a small, coarse cotton bag, asking for a morsel of food. Her lips parted and there came a strange sound, such as is only made by those who are deaf-and-dumb. Meanwhile her big eyes were looking anxiously to see if a dog lurked in any corner; but, seeing none, she grew more bold, and pointed again to the wounds on her legs, indicating how dogs had come up behind and bitten her.

"Cannot the child speak?" said the lady in blue, then called out to some unseen companion: "Come and see this poor mite. She seems to be deaf-and-dumb, and her legs are bleeding from horrible dog-bites."

Instantly the door-curtain of a room was lifted and a tall lady in grey stepped into the courtyard, followed by another dressed in brown. The Grey Lady walked quickly across and stood looking down at the child; but the Brown Lady, after one glance, turned off to the kitchen and came out holding a bowl of steaming broth in one hand and a large piece of bread in the other.

At the sight of food the child's face beamed, and she threw down her tiny stick and bag to take bowl and chop-sticks from the hand of her new friend; but, before she was allowed to eat, the Blue Lady took her two grimy hands, held them in her own, and pointed to the sky, to show that thanks must be given to God in heaven. The child seemed to understand, for she gave one quick nod and looked upward before she fell on the food.

When it was finished she again pointed to her legs, so the Blue Lady bent down and examined the wounds, and then called for a basin of water, while the Brown Lady went indoors and brought old linen and bandages with which to dress them.

Though the child could neither speak nor hear, she seemed to understand everything, and when the Blue Lady, pointing at the sun, told her to come again next day at the same hour for another bowl of food, she grinned and nodded, then picked up her stick and went out of the courtyard, looking cheerfully back, as much as to say, " I have found some good friends to-day."

CHAPTER TWO

NEXT day there was no little tap, tap, tap
at the courtyard door, but instead a great
squawk and a yell, followed by a volley of
oaths from someone calling down curses on
the heads of the three ladies.

"Where is that fierce dog which bit my
poor little girl yesterday? Can't you keep
the brute tied up? My child's legs are torn
to bits. I'll go straight to the Mandarin, and
he shall deal with you."

The speaker was an angry, shrill-voiced
woman, evidently mother to the little dumb
child of the day before. She, however, was

no beggar, but was decently dressed, and the reason of her visit was quite evident : she wanted money, and was out to make trouble. The cook thrust his head round the kitchen door, looked her once up and down and spoke :

" If you think that we are the kind of people to give you money just because you come here storming, you are quite mistaken. We have no dog, and never had one. No one but our ladies would have bandaged the legs of your good-for-nothing child and used the most expensive ointment. You are a fine one to dress up as you do, and your child with not a rag to cover her. Why should she be begging ? Are you a beggar too ? "

When she realised that there was no dog on the premises, the woman was somewhat taken aback, and not knowing what to say, she turned her abuse on the child.

" It is just like that little idiot to mislead me. She pointed to this house, and as good as told me she had been bitten by the dog. I'll thrash her for this."

The Grey Lady now appeared on the scene.

" What is this noise ?   Are you the mother of that starving child who came here yesterday ? You had better not talk so freely about thrashing her, for when a woman dressed as you are drives her child out to beg, she may get into trouble over it."

The woman saw that these people were not easily frightened and had no dog, so, after more blustering, she walked off muttering curses. As the cook shut the door behind her, he said to the Blue Lady :

" Teacher, don't you touch that little girl again. Let her sores look after themselves. The woman is a bad lot, and her child must go hungry."

The cook and the ladies were still talking when Grannie Fan appeared on the scene. Someone had told her that a woman from West Street had been round abusing the missionaries and accusing them of setting their dog on her child, so she had come at once to help, feeling that she could deal with such a

woman better than they could.   She was soon
sitting cross-legged on the warm *kang*,[1] with a
cup of tea by her.   The cook used no tea-pot,
but ran across with a boiling kettle and poured
the water on to a pinch of tea-leaves and dried
jasmine petals in a dainty cup without a handle,
but with a china lid.   This served the double
purpose of pot and cup.

While Grannie Fan sipped they all talked,
the cook standing in the doorway half in and
half out of the room.   He was disgusted with
the whole business, and had his say first.

" It is like her impudence to come to our
house and make a scene !   Our ladies were
much too gentle with her.   Neither she nor
her child must be allowed inside the door
again.   If she comes, you just leave her to me."

" I have seen that *ya-ba*[2] about the town,"
said Grannie Fan.   " They call her ' Gwa
Gwa.' "

" ' Gwa Gwa '—' Little Lonely '—what a sad

---

[1] *Kang*, a brick or mud bed heated with a fire.
[2] *Ya-ba*, the Chinese word for deaf-mute.

The Blue Lady.

The Grey Lady.　The Brown Lady.

name for a child!" said the Brown Lady. "But she must not be punished more than we can help for her mother's faults."

The cook sniffed, and Grannie Fan shook her head; but the Blue Lady declared decisively, "Little Gwa Gwa must never be turned from our door," so, when the tap, tap, tap was heard again next day, she hurried to welcome her small friend, who stood there smiling, asking for more, and quite sure that she would get it.

B

CHAPTER THREE

GRANNIE FAN'S sharp eye always showed when she was hot on the scent of a mystery.

"There is more in this than you think," she whispered. "I just wonder if that woman is her real mother at all. I have some shopping to do, so I will be off now, and as I go up West Street I shall drop in on some friends I have there. Whatever there is to be found out, I think I shall soon know."

A few minutes later she set out on this little

18

job of detective work. Her head was neatly tied up in a black silk scarf, in her hand she carried a coloured kerchief in which to wrap the things she intended to buy, and her whole appearance was so demure that none would have suspected her real business. She was away for several hours, and came back full of information.

"It is just as I thought, Teacher," she began. "I guessed rightly, and that woman is no mother of Gwa Gwa's. The child does not suspect it, for she was bought when she was only three weeks old, and they gave one and sixpence for her. The neighbours in West Street know about it, but no one dare say a word openly, for the woman's temper is terrible."

There was a grim look in her eye as she added:

"Two years after she bought her she had a boy of her own, and when she saw that Gwa Gwa was dumb, she turned against her."

As Grannie Fan was speaking there was the loud sound of a bell, and the Brown and Blue ladies hurried off, because this was the signal for the Children's Service.

Every evening at sunset you might have thought that the Pied Piper of Hamelin had come to Spring-of-Wine. Just as the sun dipped, a boy went down Jade Street ringing a bell, and children poured out from every door and alley, skipping, dancing and singing as they followed him back to the large open space where a big tent stood. This evening the crowd of children had already gathered, so the Blue Lady sat down at the harmonium and began playing gay tunes, while the Brown Lady sorted out a pile of musical instruments. There were tambourines, mouth-organs, flutes, jews'-harps, triangles and jingle bells.

The children all clamoured for an instrument, but they knew that only the well-behaved were allowed a place in the orchestra, so the next few minutes were spent in selecting the musicians, and then, as the tent was

Scraggy Boy and Wee Pup

quite full, they all climbed to their places on the platform.

Standing at the back were the tall boys with mouth-organs who sustained the melody, and down each side were the time-markers with their tambourines, while in front stood the smaller children with the other instruments. The smallest was little Moth, who jingled her bells in and out of time, but everyone who looked at her always said, " What a darling she is ! "

At a sign from the Brown Lady all rose to their feet and sang a greeting, with pauses for deep bows at the right moment, then burst into song, accompanied by a great volley of music from the tambourines, jingle-bells and flutes, while the harmonium sounded its loudest.

Each of these children in his own home saw father and mother burn incense to a wooden god, but when they came to this service the children never wearied of the songs, and those they sang most lustily were all about the true and living God and of how He loved them.

Gwa Gwa turned out to be dumb and cheated her."

"How did she cheat her?"

"Well, she says she paid too much for her."

"Teacher," said Joy Babe, "I live next door to Gwa Gwa, and I can hear her crying at night. They won't let her sleep on the *kang*, and all winter she lay on the icy mud floor."

"Poor little Gwa Gwa! I hope that you are all extra kind to her, and that you never tease her about not being able to speak," said the Blue Lady.

"Oh no, Teacher. We wouldn't do anything like that," answered all the children together.

"I gave her half a potato one day when she came to our door," said Sapphire, looking up for approval.

"If you children were half as good as you say you are, what a happy town this would be!" said the Blue Lady. "Now off you go, and come again to-morrow."

CHAPTER FOUR

Where did you come from, Lonely dear;
Out of the nowhere into here?

THIS is what the ladies wanted to ask, but Gwa Gwa could not tell them, and her mother would not. Other people did, though, and by degrees they learnt a lot more about her than she herself ever knew.

Midday generally brought the grandest callers to the missionaries' house. Lady Ma always came in a carriage with a whole retinue of attendants, and several nephews and nieces, besides her own children. Before she got out of her carriage, the outrider dismounted and came ahead to ask whether the missionaries were at home, and whether it was convenient for them to receive his mistress.

When the three ladies heard that Lady Ma was at the door, they all came out to meet her, while the cook hustled round, bringing a kettle to the boil and spreading out plates of cakes. There was a great deal of bowing, and a great many polite things were said as the caller was led to the seat of honour in the guest-room. As the cook filled her cup with tea, the Grey Lady rose, took up the chop-sticks, and with them helped her to some of each kind of cake that was on the table, adding a handful of melon-seeds, some peanuts and a few sultanas, while Lady Ma half rose and bowed graciously, begging the Grey Lady not to trouble about her. Meanwhile the Blue Lady distributed handfuls of sweets to all the children, who stuffed their pockets with the good things.

Gwa Gwa happened to be sitting in a sunny

corner, devouring a bowl of hot dough-strings, and Joy saw her at once.

"Look, Ma-ma, there is Gwa Gwa," she called out; "and just see her legs—they are tied up with clean bandages where the dogs bit her."

"Ah," said Lady Ma, "what kind hearts these missionaries have!"

"Do you know the child?" asked the Grey Lady.

"Yes," said Lady Ma, "she often comes begging at our door; but she is an independent child, and if we give her something to eat, she does a little job in return. The fact is, she is well born, and she cannot take to begging."

"Well born?" exclaimed the Brown Lady. "Whose child, then, is she?"

"I will tell you all about it," said Lady Ma; then, turning to the children: "Now, then, Snowflake and Peony, run away with Joy and play in the flower-garden."

As soon as they were gone she lowered her voice:

" Gwa Gwa's own mother lived away in the Tibetan hills, and when the child was born she did not want her, so a relative of hers found a foster-mother for the baby, and it was that woman in West Street. She had no child of her own, and when she bought Gwa Gwa she was very proud of her because she was so pretty. I remember that as a baby she used to wear a satin cap with a little cat's face embroidered on it and silver bells dangling from each side."

Meanwhile Snowflake had slipped back to hear the grown-ups talk secrets. Now she broke into the conversation :

" Ma-ma, Peony won't come to the flower-garden. She says she is hungry and wants more sweets."

" Naughty Peony ! Take this to her "— giving her a double handful of monkey nuts— " then, precious, you may run and see if the carriage has come."

As soon as the child was gone, Lady Ma went on with the story :

Only the Well-Behaved were allowed a place in the Orchestra.

" When the girl turned out to be dumb, the woman was very angry, and from that time she turned against her and ill-treated her. Later on a boy of her own was born, and then she had no further use for Gwa Gwa, so she turned her out to beg."

" What a sad story ! " said the Blue Lady. " I thought the woman had a very cruel face, and I could see that the child was terrified of her."

" Oh, yes, she must be," said Lady Ma; " but of course she will be all right now, for you Christians are always kind to the poor, and I am quite sure she will not go hungry any more."

" Ma-ma, Ma-ma, the carriage is here," said Snowflake; " let us go home."

" All right, precious, I am coming. Here is a copper for Gwa Gwa."

The Grey Lady walked the whole length of the courtyard with her visitor, begging her all the way to step slowly and to be sure to come again soon. At the street door there were more bows and more compliments. The driver set down a little stool for his mistress to step on as she got into the carriage, the outrider leapt to the saddle, and the children scrambled into the second carriage, except Peony, who sat by her mother.

When they were gone, little Gwa Gwa caught the Blue Lady's eye and pointed to her legs.

"Yes, little girl," said her friend, "I will change the bandages, and you must come again to-morrow for another good meal."

Though Gwa Gwa was deaf, she understood quite well, and in her heart she wondered why these people were so different from everyone else in the town, and why they never drove her away.

CHAPTER FIVE

STANDING just outside the courtyard door
where Gwa Gwa first tapped her little stick,
and looking up, you would see a range of high
mountains covered with snow and ice.

All through the summer the ice-fields
glittered, and when it was very hot the townspeople would look out and think how lovely
and cool it must be up there; but everybody
knew that the Tibetans who lived in the hills
were a fierce people who shot strangers at sight,

31

and that it was not safe to go among them. It would be all right if they invited you; but the trouble was how to get the invitation.

Early one summer morning the three ladies were having their breakfast in the flower-garden, when an odd-looking man strode in. He was very tall, and looked very strong. He wore a pointed yellow cap, which made him look still taller, and round his shoulders was a red shawl. His boots were of purple leather. When the ladies looked up, he stretched out his right hand, palm upwards, and with the fingers of the other hand he caught the skin of his throat and pulled it forward. They knew what this meant: here was a Tibetan, and he had a favour to ask.

When a Tibetan pulls on the skin of his throat it means that he is going to ask for something, so they called out: "Come and sit down, Lama, and have a cup of tea."

The Tibetan never says "no" to a cup of tea, and the Lama walked towards them right across the flower-beds. He knew nothing

Mid-day Callers.

about gardens, and treated this one like a bit of meadowland.

He sat down on the ground while the Grey Lady went to a cupboard and brought out a skin of butter which smelt very strong. She took a good lump of it, and when she had poured out a large bowl of tea, she stirred in the butter, because she knew that a Tibetan likes good tasty butter in his tea. On the table was a pile of rolls of bread. They were not baked, but steamed, so instead of a crust they had a thin white skin. She put five of these on a plate and set it in front of the Lama, because when the Tibetan eats, he eats a lot.

As they drank they talked, and the Lama told the ladies that he had come because his old mother was very ill, and he wanted some medicine for her.

" What is the matter with her ? "

" There is a pain inside her."

" Where is the pain ? "

" That I cannot say, for it is always moving about."

C

" Does it seem worse after she has eaten ? "

" Yes, yes, that is it. I see you know all about it. Will you give me something to stop the pain ? "

The lady in blue smiled and went to a side room, from which she brought back a little box with some pills in it.

" Lama," she said, " be very careful of these. They are for your sick mother and no one else. One disease, one remedy. She must take only two a day—one in the morning and one at night—and each time she takes one she must slowly drink a whole bowl of very hot water."

The Lama put the box of pills down the opening of his high boot because he had no pocket, then he drank three more bowls of butter tea and finished the bread. After this he stood up and bowed very courteously, with both hands outstretched.

" My home is three days' journey from here over yonder hills," he said. " It is hot in the city, but up there it is very cool. Will you not come and see us? Our pastures would be good for your horses."

Then he flung his red shawl around him and strode out. This invitation was what the missionaries had been waiting for. Now they knew they might go quite safely among those nomad people, because when a Tibetan asks you to his home, and you go as his guest, he will see to it that no one hurts you.

CHAPTER SIX

THE next person with whom to get in touch was Mr. Ban. He was a farmer whose land lay right up on the foothills of the Richthofen Range, and he grew potatoes for a living.

From childhood he had mixed with the Tibetans, and every year he bartered some of the produce of his farm for their unbroken colts, which, properly handled, made such valuable riding-horses.

He was certainly the best man with whom to talk things over, so a message went to him, and next day he turned up full of helpful advice and willingness to do his share.

36

Tibetan Prayer Wheel.

" The right time for you to go is before the sixth day of the sixth moon," he said; "for on that day all the tribesmen come to the Temple of the Golden Buddha for the great festival of the year. The Lamas there all know me, so I will go up with you myself. If you come as far as my farm in your carts, I guarantee that next morning there shall be as many horses as you need for the two days' ride up the passes."

The three ladies fell in with the plan, and at once began preparations for the trip. They would have to carry all the food for the whole party for as long as they stayed, as there was nothing to be bought up there. Each man would consume one pound of flour per day and half a pint of millet. They could be allowed only a taste of vegetable, but must certainly have plenty of capsicum chopped and frizzled in oil, with as much vinegar as they could carry. There would be six people—one man to look after the horses and keep them from straying, another to cook and mind the tents, and Mr. Ban would act as guide and general adviser.

When Joy's mother heard of the expedition, she sent her little girl round with a large wash-hand basin full of her own home-made vinegar, which was much better than what one could buy in the shops. It was dark, thick and strong, and every one was pleased, because a little would go a long way. The cook dipped the tip of his finger in the basin, licked it and smacked his lips saying, " This is splendid stuff—very sharp." He fetched two earthenware jars, filled them to the brim, corked them with maize-cobs and set them aside.

The cook's wife sent in a present of vegetables salted by herself. There were cucumbers, French beans and a kind of lettuce which has very few leaves but a large, firm stalk. The cook chopped these fine and packed them tightly into a basket, which he had lined with grease-proof paper to keep them moist.

The next matter to be arranged was that of getting sufficient flour for making the bread, of which they would carry fifty pounds. First the wheat was measured, then sieved until it was clean and soaked in cold water for some hours, after which it was well drained. By sunrise next morning the ladies heard the grinding-stone creaking, and knew that every-one was at work.

Before breakfast they went round to see how things were getting on, and found the cook's little girl, Golden Bud, in charge of the gentle brown mule, Molly, who, blind-folded and harnessed to the pole of the mill, walked round and round, turning the stone as she went. Whenever she slackened her pace Golden Bud just flicked her with a twig and on she went again.

A boy, hired by the day, was sifting the flour. He sat on a narrow board and worked the sifter with his feet, making a tremendous racket. By the time he paused, all the finest flour was in the wooden trough, and the coarser was ready to go back to the mill and be ground over again.

By early afternoon there were fifty pounds of fine white flour in the trough, and tired Molly was led back to her stable, patted, petted and given an extra feed of the good bran. Meanwhile the cook had the yeast ready, and all through the night it worked silently, until the solid mass of dough was light and spongy and ready to be kneaded into loaves.

The moment it had risen the bread must be steamed, and that was a big business. The hired boy was out borrowing extra steamers from friends and neighbours, while the cook stoked the fire with faggots, got the big iron pot boiling, and put the small, smooth loaves ready to fill the steamers. There were eight layers of them, and each layer held fifteen loaves. When he had packed them all and stuffed up every crevice with rag, the steam from the great iron pot below cooked all together.

It was hard work, and they rested a day before starting on the next heavy job. Then the Brown Lady said :

" To-morrow we must parch corn and beans to grind *zamba*."

" Yes," said the cook. " I have bought dried peas, oats, hemp and sesame, and with some of the wheat we have in the house we should get a sack of very tasty *zamba*."

Next morning the house was pervaded with a most delicious smell of roasting grain, and the cook was mopping his brow over a big fire on which stood a huge iron pot. In it were all these grains and with a small broom he swept them deftly to and fro, so that all should get roasted but none should scorch. Later on Molly was led out again to the grinding-stone, and before dark the hired boy staggered back with a sack of meal made from the parched grain. The Brown Lady tasted it and declared it to be very good.

" Now," she said, " if we are held up by rains we shall have enough food for the whole party."

The Grey Lady was busy in the book-room sorting out packets of Gospels, some of which were in Chinese, others in Tibetan and others in Mongolian; for they were sure to see Mongolian princes at the festival.

The carter spent the whole day overhauling the harness and the wheels, and getting the beasts shod. Once he came back to say : " I shall need two thousand cash [1] worth of leather thongs and a new whip." It sounded frightening, but as two thousand cash was only worth two shillings and fourpence, it was not as bad as it seemed.

By evening each beast was shod and all were ready for the journey. The carter knew that the river was in flood, and that were there one weak place in the harness, there might be an accident and someone drowned.

" We must cross early," he said, " before the snow melts in the mountains and the floods come down. I should like to be off by four o'clock in the morning."

[1] *Cash*, term used for a small Chinese copper coin.

CHAPTER SEVEN

THE river crossing was even more exciting than the carter had expected.
At three o'clock in the morning the moon
was bright, so he called up the hired boy
and sent him off to see for himself if the water
was safe. He came back with a message
from the river-men, but it was so vague that
it might have meant anything. They just
said, "A man has gone over," but whether
he had reached the other bank was quite
uncertain.

When the cart came in sight of the water,
everyone was anxious, for the river was three-

quarters of a mile wide, and though, here and there, you could see a strip of sandbank rising above the water, yet it was evident that the channels between ran deep and that the current was very swift.

Half a dozen river-men had built a hut of branches close to the water's edge. It was their business to help travellers, and to stop them from crossing when it was too dangerous; but in spite of their help and advice, it was a very common thing for men to be drowned because they were obstinate and would have a try even when warned not to go.

There was a good deal of talk between the driver and the river-men. They said, "You can do it," but everyone shuddered when the first plunge was taken and the terrible, swift water swirled around. All were silent except the carter, who talked to his team the whole way. He had trained the beasts to obey the word of command, and Molly, though she was small, was so clever and so obedient that she could always be trusted to

Child Lamas with Scripture Pictures.

lead. The sight of the river was terrifying indeed, for the water foamed and tossed, and you could hear the rattle of the great stones as the undercurrent sucked them down.

One river-wader went ahead, grasping a stout pole, with which he tested every step he took; for if the mules trod into a hole they would certainly fall, then the cart would be overturned and someone might lose his life. The carter cracked his whip and encouraged the beasts, but he never moved his own eyes from the next sandbank; for if once the water made him giddy and he lost his sense of direction, it would be impossible for him to control the beasts and give them the clear orders they needed.

At the sandbank they halted, but only for a moment, then they plunged again and got to the next one, and so from halt to halt until only one stream rushed between them and the other bank. This stream was a very wide torrent, and when they were quite near to safety, Lolly, the shaft-mule, stumbled and nearly fell.   She would have been under water if the carter had not leapt from his place and caught her bridle, giving, at the same time, a shout to Molly to pull for all she was worth. A moment later men and mules, dripping with water, reached dry land, and that crossing was over.

It was high time, for the water was rising rapidly, as it did each morning when the snow melted.   Indeed, the river-men could not get back to their hut, and would have to wait until evening to do so, for then it was cold in the heights and the snow did not melt so quickly.

The sun was now high, and it was very hot; moreover, all were hungry, so they sat down on the ground and ate little loaves of bread before they started again.   Towards the middle of the afternoon they reached Mr. Ban's farm on the slope of the hills, and the mules stood while the carter walked towards the house, which was enclosed by very high walls, like the keep of an old castle.   He cracked his whip as he went, for the dogs were out in a moment and ready to attack. The farm stood alone, yet no robber dared to come near, because fierce Tibetan mastiffs guarded the place, and were so strong that two of them could tear a man to pieces.

Mr. Ban, Mrs. Ban and all the little Bans came out to welcome the ladies, and the smaller children put their arms round the necks of the fierce dogs and ordered them to be quiet. A few minutes later the mules were in the stable and the guests were sitting on the *kang* sipping a cup of tea and watching Mrs. Ban's preparations for a very savoury supper.

No one wanted to sit up late, but such a supper could not be served or eaten in a moment. The ladies sat cross-legged and the little round table stood between them. On it their hostess first laid out eight saucers of tasty vegetable and pickles, taking great care to put each dish in exactly the right place. Two held green celery chopped very fine, on two others was shredded raw carrot, and on two more salted cucumber was piled.

There were also two dishes of a wild desert plant called "hair strands." This was a great dainty, though it only looked like coarse black hair; little shepherd boys dug it out of the sand, but after it was soaked in vinegar, it had a very nice flavour, like delicate, salty seaweed.

Before each visitor was a small saucer and with a pair of chop-sticks she could pick as she pleased among the dainties, while the last touches were being given to the *pièce de résistance*, which was a large dish of savoury antelope. At last Mr. Ban carried it in, and as his visitors tasted the meat, he told with pride how he had shot the game. His gun was a very old-fashioned firearm, and so heavy that he always rested it on a forked stick while he took aim. This made shooting a very difficult business; for the antelopes were shy, and so swift that it seemed impossible to get within range of them. Mr. Ban's father, however, had taught his son that if he sat in a cart drawn by an ox, he could get nearer to the herd than was possible on

"Gwa Gwa's real Mother lives just here," she said.

foot; for when the antelopes saw the cart moving so slowly, they stood to watch, and that was the hunter's chance to bring down his quarry.

After supper the family with all the hired labourers and the little shepherd boys gathered for prayers in the big room; for this was a Christian household, and they enjoyed singing " Onward, Christian soldiers " to the accompaniment of the small organ.

By the end of prayers everyone was more than ready for bed. The ladies slept on the big *kang* in the storeroom, which was stacked with every kind of grain, Mr. and Mrs. Ban and all their children shared the one in the general living-room, and the hired men and shepherd boys just lay down anywhere, close to the beasts for which they were responsible. Everyone had a wadded quilt in which he wrapped himself, and in a few minutes the whole tired household was fast asleep.

D

CHAPTER EIGHT

VERY early next morning the farmyard was full of horses. The packs had to be most carefully adjusted and all girths tightened, as the steep climb ahead would take every ounce of the animal's strength. Then all mounted and rode off towards the gorge down which the torrent rushed to the plain.

For two whole days they rode in the lonely mountains, crossing and recrossing the stream many dozens of times. Once they emerged from a gloomy gully on to a carpet of blue gentian, and at other times they trod on edelweiss. Overhead the great vultures circled majestically, and once an eagle dropped a beautiful little kangaroo rat just at the door of the tent. It had long hind legs like the kangaroo at the Zoo, yet it was small enough to stand in the palm of the hand, and its big flapping ears were as fine as an autumn leaf. The strange little creature's strength lay in its muscular tail, and it could jump so far and so quickly that it was almost impossible to catch one. Among the trees were wild peacocks, and at night the wolves and other wild beasts prowled around.

On the evening of the second day they rode out on to high pasture-land, where herds of yak were browsing, and sighted the tall buildings of the Lamasery, with tents scattered here and there and strange people moving around them.

It was these people who fascinated the travellers. The women wore riding-breeches and coats of sheepskin dyed red, green or blue, with high boots and tall hats trimmed with fox brushes. Their hair was plaited into twenty or more small plaits, according to the age of the wearer, and finished off with broad bands decorated with turquoise, jade, coral and shells. They chatted away in Tibetan, and when they saw the small harmonium which the ladies had brought, nothing pleased them so much as to sit on the ground peddling with their feet and pressing down the notes with their hands.

They fed mostly on sour milk and yak flesh, which they cut in strips and hung round their tents to dry in the sun. This was very strange, but their way of praying was stranger still. The Lamasery was surrounded with prayer-wheels, some of which were so big that the stream kept them turning like a water-mill. Many were turned by hand, and some that the Lamas carried about with them were no larger than a baby's rattle.

On the eight sides of each wheel a prayer

Heating Grannie Fan's Bed.

was written, and the Lamas told the people
that every time the wheel turned, the gods
reckoned that prayer had been said eight times.

The lower branches of the trees were hung
with bleached bones, and on each bone the
same prayer was written. Over the temple
roof little flags fluttered, and on each flag was
written that same sentence, so that when the
wind blew and the flags flapped and the bones
rattled the gods would be pleased. This is
the sentence which the Lamas call their
prayer :

ༀ་མ་ཎི་པདྨེ་ཧཱུྃ

Om mani padme hum

It means : " Hail ! thou precious jewel of
the Lotus Flower !

The Lord Jesus Christ once said, " When
you pray, do not use vain repetitions as the
heathen do," and this is the kind of thing
about which He was speaking. Every day
the Christians met under the trees where

the prayer-bones rattled and prayed for the people around them. They asked that these Tibetans might learn to look up to God and say " Our Father."

Everyone was excited, because in two days time the great festival would be celebrated, when the lamasery would be decorated with hand-painted banners and the Lamas would dress up and dance.

The Lamas always wore red shawls, and had bare feet and shaved heads. Many of them were only children, because every family gave one of its boys to serve in the temple, the mother generally bringing him when he was six years old. The head priest wore a yellow silk gown and a huge hat shaped like a cock's-comb. Wherever he went trumpeters marched ahead announcing his arrival. The din was enough to make one deaf, but these strange people believed they were doing great honour to the man in yellow by all this noise. They worshipped him as a kind of god, and the name of Living Buddha which they gave him showed that they thought him different from everyone else.

He was pleased with the presents they brought, listened to the clanging of cymbals and beating of drums, and received prayers as though he were really a god; but he was only a man, and could do nothing for the sins of the poor people, for he did not even know how his own sins could be forgiven. The Christians had come to tell of God Who is love and of Jesus Christ Who is Saviour. It was wonderful news, and the Lamas took the Gospels and carried them as great treasures to the Lamaseries, which are far away in the fastnesses of Inner Tibet, where no missionary can go.

On the day of the festival the Tibetans came riding in from all sides, and after a while there was a great stir, and everyone ran towards the Lamasery where the courts were filling up with excited people. The reason of the excitement was that the Lamas were about to perform the temple dances. The dresses they wore were the strangest you can imagine, and on their heads were very cleverly made masks, which rested on their shoulders. One wore an eagle's head, another that of a yak and a third was disguised like a wicked-looking giant with a black face and yellow eyes. They danced very cleverly, skipping and swaying and acting so as to make themselves look like the animals they represented.

The audience was delighted, and the crowd of women giggled and chatted. Sometimes when the blast of a trumpet was heard they all fell on their faces and muttered a prayer. The girls were on one side and the boys on the other; but of course the boys all looked at the girls, and the girls looked sidelong at the boys, yet none of them left the proper side until the service was over and they began to make merry together.

Then it was that someone said to the Blue Lady, " Gwa Gwa's real mother lives just here. She is one of those women wearing the tall hat, but no one is supposed to know. It is a secret, and no one must tell."

CHAPTER NINE

MEANWHILE Gwa Gwa was not faring too badly in the town.

Every day she could count on a bowl of good, hot, steaming food, for the cook had orders about that, and when the three ladies came back, he gave a deep sigh and said, "Ai-ya, what an appetite that child has! She makes a bigger dinner than I do," but he

57

quite forgot that he had breakfast and supper as well, whereas Gwa Gwa had neither.

The dog-bites had healed, but deep holes remained in the calf of her leg where the wicked woman had burnt her with a hot poker. It seemed as though the woman hated her more than ever now that she had friends, and Gwa Gwa kept out of her way as much as she could.

One summer evening she was late on her rounds, for she stayed playing knuckle-bones with some children in Jade Street. She was skilful at tossing and catching on the back of her hand, and was quite a star in the knuckle-bone club. Suddenly all the children jumped up and ran away, for they had caught the distant sound of the gong which announced the Children's Service. Little Lonely could hear nothing, but she followed the crowd to the door of the big tent, and there she sighted her friends the Brown Lady and the Blue Lady, just back from Tibet, and her heart leapt with joy to think that they were home again.

There was now a group of boys and girls who came to the Service and who were always ready to champion Gwa Gwa, so gradually she had a much better time of it. Many more people than formerly would give her a piece of bread or a small coin, and several times when the ladies met her in town they put her to sit on the luggage rack at the back of their cart, and brought her home to dinner in style, so that the whole town was saying, "Gwa Gwa is in luck's way."

About this time another little girl was obliged to join the ranks of the child beggars. Her father had been a postal courier who carried the mails from Spring-of-Wine to Mongolia. Each time he went he had to cross a dangerous river full of quicksands, and one day the horse stumbled into them, and in a moment horse and rider were sucked down and never seen again. His wife was dead, and when he did not come back the little girl had to beg her bread.

Gwa Gwa understood trouble and was very

sorry for this child, who had to learn how to fend for herself, so she brought her along to her friends' house to share the good things which she herself enjoyed, and now there were two children to gobble up the bowls of food. One day when they came for their midday meal they found their three friends just stepping into the little varnished cart with its blue quilted cover.

" We are going for a picnic," said the Blue Lady, " and you may come too, so both of you jump up on the luggage-rack."

Cakes, biscuits, meat dumplings and all kinds of good things were being packed in baskets, and the two children joyfully climbed up behind and sat with their legs dangling, grinning proudly at the street urchins as they drove through the town to the lake and pleasure-grounds, where great officials sometimes entertained their friends. Here the cart stopped and the children were given a large portion of food, and told to go and eat it on the bank of the pretty lake, where they could feed the water-fowl with the crumbs, while

Photo. The Autotype Fine Art Co.
The Lord Jesus said: "I am the Good Shepherd."

FIRST PRESBYTERIAN CHURCH
2619 BROADWAY
OAKLAND 12, CALIFORNIA

the ladies had their lunch in the pagoda on the small island over the wooden bridge.

It was quite late when they came home, and at the city gate they were held up by a long string of camels which was passing slowly in. The beasts were laden with bales of cotton, and the children called out with delight when they saw that one of the camels carried her baby lying in a wooden cradle on her back. The camp watch-dog had also secured a lift, but at the gate he leapt lightly down, for he knew it was his business to keep the camels in place.

It was sunset when they got home, and there was only just time to pick up the tambourines and go over to the tent where the children were all calling out :

" You're late, teachers.   Everyone is here except yourselves."

Gwa Gwa was no longer the lonely child she had been; though she was still poor and grimy, and was ill-used in her own home, yet all life had changed since some one loved and welcomed her.

CHAPTER TEN

GWA GWA'S friends came and went a good deal, and she was used to seeing them travel off, sometimes in one direction and sometimes in another. She knew that wherever they went a crowd gathered to listen to what they said, and she also knew that when the talking was over people bought lots of books and carried them away; but what the talking could be about, or why people wanted so many books, was a great mystery to her. However, it was the ladies' way of doing things, and after a few days or weeks they always came back again, and were as pleased to see Gwa Gwa as she was to see them.

The following summer, however, there

was a different feeling about the place, and Gwa Gwa was anxious with fear of changes which might mean trouble for her. She could ask no questions, but she noticed little things, just like a dog that scents unrest in the air, and she was quite sure that this time there were preparations for some extra long journey.

Several times the Blue Lady looked into her eyes so kindly and so sadly that Gwa Gwa's heart went chill, as though she had heard bad news. At other times the Grey Lady and Grannie Fan sat together on the *kang*. Their lips moved and they looked at Gwa Gwa, then their lips moved again, and she felt sure that they were talking about her and that the Grey Lady was saying :

" What about Gwa Gwa when we are not here ? "

One morning she arrived to find carts at the door and everyone in a hubbub, so she knew that the hour of parting had come. Her heart sank, and it was no joy when the ladies were specially gentle and gave her a little present.

She sat on a stone and watched the preparations. Parcels of books were carried out, then bags of flour, millet and sun-dried bread. Rolls of bedding were hauled on to the cart, and finally the frying-pan and a big iron pot were slung in place.

A crowd of people gathered in the open space. Many of them had brought presents of cakes, sugar or slabs of brick tea—that is, tea leaves pressed into the shape of a brick and stamped with handsome Chinese ideographs. When everything had been packed, Gwa Gwa peeped into the cart and wondered, as her friends themselves did, where they would find a corner big enough to hold them.

After this, all stood in a circle, and Gwa Gwa knew that they were going to worship their God, so when they sang, she opened her mouth just as they did, and sang her little song also.

Then the ladies said good-bye all round; they bowed low to each one in turn, but when

"Let 's Forget the Brigands and Play."

they came to Little Lonely they held her hand very lovingly, and she felt quite certain that she was not going to see them again for a long time. She quickly thought of a plan, and made up her mind that wherever they went she would follow. When the driver took up his whip and started the mules with a shout, she quietly walked behind, right down the main street of the town through the city gates and the straggling suburb, into the country.

On they went till she was very tired, but still she kept them in sight, though she began to think that perhaps, after all, she would not be able to keep up. Every now and then one of the ladies signed to her to go back, and when they got on to the rough country road, the Blue Lady jumped down and, walking back to Gwa Gwa, said:

"Go back, my child; you must go." She made her understand that she could not follow them any farther; then, with tears in her eyes and a big ache in her heart, she turned to the driver and said:

E

" Press on ahead.   She must not follow us farther, lest she lose her way."

The little figure, pathetic in loneliness and desolate in prospects, stood and watched the cart which carried her friends away from her until it was finally lost to sight; then, very, very slowly, Little Lonely made her way back to the town and began the business of begging enough food for that day.

CHAPTER ELEVEN

THE weather was still warm, and Gwa
Gwa sat sadly by the road-side watching
the carts go past, always hoping that one day
the cart she wanted so much to see would
come through the great gate. Sometimes she
shared in the games of other children, and
sometimes she just sat still and pondered the
strange events of life.

It was not unusual for a fellow-member of
the Children's Service to share a cucumber
with her, and sometimes a stylish lady would
stop her cart, call her to her side and give her
a copper, because there were now a good many

people who knew Gwa Gwa as the missionaries' little *protégée*.

She need no longer be really hungry, because Grannie Fan had promised to give her a bowl of food once a day. She also saved herself many a beating by running back to the wicked woman in West Street only when all were locking up for the night, and leaving again on her rounds by dawn. But all too soon the summer cooled to autumn, and the cruel winter, so much dreaded by the beggars, set in. The piercing winds cut through Lonely's little ragged garment, and sometimes her cough was so bad that it was all she could do to struggle round to Grannie Fan for her dinner. The dogs were as fierce as ever, but now there was no one to wash the wounds torn by their teeth, and though she often cried with pain, she had to put up with it, as also with many a kick and blow from the woman, who had no mercy on her and ill-treated her because she brought home so few coppers from her rounds.

Topsy Riding Molly.

She often asked Grannie Fan, by signs, when her three friends were coming back, and always got a cheerful nod as answer, which meant: " Yes, yes, they are coming soon." But the time seemed long, and it looked as if they would never arrive.

During that winter Gwa Gwa made friends with another little girl whom she met crawling into the town one day.[1] She was a child of her own size, but as she had only one foot, she had to go on hands and knees. This little girl had also been befriended by the missionaries when she was in great trouble, so she and Gwa Gwa became begging partners for the winter months. The little lame girl was a much better manager than Gwa Gwa. She found out the best corners where they could sit with their backs against the walls of other people's heated *kangs* and get the warmth of their fire. She also knew how to wheedle the cook of the street-corner restaurant into pouring a spoonful of his chitterling soup over the scraps of dry

[1] Her story is told in " Grace Child of the Gobi."

bread in her bowl. Gwa Gwa was not a good beggar, because she was always asking to do a job in exchange for food, and very few people were disposed to find her one; but as junior partner in the firm she benefited by the business experience of her senior.

When spring returned, there were frequent festivals in the temples of the town and crowds of villagers came together to see the fun. Everyone had a pocket full of money and was liberal to the beggars, so that many an odd scrap of oil cake and handful of parched broad beans found its way into Gwa Gwa's bag.

Still the ladies who were her friends did not come back, and the house where they used to live stood empty.

Gwa Gwa gave up all hope of ever seeing them again, although Grannie Fan still nodded her head to show that they were coming; but Gwa Gwa's experience of life had taught her that people did not always speak the truth, and she thought in her little heart, " Never again shall I see these friends of mine."

Though she gave up hope, yet she still paid her daily visit to their house. She would go in by the courtyard door, over the sill on which her little stick once sounded its tap, tap, tap; she walked round the garden and looked at the rooms where her friends once lived, and then, before leaving, would sit on the curb and croon a little wail as she knew people did when someone was dead.

A whole summer passed, and the second dreaded winter had come. The early blizzards had already swept over the town, carrying sand and pebbles from the Gobi desert and strewing them down all the lanes. Gwa Gwa's rags were poorer than the year before, for not a bit of cotton-wool would the wicked woman put into her old coat, although her own children each had a wadded winter garment. There were no fairs now, and the streets were very empty, so that few extras came her way. She was so miserable that when she went to her friends' empty house, she not only crooned her little wail, but also truly wept for her own wretchedness.

But one memorable December day when she came inside the courtyard door she stood transfixed. There were bundles lying about, and steam was pouring out through the open kitchen door as though dinner was being cooked. Grannie Fan, too, was there, busily putting things in order.

Suddenly she saw her three friends standing in the doorway of the living-room and with one shriek of joy she flung her little stick into the air, ran down the courtyard, and was caught up into their arms.

CHAPTER TWELVE

THAT winter was one of the fiercest that the North-West had yet known. One blizzard after another swept down over the plain, and the cold was so intense that often no one ventured out of doors. Each evening the beggars crouched, huddled together, near the temple buildings, where the high walls kept off the worst of the blast, but every morning some little child or old person lay dead, frozen in the night.

The Christian Chinese talked over the situation with the three ladies, and together they formed a plan.

"Let us lay a heap of straw in one of the big rooms," they said. "After dark we will go out and collect the small children, and they can shelter in the straw."

"That will be splendid!" said the ladies; "and we will boil a cauldron of millet gruel each morning for the children's breakfast."

So the straw was spread thickly on the floor, a great sack of millet was bought, and the children were fetched in each night. In England children feed their canaries on millet seed, and never think of eating it themselves; but when boiled very soft it makes a thick creamy porridge, and these children enjoyed it very much indeed.

Little Lonely wandered up and down the main street or crouched in a sheltered corner; but for her, as for all the homeless, it was a bitter season. Her thin cotton rags would not meet across her chest, and she shivered as she faced the morning wind without food. She often had to wait a long time before people would give her a crust, and when they did so she would run an errand for them or sweep the snow from the doorstep, because by doing so she soothed her pride and made herself feel that she had earned her meal. She was quite happy, however, to eat the hot dinner waiting for her at her friends' house, because it was given and accepted with love which neither wants nor gives payment.

Seeing her so nearly naked, her friends bought a piece of hand-woven cloth, and Grannie Fan ran up a pair of trousers such as all little Chinese girls wear. When Gwa Gwa put them on she was so proud that she walked the whole length of the big street to show them off, and the other beggars said : " Look at Gwa Gwa's trousers."

All the pride and joy left her when she turned the corner and began to walk down West Street. She lagged and dawdled so as to take as long as possible before reaching the narrow entry which led to the courtyard.

It held five rooms, and in one of these the woman who owned her lived with her family. As Gwa Gwa reached the door a boy of her own size came out and, seeing her new garments, he seized the chance to slap her in the face.

The air of the room was heavy with opium. On the *kang* was a ragged matting, some grimy bedding and a tray on which stood a little lamp fed with vegetable oil. A man, stretched at full length, was scraping the burnt-out opium from the tiny bowl of his pipe. Gwa Gwa had nothing to fear from him, for he was drowsy with the dope he had already taken, but the woman, who was clearing up after the evening meal, was angry and irritable because the craving for the drug was on her.

By the side of the mud stove stood a bowl half-full of a sticky, grey mass of flour-and-water food. This was Gwa Gwa's portion— the scrapings of the pot after each member of the family had taken his share. The woman seized the child's begging-bag and emptied

Mongolian Tents.

it. It held four copper coins, the value of each of which was so small that it took thirty to make one penny, three little lumps of coal which Gwa Gwa had picked up on the pavement, and a bone which the cook in a food-shop had thrown to her. The woman put the coins in her pocket, laid the coal by the fire and placed the bone on a shelf. After this she caught hold of Gwa Gwa and examined the new trousers, making sure that she still wore her old pair inside. Whenever she looked at the child her eyes were full of hatred, and as she held her she pinched her arm till Gwa Gwa cried out with pain, but when she cried the woman took up the poker and beat her several times across the shoulders.

As soon as Gwa Gwa could escape she went to the corner of the room near the door and lay down on the mud floor with her begging-bag and her stick by her side. In a short time she was asleep, but while she slept the woman came quietly and slipped the new trousers off her legs, leaving her in her old rags once more. Then she went out to an old-clothes store, where she sold them for a few coppers, and with them bought a small lump of opium juice.

In the morning when Gwa Gwa found what had happened she was furious; she had to wear her old rags, but she cried and banged her stick on the floor, then, slamming the door, went out in a great rage. For the first time in her life she had had something of her very own, and now it had been stolen. She ran round to her friends' house, only to find that they were out that day, and that the cook, though he gave her her dinner as usual, was not interested in the trouble about her trousers.

CHAPTER THIRTEEN

THOUGH Gwa Gwa could not guess it, her three friends were thinking out a plan which would change her whole life. When they told their Chinese friends about it, all agreed that the idea was a good one, seeing that if it could be carried through, the wicked woman would have no more claim on Gwa Gwa and could torture her no more. The plan had to be carefully considered, so several important men were asked to talk it over with the ladies and with Grannie Fan.

"Nothing will do but to buy Gwa Gwa outright," said Grannie Fan.

"To buy her is only the beginning of responsibility," said Mandarin Lin, the wealthy merchant from Central Asia; "for after that she must still be fed and clothed."

"We would do that," said the Grey Lady; "but who would look after her when we are away on our long missionary journeys?"

"That is easy," said Grandad Fan. "My wife and I can always take her unless we are out with you."

"In which case my wife will help," said Mandarin Lin. "The child ought to have a chance, and I believe will turn out well, for they could never make an ordinary beggar of her."

The only fear was that the wicked woman, out of spite, would refuse to sell Gwa Gwa, so for a whole hour the circle of friends discussed the best way of approaching her.

In the end Mandarin Lin's idea was accepted, so he went home and called a trusted servant to his room. They talked the matter over, and

Camels carried them over the Sands.

the trusty man, who knew the kind of woman she was, was full of helpful suggestions.

"Give me two dollars in my pocket," he said, "that she may hear the chink of silver; that will fetch her. She is an opium smoker, and would sell her soul for a lump of poppy-juice, let alone a *ya-ba* whom she hates."

With the dollars chinking in his pouch, and the long stem of his pipe sticking out of his waist-band, the trusty man sauntered down West Street, exchanging a word with many as he went, for he was on speaking terms with most people in the town. Near the end of the street was the shabby doorway, and by it stood a small boy with a wooden tray slung round his shoulders. On the tray was a pile of greasy meat dumplings. This boy was the wicked woman's son, and she had made the dumplings in the hope that he would earn five coppers by selling them. Five coppers was the price of her evening dose of opium.

When he reached the doorway the trusty man squatted down on his heels, rammed a

F

pinch of tobacco into the bowl of his pipe and lit it.

" Business good ? " he asked the boy.

" No," was the answer.   " No one wants mutton dumplings now."

Just then a shrill voice sounded, and the wicked woman came through the doorway, scolding the boy for wasting his time.

The trusty man spoke.

" The boy is all right," he said, " but no one wants his dumplings.   Is there not any-thing else he could sell ? "

" He's a lazy good-for-nothing.   I have the most worthless children in the town.   Just look at my girl; she is a *ya-ba*."

" Why not sell *her* ? " he asked.

By this time half a dozen bystanders were ready to join the talk.   This was a great joke and one of them laughed and said :

" Who would buy a *ya-ba* ? "

" Who knows ?   Someone might do so," said the trusty man, and as he spoke he rose to his feet and the coins chinked in the pouch.

" I happen to know someone who wants a girl to serve her, and she might not mind her being a *ya-ba*."

He moved on, but the seed had been sown and, later, when he walked down West Street again, the dumpling boy was on the look out, and ran in to call his mother.

Very few words were exchanged, but the trusty man murmured : " Come to Mandarin Lin's house to-morrow, when the midday gun is fired."

CHAPTER FOURTEEN

NEXT day when Gwa Gwa called at her friends' house there were all sorts of jobs for her to do. She swept the court, carried pails of water, and then collected firewood in the garden; but she never suspected that she was being kept at hand while Mandarin Lin was talking over her future with the wicked woman from West Street.

The woman had come punctually at the time when the midday gun was fired, and was shown to the office where he did business. It

The Baby Camels were Troublesome.

was a lovely office; in it were beautiful red divans and a table with a red skirt round its legs. On the table stood a teapot and two cups, an ink-slab and brush for writing, and the large square seal with which " Big Man Lin " stamped his documents.

She was rather awed at all the grandeur, and felt she might have done better if she could have talked it over in the kitchen with the wife, but the trusty man was there, and that helped the proceedings.

" It is about that *ya-ba* of yours," he said. " How much do you want for her ? "

" That child has cost me a lot of money, and I cannot let her go for less than twenty thousand cash," was the answer.

" Twenty thousand cash ! Who has money to fling around like that ?" snorted the trusty man.

Both he and she were first-class hands at driving a bargain, and who knows how long the argument might have lasted had not Mandarin Lin stepped in.

" Bring me fifteen thousand," he called out,

and handed the strings of coppers to the woman. Then he issued a further order, "Fetch the child," he said.

Gwa Gwa was brought in. She looked terrified when she saw the woman; but Mandarin Lin showed her a big paper which lay on the table and the pile of money which the woman was folding in a cloth. Then she understood, and her eyes shone as the big seal was pressed on the document which declared that Gwa Gwa ceased to be the wicked woman's property and became a child of the Christian Church.

Happy Gwa Gwa went back to her hot dinner with more odd jobs to follow at the ladies' house, and was kept so busy that it was sunset before she knew it. Then, thinking that she must still go back to West Street to sleep, but with a terrible fear as to how she might be treated when she got there, she seized her stick and her bag, but the Blue Lady took them from her hand and signed to her that the wicked woman would not expect her

back that night.   Then they went to a side
room, and there was a wooden tub of steaming
hot water and a suit of clothes just her size.

Off went the rags and into the tub went
Gwa Gwa.   It was the first bath she had ever
had, and she laughed and clapped her hands
when Grannie Fan fetched a brush to get the
dirt off, and scrubbed her down from head to
foot.   When she came out of the water her
head was shaved and she put on the new suit.
There were a pair of blue cotton trousers lined
with white, and cosily padded with wadding,
a little white under-jacket with an outer coat of
dark blue, and there was even a pair of white
calico socks.   She slipped her feet into an old
pair of the Blue Lady's shoes, which were
much too big for her and had to be tied on
with string, and when she was tidy she went to
the ladies' room and bowed low three times to
show how grateful she was for all the wonderful
presents.   Then she turned and bowed to
Grannie Fan to thank her for making them.

She was told that she would never go back to

West Street, but would stay on in the ladies' house and live with Grannie Fan who now had a room in the courtyard. She had to keep the room clean and heat the *kang* by burning thorns and stable manure inside it, so that the mud bed should always be warm and comfortable.

That night, instead of curling up on an icy floor, Gwa Gwa stretched herself on the warm mud bed which was gently heated by the smouldering fire beneath.

Grannie Fan used a sausage-shaped pillow finished off with a circle of embroidery at each end and stuffed with the husks of buckwheat, but Gwa Gwa had no pillow, so she took a small faggot of wood, slipped it under the back of her neck, drew the wadded quilt up to her chin and fell sound asleep. Before they lay down side by side, Grannie Fan and Gwa Gwa both knelt, and Grannie prayed aloud. No one knows what Gwa Gwa prayed, only it is certain that she was very grateful to somebody for something.

CHAPTER FIFTEEN

A WEEK later the wicked woman suddenly appeared in the missionaries' courtyard. Gwa Gwa was the first to see her, and
fled in terror to hide behind the door. At the
sound of her harsh voice the cook stepped out,
longing for a chance to speak his mind to her,
but the Grey Lady was ahead of him.

" What do you want ? " she asked sternly.

" Oh, there is just a little matter I wish to
talk over," was the answer.

" Say what it is," commanded the Grey Lady.

" Well, it is about the suit of clothes that Gwa Gwa was wearing the day she went to Mandarin Lin."

" What about it ? "

" I have not had any money for them, and Mandarin Lin has said nothing about buying them."

" Is that the only thing you have come to say ? " and the Grey Lady's voice sounded very severe indeed.

" Yes, that is all."

" Well, here they are, and since that is all you want, you may take them and go."

As she said this the Grey Lady led the way into the stable and pointed to the corner where the bundle of rags had been thrown until there was a bonfire on which to burn them.

The woman stooped and gathered up the filthy things, then walked off, turning her head in every direction, hoping for a glimpse of Gwa Gwa, who was nowhere to be seen. When she reached the door the Grey Lady spoke :

" This is to be the last time that you come

here. In future if you have anything to say
go to Mandarin Lin and tell him."

But the wicked woman knew better than to
risk an interview with the Big Man.

The fact was that all sorts of things were
being said about Gwa Gwa among her neighbours in West Street, and she had hoped to
find out which of them were true.

Some said that the ladies had sent to their
own country for a marvellous medicine, one
dose of which would cure deafness. Others
said that Gwa Gwa was already talking, and
one little spy reported that she not only spoke
Chinese, but English too. Some said that she
was dressed in beautiful clothes, and others
that she was treated like a child of the house,
and ate the same food as the ladies; but the
wicked woman had to leave without satisfying
her curiosity, for Gwa Gwa remained crouch-
ing behind the door until she was off the place
and the cook had shut the front door firmly
behind her.

Gwa Gwa had, of course, watched the woman

through a crack, though the woman could not see her. She felt much safer when the woman was gone, because she could not know that once the redemption money had been paid that cruel tormentor of hers lost all power over her, and though she might rage, she could never touch her again.

Gwa Gwa had been bought so as to be freed, and no one would have any right over her but the right of love; but the affection of her friends was going to provoke a response in her which would make her yield them her most willing devotion.

Later on she would learn of the Saviour Who redeemed her, not with gold or silver, but with His own most precious blood. He had died for her, and nothing evil would have any power over her if she trusted in Him. She would hurt her friends very deeply if she ever ceased to love them, but she could wound her Redeemer most cruelly if she shut her heart against Him.

"Lonely" was an impossible name for the

Good-bye to the Camels.

child of a Christian household, so she was given the new name of Ai Lien, which means Love Bond, and everyone called her by this name except the three ladies. To them she was "Topsy." Ai Lien was too difficult a word for the child to lip-read, but she soon learnt to articulate the name " Topsy "; in time she learnt to write it also, though at first she often made a mistake and spelt it " Tospy."

Now, all this happened at Christmas time— indeed, it was on Christmas Eve that she came to her new home. She knew nothing about Christmas or what it stands for, but the group of people who cared for her were disciples of the Lord Jesus Christ, Who was born in the stable of an inn because there was no room for Him in the house.

He had told them they were to look after children who were in trouble, and when they asked Him about Gwa Gwa, His answer was : " Suffer her to come to Me ; " so they brought her to Him, and the coming of Topsy made this Christmas one of the happiest they had ever enjoyed. In fact, they were so happy that she must have wondered at it, and to this day, when she wants to speak about Christmas, she always calls it " The Happy Day."

CHAPTER SIXTEEN

TOPSY had been her own mistress for all the hours of daylight since she was six years old. Each day had brought difficulties which had developed her will-power and self-reliance, for in the beggar world she had learned how to fight for her rights and hold fiercely to whatever came her way. She had had no training in gentleness, yieldingness, and unselfishness, for these were virtues for which the people with whom she associated had no use.

Her new life brought in a fresh set of experiences, and in her new home she was expected to learn how to share with others, and above all to yield her own will and obey her three Ma-mas and Grannie Fan.

Her world was now peopled with those who treated her kindly, but who expected her to do as she was told, and this was not an easy lesson to learn. The first struggle was over a little bundle of snippings from Grannie Fan's dress-making. Topsy had collected a tiny packet of odds and ends of prints which was her very own. It was a priceless treasure, and when she also became the proud owner of a needle she instantly set to work to make a gay little patchwork case in which to keep it. This was all right, but when she was called from her sewing to sweep the floor of the ladies' living-room she coolly indicated that she would come when she had finished her needle-book. This led to a first-class tussle as to who was mistress, and Topsy found she had to yield, though she did so grudgingly and of

The Forest Camp.

necessity, and with a private determination not to do more of it than she could help.

The next trouble came when Topsy saw the plates of cakes and sweetmeats laid out for guests. She knew that she would be given her share when the callers had left, but here was a glorious opportunity, when everybody was busy, to seize a few extra goodies. She did so; but when her Ma-mas came into the room, her face flushed such a deep scarlet that her secret was out. Even before she was questioned she was shaking her head, denying that she had taken anything.

Visitors being expected, Topsy was wearing her Sunday best trousers, which were wide round the ankle, and not tied in with a band like those she wore every day, and even while she shook her head to convince her Ma-mas that she had not done anything wrong, the sweets came rattling down the open trousers and rained on to the floor at her feet. She had stuffed them down the belt of her garment, quite forgetting that there

G

was nothing to hold them from falling to the ground !

Poor Topsy spent the next hour weeping in the corner. She was quick to learn, and before long she knew that when she wanted a thing she must come and ask for it, and also that while helping herself to cakes was naughty, this was a small offence compared with saying that she had not taken things, when she had really done so.

The walls of her room soon became the picture-gallery of the house, because she loved pictures more than anything else. At first a scrap of coloured paper or the wrapping of a match-box satisfied her craving for a bit of colour, but gradually, as she understood more, the scraps of coloured paper were replaced by pictures cut from the illustrated magazines which sometimes came to the house.

One day the Blue Lady called her to her side and showed her the most beautiful coloured picture she had ever seen. It showed a shepherd followed by a flock of sheep, and he was carrying one little lamb in his arms. Topsy saw at once that the little lamb was very tired and that the shepherd was very kind.

She could hardly contain herself for joy when she was allowed to pin this picture to the wall over her bed and every evening she kept her eyes fixed on it all the time that she knelt by Grannie Fan's side while the old lady said her prayers.

No one could tell what was going on in the child's mind, but the ladies felt that some angel must have been sent to teach her, for when, later on, another picture of the shepherd came, she knew the meaning of it at once.

This new picture showed a high rock with a huge eagle hovering overhead; at the foot of the rock was a tiny lamb caught in the thorns and quite helpless to escape; a shepherd was reaching down to rescue it. Topsy had often seen a great eagle swoop down and pick up something from the ground, and knew that if the shepherd had not been there, this lamb would certainly have been carried off in the cruel talons of the bird, to its nest in the mountains, there to be torn to pieces.

With pictures and signs the Blue Lady made Topsy understand that above the bright blue sky she had a Friend who had always loved her, and that when He saw she was in terrible danger, like the little lamb in the picture, He had sent someone to bring her to a house where she would be safe.

She grasped the idea in a moment, and from that day she always saw herself as a little lamb who had been rescued from great danger by the Good Shepherd Who had told her three friends to take care of her.

Four Gold Coins! How rich the King must be.

CHAPTER SEVENTEEN

EVIDENTLY plenty of people knew who Topsy's mother was, though they only spoke of it in whispers, because it had been agreed between her and the wicked woman that no one must know about the selling of the baby. Only a few, however, knew about Topsy's father—that he was a Mongolian Chief who rode over each year to the great Tibetan festival, taking a present from his tribe to the Living Buddha of the Lamasery.

He never bothered his head about baby Topsy, for he was far too busy with his flocks and herds to trouble about little girls and their

Tibetan mothers. Though he never spared her a thought, yet there she was, and each year she looked more and more like a Mongol. She had the strong build and the merry, spontaneous ways which were such a contrast to the quiet, restrained dignity of the Chinese girls around her. As for riding—why, no one who saw Topsy astride a pony could doubt that she was a child of the Mongolian plains, so fearless was she and so sure of herself.

In Topsy's new home a journey to Mongolia was under consideration, and while it was being discussed, Grannie Fan had a splendid idea. She said :

" There is room in my cart for Ai Lien, so what about taking her with us ? She would be most useful in guarding the sleeping-tent while we are preaching."

Everybody liked the proposal, and when Topsy found that she, too, was going on a missionary journey, she was wild with delight, and straightway tidied her little bundles of treasures with as much care as Grannie Fan put into sorting out what she needed for the journey.

Grandad Fan wanted to begin the Mongolian trip with a visit to Lone Hill Temple, where, once a year, there was a great festival in honour of the large idol which was said to control the weather at harvest-time. No farmer could afford to overlook such an important idol, so everyone who could manage it brought an offering and burnt incense at the temple.

" If we leave here Tuesday midday," said Grandad Fan, " we can pitch the tent on Lone Hill, and spend Wednesday and Thursday at the fair. It will take us only ten miles out of our way."

The road to that remote temple was generally quite deserted, but on that Tuesday it was alive with pedlars carrying their goods to the fair. They slung their wares across their shoulders together with the boards for putting up a stall, for the villagers liked to buy a cap for the baby, a new brass lamp, a sieve for grain or a wash-hand basin, so all such goods were displayed to attract buyers.

Up near the temple were dozens of men building mud cooking-stoves, erecting booths and raising squares of cloth to shelter the stall-holders from the burning sun. Cooks were kneading dough, chopping meat and onions, scraping carrots or mixing the filling for the mutton dumplings which everyone would want to eat. One man stood over an iron saucepan of boiling fat and dropped dough cakes into it, fishing them out a moment later, all golden brown. These dainties were Topsy's favourite morsels, and she had a glorious half-hour spending three coppers that Grandad Fan had given her.

By dawn bullock-carts packed with women and children were creeping over the plain, while the men-folk rode horses or donkeys which cantered along at a great speed, and at midday the theatre band struck up a wild din with cymbals, drums and blaring trumpets.

Before the first cart-load of villagers alighted,

the missionaries were ready for them in a big white tent hung round with pictures and with tables of bright-coloured books down the centre. There were benches where people might sit and rest, and one of the ladies played so gaily on the harmonium that crowds came to hear the music. They listened to some wonderful things that day, for many of them heard for the first time that God loved them, and loved so much that He gave His Son to die for them.

Among the pictures was one they liked better than any of the others. It was about a boy who ran away from home and spent his father's money. In the end he was so poor that he had to feed pigs. It showed how one day he felt so sorry for the way he had treated his father that he determined to go home and say so. Then his father forgave him and even made a feast for him, and gave him a suit of new clothes and a pair of new shoes which he must be very careful not to soil by going to places where he had no business to be.

The people could read this story for themselves in the book bound in yellow, called *Lu-gia Fuh-yin*.[1]   After they had heard the story told, they bought so many copies of this book that there was not one left on the tables.

It was all so surprising.   They had always heard that gods were terrifying and would hurt them whenever they could, yet here was the preacher saying : " That wilful son is like you and me, and the forgiving Father is like God " !

Could it really be true ?   Some of them went to Grandad Fan and asked him straight out about it.   He said, " Yes, it is quite true; I know because God forgave me."

" Then do you not burn incense in the temple ? "

" No," said Grandad Fan, " I do not.   God asks us to love Him with our whole heart, mind, and strength, and to love other people as we love ourselves.   The idol though it has ears cannot hear, and though it has

[1] Chinese for the Gospel according to St. Luke.

eyes cannot see; but God sees you, knows you and loves you."

Some went home to think more about it, and nearly all bought copies of the Gospels because the ladies said, " This book tells you all you need to know about God," so the people in each cart carried away pink-, green- or yellow-bound Scriptures in their hands to read at home on leisured winter days. At sunset Topsy gathered up the books that were left over and put everything in order for the next day.

When the fair was all over and the last peasant had gone home to his farm, and while the pedlars were demolishing the stalls, and the little temple attendants were sweeping the litter from the temple-floor, the big white tent was folded and carefully laid at the back of the cart. Before daylight everyone must be ready, for at midday the sun was hot, and for the beasts' sake there must be an early start.

Thus the whole caravan moved off towards the sandy desert in the North, leaving the deserted temple and the mud god behind.

CHAPTER EIGHTEEN

AFTER a few days of travel the carts were
abandoned and camels hired to carry the
party over sands that were so loose and so
heavy that only camels could go through them.
The row of beasts all knelt for the luggage
to be strapped to their backs; then each rider
stepped on her camel's neck and the well-
trained creature raised its head and lifted her
to the natural saddle between the two humps.
Topsy gripped the tuft of hair very firmly,
because she knew that there would be a terrible

The Brigands could roam over the Housetops.

upheaval when the beast unfolded its legs and stood. When all was ready the drivers jerked each rein in turn, and at this signal the great creatures stretched out their hind legs, then extended their front ones, and the rider was lifted high in the air. The caravan then moved on very evenly, and Topsy thoroughly enjoyed being swung to and fro and flicking her camel with a twig of *saxaul*.[1]

They rode in this way for several days before coming to tents which they might easily have passed by and never seen, had they not known how to look for the signs of an encampment. As it was, they kept their eyes open for some such trifle as a tiny tuft of lamb's wool tied to a branch, or a thread of scarlet in a bush. Such signs showed that they were near tents, and must dismount to force their way on foot through the thicket. Soon they heard the sharp bark of dogs, and in answer the camel-drivers walked ahead and cracked their long whips, and when the dogs saw the whips they

[1] Species of tamarisk.

kept their distance, though they still showed
their teeth and snarled.   Then the tents came
in sight, camouflaged with rough hurdles of
interwoven tamarisk.   At the sight of strangers
the women shouted to the men, for a stranger
might be anyone, from a tax-collector to a
traveller in distress, or a scout from a brigand
band.   The men soon appeared, each carrying
a gun and having a big knife thrust down the
side of his boot; but when the travellers threw
out their hands to show that they were quite
unarmed, all suspicion vanished, no one was
afraid any longer, and the headman lifted the
door curtain of his tent and asked the ladies
in.

A   tent   looks   wonderfully   comfortable
inside, especially if a blizzard rages without.   In the centre is a glowing fire of dried
cow-dung, which is fed with tamarisk roots
when a blaze is needed; the blue smoke curls
upward and escapes through an opening in the
tent roof.   Standing near the fire is a big
brass jug of stewing tea, and a cauldron hangs

from the chain of the tripod ready for heating up camel's milk. Facing the entrance is a raised seat covered with a scarlet rug, and behind it stands a table spread with small brass bowls brimming with cold water. This is the seat of honour in which the master only may sit, and the table with its little bowls holds the offerings he makes to his gods. Round the sides of the tent are boxes inlaid with bright metal; these hold skins, the spare leather boots of the family and the heavy silver ornaments which the women love to wear.

As the visitors entered, the master welcomed them by offering each a pinch of snuff, to show that he was pleased to see them. A few minutes later they were all sitting on the ground round the fire, while the elder son's wife took china bowls from one of the inlaid boxes. The ladies, who knew the nomad's customs, were glad to see that the bowls had been washed clean; for sometimes they were just dipped in milk and polished with the hostess's tongue.

The master than produced a fine lacquered box, from which he offered *zamba*, which the guests stirred into the camel's milk and ate with great enjoyment.

The tent was of thick felt which the women had trodden from the hair of goats, so that it was both warm in winter and cool in summer. The felts were laid on a wooden frame-work very cleverly made, and finished with a dado of lattice-work. Inside, the dado was decorated with bright-coloured wool woven over coarse desert grass. It all looked very handsome, and was beautifully done.

The tent-dwellers were always busy drying cow dung for fuel, tanning skins, stitching boots, twisting rope of cows' hair and weaving decorations, in addition to the daily round of milking a huge number of goats, ewes and camels. Making the butter was heavy work, for the cream had to be churned with a big wooden beater in a leather churn, and then stored in smaller skins to be kept for a long time before it was ready for use. No one,

The Cook brought a little Brigand Recruit
to the Children's Service.

except the Mongolians themselves, likes their butter, for they think it unlucky ever to wash the churn or the butter-skins and, in consequence, it has a very queer taste.

The baby camels are troublesome, for when the mothers are sent off to pasture the babies are reared on the bottle, or rather on the horn, for they are fed from a bullock's horn pierced with a suitable hole and fitted with a leather mouthpiece.

The men had to drive the herds from one pasture-land to another and round them up lest they wander too far. They enjoyed this rounding up, because it meant galloping long distances, and that was great fun. At least four times a year the whole family moved to find fresh pasture. They were very kind and friendly to peaceful guests, but fierce fighters if attacked, and they never went out without a big knife hidden somewhere and a gun slung over one shoulder. They always left *zamba* and milk at the tent door, that a hungry traveller might refresh himself, for the Mongol

H

law of hospitality required it; but if anyone stole from the tent or from the herds, he was tracked down though his pursuers might have to follow his traces for days, and when he was caught he would be shot.

CHAPTER NINETEEN

THE Mongols liked Topsy. As soon as
they caught sight of her they would
whisper and nudge each other. Then one
of them would say :

"That little girl belongs to our people.
Can she speak our language ?"

When they heard that she was dumb, they
petted her, smoothed her black, shining plaits,
and said she was a dear little girl. Topsy
liked them, too, and she loved to play with
baby camels in their nurseries, and to cuddle
the tiny kids and lambs which were cared for

inside the tent until they were strong enough to go outside.

At night the wolves prowled round, hoping to pick up a lamb for supper, and Topsy, when she saw the Mongol shepherds folding the lambs so carefully, remembered her picture of the Good Shepherd. It was not only a lamb that the wolf was after; he would have made short work of Topsy herself if she had wandered off after dark, and she knew better than to go outside the tent.

The missionaries moved from one Mongolian encampment to another, and each seemed better than the last, but most wonderful of all was the tent in which the Prince of the tribe lived. His seat of honour was spread with scarlet brocade, and Topsy gazed with admiration at the Princesses' lovely head-dresses and the satin bags worked with silk, jade and coral into which they slipped their long black plaits.

They were kind to Topsy, and brought out a beautiful golden-lacquered box, from which

On Trek.

they took *zamba* for her tea. After the
Prince and the ladies had talked for a long time,
they all walked to the Prince's pastures, where
hundreds of his horses were grazing, guarded
by mounted herdsmen.

One morning they started early, as usual;
but about ten o'clock a horrid red glow came
over the sky, and the camels lifted their heads,
sniffed the wind and called to each other.
The camel men said, " There is a sand-storm
coming." Suddenly there was a howl, and
the sands were caught by a tearing whirlwind,
while the riders clung to their camels' humps
lest they be thrown from their places. The
drivers shouted a command and the obedient
beasts knelt, stretching out their necks and
burying their noses in the sand. All dismounted, and each traveller sheltered behind
her camel.

Topsy held on to hers and hid her face in
its long, soft hair, for the sand and grit blinded
her, and she was afraid that if the wind caught
her it would sweep her right away. Only

the camel-drivers were not frightened, because they had often seen such storms before, and knew that after a few hours the wind would drop, the sun come out and the sky be as blue as though there had been no storm at all.

As they travelled on they reached forests of desert poplar, a strange tree, of which the lower branches bear leaves like a willow and the upper ones leaves like a poplar. When the camp was pitched, Topsy was accustomed to help collect camel dung or bits of desert scrub for firing, but in the forest there was no such need, for the men hauled in great tree-trunks and made a huge blaze. The kettle boiled almost at once, and they all had as much tea and *zamba* as they wanted. How they enjoyed it, and what a lot they ate, for the open-air life made everyone hungry!

From the forest they came out among sandhills. It was a regular labyrinth, and each sandhill was so like every other that they could never have found their way but for the camel-drivers, who spend their lives in the desert and recognise all kinds of little landmarks that other people do not see. The regular caravan route passes through this wilderness of shifting sands, and to save travellers from losing their way and perhaps dying of thirst, the Mongols had set up a great wooden support from which hung a bell. In clear, fine weather the bell is silent, but as soon as the wind rises it begins to sound, and when the terrible *buran* [1] blows and the air is thick with flying sand, it swings to and fro and gives out its loudest clang. In giving directions the Mongols would always tell the traveller to which side of the bell he must keep, and they would warn him :

" If the wind blows and you can see nothing, listen for the bell and take your bearings by it."

It was late afternoon when Topsy and her friends reached the dunes where the bell was, and they were anxious, for it seemed impossible to trace the way. The wind was high and the

[1] *Buran*, the desert wind-storm.

crest of each sandhill was blown about like spray. Every one was listening for the sound of that bell when, suddenly, the clanging came quite clearly—" ding-dong, ding-dong "—and they knew they were safe, and that three miles farther on they would find a water-pit. They pressed on for fear of being overtaken by the darkness, and, sure enough they came to a place where four deep holes were dug in the sand, and at the bottom of each, water was oozing through. The water was dark brown and had a horrid taste, but the travellers were so happy to find it that no one said, " How bitter the tea is to-night."

They carried some thick stems of *saxaul*, which is splendid fuel, and boiled the water for some time to make quite sure that it was safe to drink it.

Next day they sighted a farm, and knew that they were nearing Eyelash Oasis. It was a lovely name, and it was a lovely oasis. The river is very blue just there, and its banks are planted with poplar trees which wave and rustle in the lightest breeze. So the people say, " The trees are like eyelashes veiling blue eyes," and call it Eyelash Oasis.

The travellers' faces were now turned homewards, and they must say good-bye to the camels and take up the carts again. The river was too full for fording, so a ferry-boat took them over. This was so large that it held both carts and mules, but it took all the strength of twelve men to punt it across. Everyone gave a hand in pushing the carts on board, but it was of no use to push the mules, for they only reared and danced on their hind legs, so the boat was drawn as near as possible to the shore and planks were laid from the deck to the water's edge. The beasts hated it all, but little brown Molly, who was everyone's pet, understood at once what was expected of her and walked ahead over the narrow boards, and when the others saw this they took courage and followed her.

The boatmen seized the long wooden oars and swung the boat round until the current caught her. It would have swept the boat downstream, but that the men were so strong and knew their business so well. They pulled and pulled, steering for a point on the opposite bank which was half a mile higher than the place where they hoped to land, and at last they brought her round just at the right spot where landing was very easy; here the carter needed only to flick the beasts until one by one they jumped from the boat on to the bank. The first to be overboard seized the chance of a free canter while the carter was still busy with the others, and raced for some fields, where young wheat was growing; but Molly, the model, never did any of these bad things.

CHAPTER TWENTY

IT *was* nice to get home again. Everything looked so clean and so comfortable. The garden was full of flowers, and the apricot trees were full of green fruit. Topsy was glad these were still unripe, for, like every little Chinese girl, she liked crunching green apricots fresh from the tree, and immediately shook a bough and brought down a shower of them, with which she filled her pockets.

There was a very nice dinner ready for the travellers, and besides six saucers of vegetable there was a pewter fire-pot bubbling over with good things. It was a round pot, made to

123

stand on the dinner-table, and it had a place for fire in the centre so that the meat and vegetables might be kept boiling.

There is a great art in making a first-class fire-pot stew, and Grannie Li was renowned for it, so she had been fetched in for the occasion. This is how she made it; she first laid a foundation of sliced yam, and over it placed shavings of mutton, covering both with chunks of potato and chopped onion. Next came meat balls, fried brown, and laid on strips of bean curd, and on the very top was the greatest dainty—namely, pancake sandwiches.

To make these last Grannie Li fried pancakes as thin as sheets of paper. On one of these she spread a thick layer of savoury mixture and covered it over with another pancake. Then she took her sharp knife and cut each sandwich into fancy shapes such as stars, diamonds and crescents. These she laid out very prettily on the top of the meat balls and garnished the whole with garlic shoots chopped fine. The golden-green shoots

The Great Wall of China.

FIRST PRESBYTERIAN CHURCH
2619 BROADWAY
OAKLAND 12, CALIFORNIA

sprinkled over the yellow sandwiches made the dish look very attractive.

But the real art of Grannie Li's fire-pot cookery lay in the flavouring of the soup with which the pot had to be filled.   No one could tell exactly how many little things she put into this gravy to make it right, for that was her own secret; this time it was so good that she tasted it very often, and felt very proud when the pewter lid was lifted and the ladies dipped their little china spoons into the soup and said :

"This is the best fire-pot stew that Grannie Li has yet made."

When Topsy sat down to table with her Ma-mas and her friends around her, she remembered for a moment how lonely, how hungry and how sad she used to be, and when she saw them saying grace there was something in her heart which is best expressed by the words :

"Thank you God for my good friends and for my lovely dinner."

CHAPTER TWENTY-ONE

TOPSY came back to her room with great
delight. She had her own wadded bed-
covering made of pretty-coloured chintz, three
good meals a day, and was given a great deal
of love by her three Ma-mas and by Grannie
Fan. Grandad, also, often patted her head,
smiling at her and speaking a kind word
which she was able to perceive, though not
to hear. She had other friends also, such as
Mandarin Lin's wife, who sometimes took her
home for the day and fed her on doughnuts
and freshly roasted peanuts.

She really was very happy, and life would
have been perfect, she thought, if only she
could always have had her own way about
everything.

But that could not be, for somehow she had
to find her place in a picture where there was
a background of home, and while the solitary
Topsy had looked quite all right as an isolated
beggar-maid, the great big TOPSY in the
pretty picture looked very ugly. If she were
ever to fit in nicely, she would have to shrink
a bit. Too often Grannie Fan had to report
her to the Blue Lady and say, " Ai Lien
has been naughty again." Then she would
have to stand in the corner or eat dry bread
for dinner, and, occasionally, the Blue Lady
made her stretch out her hand and gave
her several sharp raps with a ruler. Of
course it did not hurt her much, because
she was accustomed to being beaten with a
poker or a horse-whip, but she was ashamed,
and went back to her room sobbing. However, when evening came she would make a

low bow to the Blue Lady to show that she was sorry, and afterwards would come up close to her side and make her understand how good it was to really belong to some one, even if she *were* punished. Yet even after this, that iron will of hers drove her to further naughtiness, and there had to be more punishments and more unhappiness all round.

But one day something wonderful happened, for the postman who brought the weekly mail handed in a long roll which was addressed :

> Topsy
> C/o The Missionaries
> Spring-of-Wine
> Kansu, China.

Via Siberia.
. . . .

Topsy was wild with joy. She had not dreamt that the postman could ever bring a parcel for *her*, yet here was one, and it came from a far-away country, sent by someone

Topsy and a Turki Playmate.

whom she had never seen! She opened it with uncontrollable excitement, and drew out an illustrated paper. Her delight knew no bounds, for there were pictures enough here to cover all her walls.

Among the pictures was a coloured one of a little girl standing very demurely, with roses at her feet. She had golden hair, blue eyes, and was wearing a beautiful dress with sprays of flowers on it.

Now, Topsy had never even thought of a child with golden hair, for all those whom she knew had black locks. She saw that this little girl's skin was pink and white and that her eyes were blue, which was more wonderful still. She took the picture to the Blue Lady, who sat down and explained that this was little Princess Elizabeth, and that perhaps some day her father would be King of England.

This was a perfect fairy-tale to the child, and the little golden-haired girl looked to Topsy like a fairy, so she asked every kind of question about her, using signs that no one

I

could mistake. Almost the first question was :

" Can I see her father and mother ? "

Fortunately, in another illustrated paper there was a picture of them, and this gave her great joy; but when she learnt that the grandfather and grandmother of the little Princess actually were King and Queen of the land to which her Ma-mas belonged, the thrill went beyond all telling !

Nothing would satisfy her but to see their picture also. This was more difficult, because there was not one at hand; but luckily the Grey Lady remembered that she kept her spare pencils in an old box of Cadbury's " King George " Chocolates, so she brought it out. Nothing could have impressed Topsy more deeply, for she saw King George in the midst of gold coins, and that helped her to realise what a very great King he must be.

A little later another box of chocolates came by post, and Topsy was allowed to eat one of them. The connection between the

King of England and chocolates was not too easy to make, but she decided that he was a great monarch, whose kindness was such that he distributed chocolates about the world to his distant subjects.

The picture of Princess Elizabeth was, of course, given a place of honour in Topsy's gallery, and as she sewed or sat at her little spinning-wheel, she would think and wonder about that other little girl.   Although Topsy was deaf-and-dumb she never lacked the means of making herself understood by clear and accurate signs.   These were some of the questions which she asked.

" Is she always good ? "

" Can she read and write ? "

" Does she spin as I do ? "

" Does she always do as she is told ? "

" Does she say grace before she eats ? "

" Can she knit ? "

" Has she a picture of the Good Shepherd like mine ? " and many more besides.

Next time that Topsy was naughty, the Blue

Lady went to her room and turned the picture of Princess Elizabeth to the wall. " This little girl," she said, " must not see Topsy in a temper." So, for a whole day, Topsy never saw her face, and this made her realise how ugly her tempers were, and that she must be good because she was ashamed and hurt when the little Princess she loved so well turned away from her. So Topsy quickly gave up her wilful ways and became much more obedient. Everyone in the house was glad about this, for everyone was happier when she was good, and though she was only a little child, she could cast a gloom over the whole household. The three ladies often said to one another, " How strange it is that Princess Elizabeth, who has never heard of Topsy, should make such a difference to her," and they knew that this was a very good example of what people call influence. The dictionary says, " Influence is action invisibly exercised upon someone," and so it was that a little girl, thousands of miles away,

"Do you remember? I was like this when I
came to you."

"Let us in," they whispered. "Brigands are pouring in at the East Gate and everyone is hiding. We dare not stay at home."

"Come in, come in," said the Grey Lady; "tell us all about it."

A man's voice was heard: "Go at once to Grannie Fan's room. I will tell the ladies what has happened."

The speaker was an important business man, but his knees were trembling and his voice was shaky with fear. The women and children went straight to Grannie Fan's room, where Topsy lay sound asleep. When she woke up and saw the room full of people, she could not think what had happened, but realised that they were all very frightened of something, so she was frightened too.

Meanwhile Mr. Kung was telling the ladies what had happened.

"It is the Baby General," he said, "who has arrived with an army of several thousand men."

"Baby General" did not sound very terrify-

ing, but the ladies knew about this famous
" Baby," and they understood why Mr. Kung's
knees shook at the thought of him.   He was
not such a " Baby," after all, for he was nineteen years old, though that is young to be
General of a Brigand Army.

He had been a very naughty boy who had
run away from home when he was fifteen, and
such a lot of other bad boys joined him that
they formed a brigand band.   They stole
horses from the farmers, rifles from the arsenal,
food from the shopkeepers, money from the
bankers and clothes from the pawn-shops.
Then they roamed about the country, earning a
terrible name for themselves with all their wild
doings.   When they seized a town they opened
the prison doors and said to all the prisoners,
" Come along and join up with our Baby
General."   The prisoners were glad enough
to be free, so they threw off their chains and
went looting and killing with them.

" The General is raging mad," said Mr.
Kung.

" What about ? " asked the Grey Lady.

" The trouble began in the baths," he said. " His cousin was his A.D.C., and after a long ride they both ordered hot baths. People heard them quarrelling in the room, and after a time the A.D.C. rushed out, ordered his horse to be saddled, and rode off, taking a lot of the men with him. The General has not got over his fury, and he will need recruits, so it is a bad look out for Spring-of-Wine."

By daylight the town was taken over by the brigand army. The General set up head-quarters at the Law Courts, where the fright-ened people brought him presents, in hope of putting him in a good temper. The peasants brought live sheep and goats, fowls and vegetables. The food-shops sent bread, cakes and sweetmeats, and the shoemakers of the town clubbed together to give enough shoes for each brigand to have a new pair. The City Magistrate sent cartloads of wheat, but that cost him nothing, for he took it out of the city granaries.

The brigand Chief of Staff graciously accepted all the presents and said, " Hao, hao, hao," which means, " Very good," and the brigand cooks set to work to make a feast worthy of the occasion.

When the soldiers had eaten as much as they could swallow, they went out to find billets; this meant turning families out of the best houses and settling themselves in. When they saw the big tent just outside the missionaries' house they said : " This is just what we are wanting to shelter our horses," so they took it, but they did not turn the ladies out of their home.

All the houses in Spring-of-Wine had flat roofs, and by jumping from roof to roof one could get from one end of the town to the other without ever coming down. This was very useful to the brigands, because they could roam about on the house-tops and spy out who kept horses, who had grain, and who fed chickens. The stables were all empty, but some clever people fed a horse in the inner room of their house, blocking the entrance with a cupboard. There was a popular saying, " Brigands have long ears," which meant that they pulled the lobe of the ear to catch the sound of distant neighing, and once they heard it the horse was soon out of the inner room and into their own stables.

Their noses were as sharp as their ears, and if anyone fried a little mutton or roasted a chicken, some brigand would know it at once, and drop from the roof to ask for his share, which of course meant all of it except the bones.

Their eyes too were marvellously quick and always on the look-out for likely recruits. It did not matter how young the boy was, he could put on uniform with puttees and march to the drill-ground where relays of men learnt the art of warfare through all the hours of daylight. The lads liked practising the sword exercise, but their mothers wept at home because they did not want their boys to be brigands.

There was no smell of roasting or frying

from the ladies' courtyard, but one night there was a rattle of firearms on the roof as men played with the triggers of their guns and with hoarse voices demanded money. It had to be given, but Topsy hated to see the dollars handed over, and she was still more angry next day when she found that the lovely black mule Kara, and the strong grey beast Boz, who pulled so well in the shafts, had both been carried off in the night.

Everyone was breathing whispered curses on the Baby General and his men, but when they brought their presents they bowed before him and called him " Your Excellency."

The town-hall secretaries were hard at work writing out posters on strips of scarlet paper in the most polished style and with great flourishes of the brush :

> " All honour to the Baby General."
> " General Ma Chung-ying, deliverer of the
>   North-West."
> " Peace and safety come in the train of
>   General Ma."

The Pagoda near Red Temple.

" Down with imperialism; long live the
mighty General."

At last it began to be whispered that the
army was going to move, and the ladies were
among the first to hear it, for a Christian tin-
smith slipped in and told them.

" We shall not have these people here for
long," he said.

" How do you know ? " asked the ladies.

" Tin mugs," he whispered. " The A.D.C.
has been round and ordered four thousand of
them. We shall be up all night working, for
he says the order must be complete in three
days. They will not want tin mugs here, so
it means that they expect to travel."

By next day everyone knew that five hundred
pairs of bellows were on order, and there was
wild but secret rejoicing at the news. Bellows
meant camp-fires; camp-fires meant a desert
journey; and a desert journey meant that the
army was moving to Turkestan across the Gobi.
With luck it might never come back again.

Anxious to see the back of this brigand

band, the masters urged on their apprentices, and the apprentices worked as they had never worked before, to get those mugs and bellows finished, though they knew they would get no money for their work. They would not have the army delayed one hour for want of equipment, so on the third day everything was complete. That same afternoon the order went out to the blacksmiths to be ready to shoe every horse in the regiment. Then indeed the town knew they were going soon, for shoeing is the last job to be done before leaving on a desert journey.

By dawn next day the army moved, and the town gave itself up to rejoicing. There was a three days' fair, with theatricals and merry-making, and people sent each other presents because they were so happy.

The complimentary posters to the Baby General all came down, and every man spoke his mind about " General Ma, Scourge of the North-West."

CHAPTER TWENTY-THREE

THE hottest weather was past, and the Festival of Autumn was soon to be celebrated. This was the best time for missionary journeys, as the weather was neither too hot for preaching nor too cold for camping, and farmers had time to listen.

Mandarin Lin was consulted about the difficult matter of buying a new team of mules.

"The roads seem to be clear of brigands," he said, "and the people in the City-of-Sands[1] have wanted you there for a long while; but the

[1] Also called Tunhwang.

question of mules is certainly a problem, for that Baby General carried off every good beast from the near villages."

"Poor Kara!" said the Grey Lady. "I fear we shall never again own such a handsome beast."

"Poor Boz!" echoed the Brown Lady, "A more willing creature I never knew."

"Well," said Mandarin Lin, "we must do our best. I know a farmer in Spirit-Water village who hid two mules; they are fairly good animals, but one of them is said to be the ugliest creature within fifty miles. I am not even sure that the man would sell, and in any case the price will be very high."

"Could you see him and find out?" said the Grey Lady.

The man at Spirit-Water was far too wary to take two mules to town and start everyone talking, and thieves plotting, so Mandarin Lin went over himself to look at them. His report was favourable. One was a strong white shaft-mule, and the other a well-trained

School in the Garden.

puller for the traces, but of a strange pink colour.

"Oh, dear!" said the Blue Lady; "how queer we shall look with a pink mule in the traces!"

"I should not mind it being green so long as it could pull," said the Grey Lady.

So a message went to the man, who ventured to bring the beasts into town, in the hope of not having to take them home again.

The carter pulled open the mules' mouths, looked at their teeth, and declared them both to be "eight-year mouths," which meant that the age was anything between eight and eighteen. A quick glance, however, had shown him that they were suitable for his purpose, but hoping to get them cheaply, he made the most of every defect, down to a scallop on the edge of the white mule's ear where a stable companion had nipped a piece out.

On the general appearance of the pink mule he was frankness itself.

K

"I should be ashamed to be seen out with such a creature," he exclaimed.

"That reddish shade has only shown up recently," said the farmer. "The fact is," and here his voice sank to a whisper, "the Baby General's men came to my place and stole all the grain, so my mules have not been fed too well lately; but if you will give them extra rations for a few days, that creature's coat will turn to a lovely chestnut."

At this point the Grey Lady broke in :

"What is your price for each one?" she asked firmly.

The price might not be discussed audibly, so the carter and the farmer thrust their hands up each other's wide sleeves and held a mysterious conversation by means of squeezing each other's forearms, thus literally keeping the price up their sleeves.

It took a long time to squeeze out the bargain, but in the end the carter followed the ladies to their guest-room and said :

"The man will not agree for less than

seventy dollars for each" (four pounds ten shillings).

"Out of the question," said the Brown Lady. "We will give no more than three pounds ten for the white mule, and three pounds for that terrible pink creature."

For yet another hour the price was discussed, but was finally fixed at one hundred and sixteen dollars for the two beasts. The large silver coins were counted out, and each one was rung to be sure that it was genuine, then the farmer went off, grumbling aloud at the poor price he had got; but when he was round the corner he chuckled at the splendid bargain he had made, while the carter led the mules to the stable not dissatisfied with his new team.

CHAPTER TWENTY-FOUR

THE team of animals was now complete, but not the team of men. Grandad Fan was lying very ill—so ill that everyone thought he was dying—and the ladies delayed their departure until they should see how the sickness turned. When he rallied it was decided that Topsy should go ahead with her Ma-mas to the City-of-Sands, and that Grandad and Grannie Fan would follow them later on.

At that time no one realised what a tremendous decision this was, and how it would change the whole course of Topsy's life.

No one thought much of it, yet her whole future hung on this decision, and later on the three ladies realised that if Topsy had been left behind then she would never have come to England. Topsy folded her new coat, resorted her packet of treasures, stowed them away in her wadded quilt, and laid the bundle safely in the cart.

On the first evening they reached a place called Kiayükwan, a difficult name to remember, but an important one, for it is the fortress at the north-west end of the Great Wall of China. That enormous wall was built two hundred years before the birth of Christ, to keep the Tatars from the north out of China. It is over fourteen hundred miles long, and so wide that in parts two carriages can drive abreast on it. It begins at the sea-coast at a place called Shanhaikwan, and goes right over the tops of mountains and down into the valleys, to end twenty miles from Spring-of-Wine.

Here the ladies stayed and preached to the people who lived in the great fortress.

On the third day a boy, who was taking his donkey to the spring for a load of water, came running back shouting the alarm, "There are horsemen galloping over the desert." When they heard that, the people fled in all directions, calling out one to another, "The brigands are back again."

The carter spoke but one word, and that word was "Go." With the help of the second man he dragged the mules away from their feed, harnessed them and packed the cart at record speed.

Even so, before they were clear of the East Gate there were shouts of soldiery and the clatter of horses echoing in the archway of the West Gate.

The best way to keep out of sight was to turn north and follow an arm of the Great Wall which led to a small oasis where only a few families lived. If they could but escape the brigands' notice, there was a good chance of getting away. They had only gone a short distance, however, when a shout from a horseman stopped them, and galloping up he challenged :

"Where are you from? Where are you going? What is your business? Show me your passport."

This was not at all pleasant, but before they had time to produce the passport there was another shout, and a second man galloped up. This one saluted and then delivered his message : "These ladies may go forward; they are the missionaries from Spring-of-Wine."

Before sunset the tents were pitched by the little stream which watered the oasis, but it was not till after dark that the peasants dared to creep round and ask questions. They were all very frightened and, like Topsy, hated the sight of guns and knives.

All night long, stealthy footsteps came and went. The people were hiding sacks of grain, and burying their money in the hiding-places they had prepared beforehand.

No member of the party wanted to delay, so next day they were off early, travelling by side roads to avoid meeting roaming bands of robbers. They missed some of them, but they met others, and Topsy was terrified when a dozen fierce men levelled their guns on the carters, and thrust their bayonets into the baggage. Just then the officer they called " Colonel " came up, and, seeing who the travellers were, called his men off. The fact was the " Colonel " knew the missionaries and had been several times to their house at Spring-of-Wine, and he felt very sorry that they should have been threatened.

At last, after fourteen days of travel, and many more of camping by the roadside, they reached the City-of-Sands. This name was given to the town because it is surrounded by mountains of sand. The sands shift with every windstorm, so that the shapes of the hills are constantly changing.

In the first inn in which they stayed they found a lot of people who were neither Chinese, Mongol nor Tibetan, but Turki. The women wore a white veil over their heads, and a gold-embroidered cap, with a plait of hair falling down each side of the face. They spoke their own Turki language, which the Chinese could not understand at all—but differences of language meant nothing to Topsy, who soon made friends with the girls. They raced each other up and down the court-yard, and played with the camels which had come from Turkestan, on the other side of the great desert of Gobi, where is the home of these Turki people.

Everything seemed very quiet in the City-of-Sands until one morning the town was invaded by a crowd of Turkis riding hundreds of little donkeys. The younger women had babies in their arms, and the older ones had bundles of clothes tied to their saddles. The children sat two or three on one donkey, and all were very hungry and terribly tired.

They all talked about a town called Hami, where they lived. " Our homes have all been burnt," they said. " The Palace of our Prince is in ruins; thousands have been killed, and we only have escaped."

" And who did all this ? " the ladies asked.

" The Baby General," was the answer.

No one ran races that day, nor played at being a camel-driver on the desert, because everyone was moving furniture to make room for the new-comers and the children had to help. All the families who had used two rooms now had to squeeze into one, and with eight or ten children this was not easy to manage.

The landlord of the inn could not refuse to take in more people, because there was no-where else for them to go, but the shouting and quarrelling, and the flies from the stables, made the inn a most uncomfortable place to live in.

CHAPTER TWENTY-FIVE

EACH day Topsy hoped to see Grandad Fan walk in, but still he did not come. At last there was a letter which said : " Grandad started yesterday, and should reach the City-of-Sands next week," but he did not come, and as days and weeks went by, everyone became very anxious.

" The roads are so full of brigand bands that no travellers can get through, and even the postman cannot come," was the report.

" Do you think that Grandad Fan can have been caught by robbers ? " asked the cook.

No one knew, and after the letter there was

no further word until an unknown carter walked in.

"There is a message for you," he began. "An old gentleman, of the name of Fan, whose home is at Spring-of-Wine——"

"What about him?" said the Grey Lady.

"He started to come here," answered the man; "but got no farther than Jade Gate."

"Well, but where is he now?" asked the Blue Lady.

"He's back in Spring-of-Wine."

"Isn't he coming? Why did he go back? What has happened?"

"Robbers," was the answer. "The roads are full of them, and he met them near Jade Gate. They flogged him, then they robbed him, and he was lucky to get off with his life."

"Was he badly hurt?" asked the Blue Lady.

"Badly enough. It was as much as he could do to get home, but he said that I was to find you, and to say that he cannot get here, and that he warns you to stay where you are, for the main road is too dangerous for travel."

This was very alarming, but when the Grey Lady asked how far off the brigand bands were, the carter said: "For the last three days of the journey we never met one, so rest your heart, Teacher, you will be all right in this out-of-the-way place."

And so said everyone; yet only a few days later the ladies and Topsy, who had gone a few miles into the country, met a boy who carried startling news.

"Go back as quickly as you can, if you don't want to be shut out of the town," he said. The brigand General is defeated, and his army is running back across the Gobi Desert. They may be here at any time. The city gates will be shut in an hour, and the local Defence Brigade is called up."

No one stopped to hear more, and the carter whipped up the mules and came back at a sharp trot in spite of the rough road. They reached the gates only just in time to get in before they were closed. The streets were empty and silent, and even the dogs did not bark, but at the Mayor's house the boys of the Defence Brigade were reporting themselves. Each one was given a sword which the blacksmith had prepared in case of attack. They had never handled firearms, so it was thought safer not to give them guns ; they were, however, ordered on to the city wall to keep a sharp look-out and report anything unusual.

Before long they spied horsemen coming at a great speed, and before sunset there was a terrific thumping on the great city gate.

" By General Ma's commands this gate must be opened, or he will slay every man in the City-of-Sands," shouted a threatening voice.

When the boys on the wall heard these words they were terribly frightened, and so was the police force which was marshalled just inside the gate, and so, too, was the Mayor, who had to give the order for the opening of the gates, and so were the merchants in their counting-houses, and so indeed was everybody —except Topsy, who could not hear the big, boastful threat.

The boys whispered, " Better let them in," and so did the police, and the merchants. Then the Mayor said :

" If we do not open the gates the brigands will burn them down and may then kill us all. It is better not to make them too angry."   So he went to the gate and talked with them very politely.

" My lords," he said, " we are only a few very poor people in this town, and nothing we have will be of any value to you; but we are very glad to receive you, and hope that you come as friends."

" We are friends to those who treat us well," was the answer.   " That is enough talk; open the gates."

While this conversation was going on, the lads of the Defence Brigade were dropping down from the City Wall as fast as they could and stampeding home; but the brigand sergeants were too sharp for them, and next day they were learning the goose-step on the brigand drill-ground.

CHAPTER TWENTY-SIX

THE City-of-Sands was now under brigand rule, and a hard rule it was. The soldiers were so free in helping themselves to all they wanted that rich men wore beggars' coats so as to seem poor. The town was famous for its old granaries, which held such an enormous quantity of wheat that, if they were kept full, the city could resist a three-

"My Teacher lets Me hold Her Horse."

years siege.   There were rows of these huge
granaries with sliding doors, and the Mayor
was supposed to replenish them each year from
taxes which were paid in grain.

The General set up his headquarters at a
large city on the main road which was four
days' journey away, but he had spies everywhere,
and it was the report of these well-stocked
granaries that brought his men thundering at the
gates of the City-of-Sands.   They scoured the
district for carts in which to carry off the loot,
and every night a long procession of these
carts, laden with sacks of wheat, vats of oil
and stacks of vegetables, left for the camp.

Every young man they could catch was also
carried off; but these were not as many as they
had expected, and the brigands knew that some
must be evading them.   The General was angry
that there were so few recruits, so he had the
sergeants brought before him and gave
them a good dressing-down.

" What are you up to," he said, " that you
are getting so few young men ? "

L

"We have been to every farm in the oasis," they answered, "but the boys are sharp and manage to keep out of our way."

"Well, look here," said the General. "I must have a thousand new recruits this month, and you must produce them, so manage it as best you can."

Now when the General gave an order in that tone of voice, the army knew that he meant business, so the recruiting officers got together to think out a plan. They knew that the young men were there, but how to catch them was the problem.

The great desert expanse of earth and sand which lay round the farms looked so flat that one would not think a wild cat could hide there, but these boys knew its endless undulations, which are like motionless sea-waves, and knew that a man wearing earth coloured clothes could lie hidden for days. From behind these low mounds they watched the soldiers hunting for them, and as soon as these had moved on the boys came out and got on with the farm-work. They knew the country, which the brigands did not, and of course they all helped one another to evade the soldiery. At the approach of a horseman some sign, generally given by a woman, put the whole neighbourhood on the alert. Offers of money, promise of loot and boastful talk of future big posts in the army, had failed to lure them, but the new plan was more subtle.

All the officers left the place for a few days, and everything seemed to be so quiet that the boys moved about more freely, and even came to the city for an occasional game of pitch-and-toss. Nothing happened, and when, after a time, gaming-tables were set up like those at the big fairs, the young fellows became so bold that every one of them tried his luck at the game. Some of the young men made quite a lot of money, and their good fortune brought others around. No one suspected this to be a press-gang trick; but one day, when the fun was at its height, and the market was crowded with youngsters throwing dice and playing cards, a squad of the brigands closed in on them, fired rifles to frighten other people away, roped the boys together, and marched them straight off to barracks. Then the boys began the hard life of new recruits, while the soldiers swept all the money from the gaming-tables into their own pockets.

The boys were not alone in being taken off to the brigand camp, for one evening an order came that the three ladies had to go also, and of course Topsy with them. They tried hard to avoid going, but the Mayor, who brought the message, spoke very seriously :

"An armed guard has come to fetch you, and if you make difficulties it will be all the worse for you. My advice is, go quickly and quietly."

So, early on that December morning, they left in bitter cold on the four days' drive across the desert. Topsy was distressed to see the Christian friends weeping when they gathered to see them off, as though they did not expect to meet them again, and she was

Peggy.

alarmed to find that two hundred boys roped
together as prisoners, were going with them.
If one of the boys was impudent to a soldier,
he had a lash from a long whip, or even found
a murderous-looking pistol pointed at him.

In camp, life was hard, even though the
headman of the commissariat sent a handful of
ration-tickets to the ladies. On one was
written, "Give bearer twenty pounds of wheat
flour." On another, "Give bearer two
measures of millet," and on a third, "Give
bearer five loaves of bread." Each one bore
the General's red seal, but when the cook took
the tickets round to the storehouse the men
in charge just laughed at him, and said:

"We have not a loaf of bread in the place
nor a pound of flour; but we will give you a
little millet if you bring a small bag in which
to carry it away."

So the family had to be content with thick
millet porridge for dinner and thin millet gruel
for supper.

Every day soldiers came and took two of

Topsy's Ma-mas away to see General Ma.
When they came back from their first visit they
told her that a bullet had gone right through
his two legs, and described how they had to
dress the wounds. Topsy, of course, could
never go out, but she used to peep through a
hole in the paper window of her room and
watch the soldiers exercising the horses. One
day she actually saw the stolen mules Kara and
Boz being taken to water, and she gave a little
shriek, thinking that this was the right moment
to get them back again, but no one dared to
speak or even notice them, though the
sight of beautiful Kara made the pink mule
seem uglier than ever.

Topsy knew that her Ma-mas longed to get
back to the City-of-Sands, but quite understood
that they were prisoners and could not do as
they liked. As time went on they were all very
tired of the turmoil of camp life, but one day
a soldier walked unexpectedly into their room
and handed the Blue Lady a big paper.
Topsy thought it was another ration ticket, but

if she could have read it she would have understood why everyone was suddenly happy, for on the paper was written :

" The missionaries and party are permitted to travel to the City-of-Sands by special leave granted by General Ma Chung-ying. Permit issued this fifth day of the eleventh moon in the twenty-second year of the Republic.

Stamped by the Military Executive."

It was amazing to see how quickly they were ready to leave; they did not even stay for dinner, but before they left, the Blue Lady was summoned to pay a last visit to the wounded General. On receiving this order she and the Grey Lady undid some parcels of books, and selected a volume which looked very lovely; it had a glossy leather cover stamped with big gold ideographs. By the way they wrapped it up, Topsy knew that this was a present for the General, and she thought how pleased he would be to have it.

It was a Chinese Bible, and when the Blue Lady came back she described how the General had saluted when he took it from her.

While the cart was being packed, the soldiers buzzed around, and a few of them came and whispered to the ladies. They were saying :

" Teacher, if you see my old mother, tell her I am here, and she is to rest her heart about me ; I shall get away when I can."

The carts were challenged again and again by very fierce and rude men, but when they read the permit and saw the seal on it, they stood at attention and said :

" Pass on."

So the travellers passed on until they came out of the brigand lines on to the desert road which led towards the City-of-Sands.

CHAPTER TWENTY-SEVEN

IT was February and an early spring sand-storm howled round the City-of-Sands. The three ladies were in their bed-sitting-dining-room, which was rather a bare place to be all that. A mud *kang* filled one side, and by way of furniture there were only a wooden bench and a small packing-case. The " dining-room " effect was supplied by the *kang* table, which measured eighteen inches across and was twelve inches high.

The Grey Lady sat cross-legged on the *kang*, sorting a bundle of leaflets, ready for the Children's Service; the Brown Lady was sitting on the narrow bench, counting and stringing copper coins, while the Blue Lady paced up and down the room. Topsy sat on the soap-box and watched the faces of her three Ma-mas. She understood that there was something very important being talked out, and she felt sure that it had to do with the urgent matters of food and brigands, one of which was far too scarce and the other far too plentiful.

The Grey Lady spoke : " The carter has been out all day trying to buy grass, and has come back without any."

" The cook met a man who promised to bring round a bag of millet after dark. I hope he will not fail us, for the supply is very low," said the Brown Lady.

" Whatever happens we must not draw on our secret store," replied the Blue Lady, " for if that were to go we should have no provisions left for a journey."

" I am not so anxious about our food as I am about the beasts' fodder," said the Grey Lady. " We could do for a long time on half rations, but if the mules lose their strength they will never get us across the Gobi."

The Blue Lady continued to tramp the room. " Unless we can hold on to our beasts and keep them fed we are done for," she said. " I am sure that in the end we shall have to make a run for it, and it will be a terrible journey."

" There was a man selling firewood this morning, and he said that the guard has been doubled at the Well of Wild Asses, because a few people escaped that way, and that no one can get through now."

" What about trying for a pass ? " said the Blue Lady.

There was silence for a moment, then the Grey Lady spoke again : " If they refuse it we are in a worse plight than before, as everyone will know that we are trying to get away."

However, next day the Brown Lady and the Blue Lady called on the Commandant, and boldly asked him for a permit to leave the City-of-Sands. He looked surprised, and said that he was not allowed to sign travel-permits. Then the Blue Lady waxed very bold :

" Would you ask General Ma to give us one ? " she said.

" I will certainly *ask*, but . . ." The Commandant said no more, and scribbled a note which he handed to his Secretary. " Your request shall be included in to-day's dispatches," he said ; " but I cannot guarantee a favourable answer."

Ten days later the answer was brought by the Town Clerk, and it was a very decided " No." He sat and talked of many things, while the ladies tried not to show their disappointment. Before leaving he gave a quick glance around, to make sure that no one was listening, and then whispered, " Let no one persuade you to try to get back to Spring-of-Wine—you would be stopped at Jade Gate, and you know as well as I do the kind of men they have down there. Keep out of their clutches."

Every Monday I wash My Clothes.

When he was gone, the Grey Lady said, " This is exactly what I was most afraid of. He has just made it impossible for us to move."

The official who had been appointed to keep an eye on the ladies, must have seen that they had apparently given up all thought of leaving. Their daily life seemed concentrated on their missionary work, and on the difficult business of supplying the house with food.   When they went out they frequently brought back a pound of flour, an onion, or a carrot, and Topsy often collected a small bundle of firewood.   Although the shops were closed, the sight of hard cash was very tempting, and would often secure some scrap from a private store.

Every few days the ladies made an excursion among the farmsteads.   The oasis was very much like an island, only that it was surrounded by sand instead of by water.   The people in the farms were always glad to see them, and the sentries at the City Gates were so used to their comings and goings that they always had a friendly word for them. But life was getting harder and conditions daily grew worse, until people were dying in the streets of hunger and of fever.

The brigand General had commanded that the missionaries should not leave; but they were asking Someone else about it. Each morning, before the front door was open, the household met to pray. First they sang a hymn, and the hymn said :

> " Guide me, oh Thou Great Jehovah,
>   Pilgrim through this barren land."

The tune was nice, and everyone liked singing it, but the hymn quite clearly asked for something which it seemed very difficult for God to give. It asked for guidance and the missionaries could not see what the next step was to be, nor how God would guide them. What happens when people are guided ?

There was still another verse which ran :

> " Let the fiery, cloudy pillar
>   Guide me all my journey through."

How was that going to be done ? Would

they really know which way to go? When
they had sung the hymn they prayed, and they
always asked God not to let them make a
mistake. They did this day by day, and still
they could not see any way out of their difficulty.

All through March they went in and out
among the farms and always watched for a
" fiery, cloudy pillar " to point the way of
escape.

In early April God spoke in their hearts
and said, " Go now." They felt sure it must
be God speaking, because He said it to each
one of them separately, so they dared not delay.
One day they moved about as usual, received
callers and chatted with the children who
played in the courtyards, but at nightfall,
when the front door was shut, instead of going
to bed, they set to hard work. All the fodder
and millet in the secret store were pressed into
sacks and hoisted on to the carts. No one
spoke above a whisper, lest the neighbours
should hear and report that something unusual
was happening at the missionaries' house.

At daybreak the bedding and bundles of clothes were strapped to the luggage-rack and all was ready.   None of the many callers who spied through a hole in a paper window could suspect that the people had really left, because the bed-sitting-dining-room looked much as usual; the tiny dining-table was there, the bench stood against the wall and Topsy's packing-case was in its corner.   There were even a few tins left on the table, as though they would be required for supper, and the blue cotton door-curtain hung in its usual place.

At the very last moment the cook called out, " Food is ready," and all gathered for a bowl of his famous " fugitive stew," the dish he made from the most unpromising materials, yet which was always appetising, and the name of which was a reminder of numerous flights and perils.

The sentries at the gate must not see how full the carts were, for that would give the situation away, so Topsy walked with two Mamas as far as the moat outside the city wall,

Topsy has Her own piece of Garden.

and the Grey Lady dropped the curtain behind her and sat so as to hide the baggage.

The road they must follow led due north, but, in order to conceal their plans, they left the town by the south gate, and took a round-about way which brought them in the end to the farms in the northern part of the oasis.

Topsy knew that they were running away, and she proved to be a first-class conspirator; she could not say anything foolish which would betray them, but her eyes were so sharp that nothing escaped her. At last they reached the very edge of the oasis, and the desert lay before them, with Wild Asses' Well just ahead.

Here there was a farm, so they stopped and asked for boiling water to make tea. While they drank, a few questions seemed quite natural.

" Is that Wild Asses' Well over there ? "

" It is," said the farmer.

" I heard there was a full guard of soldiers there."

M

" So there was until to-day, but they all rode off this morning."

This was a surprising answer, and some of the party remembered about the " fiery, cloudy pillar " which was to lead them.

" Where have they gone ? " asked the cook.

The farmer grinned. " They went toward the City-of-Sands, but wherever they have gone it means trouble for someone. We are glad to be rid of them, and others will be sorry to see them come."

The carter chimed in : " Old man," he said, " are you telling me that there will be no soldiers at Wild Asses' Well this night ? "

" That is what I am saying," he replied.

A look was exchanged between carter and cook, and an order came from the Grey Lady :

" It is late, and we must not stay talking any longer. Finish your tea and we will be off."

An hour later, as the grey evening light faded towards darkness, the small caravan passed Wild Asses' Well and was lost to sight in the dim expanse of sand.

CHAPTER TWENTY-EIGHT

WOULD they never get free from brigands and their guns? That is what Topsy must have thought when two days later, in the middle of the desert, armed men appeared, as though they had risen from the earth. Her eyes were sharp enough, and as far as she could see there was nothing around but a vast plain of sand, yet, suddenly, here were mounted men galloping after them! She saw the cook's face go white with fear.

" We saw the marks of your cart-wheels and followed you up," the men said. " What are you doing here? Where are you going?

We have orders to arrest all who have not a travel permit."

This was very alarming, and Topsy drew farther back into the cart and sat close up to the Grey Lady, where the men would not see her. There were lots of things she could not understand, but she realised clearly enough that they were in real danger again.

The next thing she saw was the Blue Lady unfolding a large sheet of paper covered with writing in red and black ink, and stamped in many places with scarlet seals. This she handed to the men, who took it, examined it, and as they looked, some of the fierceness went out of their faces. One of them nodded, and the other looked up quite pleasantly as they refolded the paper and returned it to the Blue Lady. Then they rode off across the sands again.

Topsy little knew what a narrow escape they had had from being taken straight back to that dreadful brigand camp and made close prisoners. It was touch and go when the brigands asked for their travel permit. They had a proper passport, of course, issued by the Chinese Government, but the Baby General was in revolt against that Government, and would have thrown the passport into the fire if it had come into his hands. Had the scouts taken the ladies and Topsy to the camp, travel would have been over for them for many a long day, but God intervened, and these particular scouts, never having been to school, could not read one word, not even the Chinese equivalent of A, B, C, which is Ren, Ma, Li. When they saw the great seals on that Foreign Office passport, they were completely deceived, and could only think that they were affixed by their great Chief himself, so they galloped off, believing that this grand document was the General's own travel permit. The cook chuckled with delight when he saw what had happened, but when they were well out of sight the caravan halted, and the missionaries thanked God for this deliverance.

Topsy knew that she was not quite like other people, who were always moving their lips at each other, and as they did so made each other understand things.

But if she could not use her ears or her tongue, she had eyes and knew how to use them, for she realised better than ordinary folk, how every thought of the heart shows through the eyes and in every line of the face. All through these stirring times she watched people's faces for signs of alarm, fear, relief and confidence, and she could not be mistaken, because she did not listen to what people *said* but saw what they *thought*.

This journey was the hardest and most tiring the ladies had ever done, and Topsy saw that they were afraid of someone running after them and taking them back again.

" It will be that bad General," she thought. " I wish the bullet had carried away his two legs instead of just going through them."

They used to press on each day, long after

dark, lie down for a few hours, often in the feeding-trough of a stable, and then, after a bowl of millet porridge, travel on once more until the mules refused to pull any longer without a feed.

Every day they were more and more tired, and it seemed harder and harder to get up without having one's sleep out. Topsy had always thought of the desert as a clean place, but where there had been fighting she saw carcases of dead horses lying about, and scraps of soldiers' uniforms blown by the wind. There were bones, too, which the wolves had picked clean and left to bleach in the sands. And then the loneliness! She had never thought of going so long without meeting some fellow-creature. It was terrifying, and the feeling that wolves prowled round each night to feed on the carrion did not help to make things pleasanter.

How long did the journey last? Topsy did not know, for what with travelling day and night she lost all count of time, and only longed to get somewhere where she might sleep.

At long last they met some people. For a moment her heart sank when she saw they too were soldiers, with rifles and bandoliers filled with cartridges strapped over their chests. The next minute, however, she caught the look of relief on the carter's face, and knew that these were friendly men.

The soldiers ran up and stood in a crowd round the cart, and everybody's lips moved at once :

" Where are you from ? "

" Did you see anyone on the desert ? "

" Were you stopped anywhere ? "

" Where is that ruffian of a brigand Chief ? "

" We shot him in the leg ; how is he now ? "

" Was it you who dressed his wounds ? I wish he would come to me to have his wounds dressed ! "

While they talked, Topsy had a good look at the men of this new army, and saw that they were thin, that their clothes were shabby and that many of them looked sick, and she guessed rightly they must have had a hard time fighting the brigand General's troops.

When they travelled on, it was among the blackened walls of burnt-out farms. Every tree had been cut down, the fields were unsown and all the inhabitants had vanished. At last they came to a large town, and when they passed the gate and entered the street, the Blue Lady said to Topsy :

" This is Hami," and Topsy, looking at her Ma-ma's lips, set her own in the same shape, and repeated the word " Ha-mi."

CHAPTER TWENTY-NINE

THERE was another whole month of jogging along in a bumping cart before the travellers reached Urumchi, the capital of Turkestan. The Mongols call it Urumchi, but the city has a variety of names, and visitors choose the one they like best. The easiest to remember is Hung Miao, which means Red Temple. In this town they had friends and a house where they might stay, but Topsy's Ma-mas were troubled about their little girl, for they must travel on to England, and what could they do about her?

Grandad and Grannie Fan were two whole

186

months' journey away at Spring-of-Wine,
and brigand armies surged between. It was
impossible to send her back and taking her
on was a plan that bristled with difficulties,
the chief of which was the matter of securing
a passport for her. It looked so simple
to go on travelling as they had been doing,
but they were now coming near the frontier
of Turkestan and Russia, and they would
not be allowed to go further without pass-
ports which showed that they had permission to leave China. The three ladies had
their papers, but how could they get one for
Topsy? Then there was the further question
as to whether she might land in England.
If this permission were given, they must still
pass through Russia, Poland, Germany and
Belgium, and each of these countries would
have a say as to whether three English women
and a little Chinese girl might cross their
borders.

They often talked to each other about
Topsy's passport. The Grey Lady would say :

" It is going to be very difficult," but the Brown Lady would answer :

" If God has given us Topsy to care for, He will make a way for her to go with us."

The Blue Lady did not say anything at all, because her heart was so heavy at the thought of handing Topsy over to someone who would not love her as she did.

At last they came in sight of the great town of Red Temple, and saw two horsemen galloping at full speed over the plain. One of these they knew to be their friend the English missionary, and the other his Mongolian groom, who rode everywhere with him.

After a word of greeting the friend said :

" You would never guess who is spending a week here."

" If we could never guess, then tell us quickly," said the Brown Lady.

" It is one of the British Consuls from Kashgar. He has come all the fifty-four days' journey, though there are only two British subjects here. We were afraid he would be gone before you arrived, but you are just in time, and you are asked to a party to-night where you will meet him."

The ladies exchanged glances, for they knew that if anyone could help them to get a passport for Topsy, it was this very Consul.   It seemed to them that God was making a way for her.

When it came to dressing for the party, they took out the best Chinese clothes they had, and seeing how shabby they were, said to one another, " However can we go to a party in these things ? " but when they got there their Chinese hostess and all the other friends were so cordial and so glad to see that they had come safe and sound out of the brigand camp and all its dangers, that they never once gave their clothes a thought.

The British Consul was very kind. He wanted to know everything about Topsy, and promised to help all he could with the passport.

" Give me every bit of information you can about her," he said, " and to-morrow, when

I see the Chinese Governor, I will speak of her; but," he added, " if she is to travel across the world, she must have a Christian name and a surname too."

Topsy had no family name, so one must be found for her. Each of the ladies had a Chinese surname, and that of the Blue Lady was Gai.

" That would be a very good name for Topsy," someone said, " especially if you spelt it English fashion, Guy. Then her own first name, Ai Lien, would easily change to Eileen, and Eileen Guy would be a very nice name for her."

So the matter was decided.

On the very next day the Chinese Governor granted the British Consul's request, and stamped a little passport book for Eileen Guy. On the front page was her photograph and her description. Everything about her was declared, even her height and the colour of her eyes and hair. So far, so good; but they could not move on until permission came from Moscow for the three ladies and Eileen Guy to cross Russia, and that permit took three months to come.

Every few days they went to a big building with a sign of the hammer and sickle over the door, and there they saw a very stern lady, who sat at a table covered with papers of all sorts. She always shook her head and said, " No, nothing has come." At last, one day, in early autumn, the stern lady, instead of saying " No," as usual, put out her hand and took up a paper which said, " Eileen Guy may travel through Russia on her way to England." For the first time in her life Topsy cried for joy. The tears just came brimming up, and when the stern lady saw it, she jumped up, took her in her arms and kissed her.

After that all was bustle, sorting and packing and the tailor made a warm coat for Topsy, because she was going through Siberia, which was very cold. She stood by and watched him cut it out, because she was told that in England there would be no Chinese tailor, and she would have to make all her own clothes.

When they left Urumchi the travel-cart was different from any which she had seen before, and was drawn by three horses with shaggy manes. The middle one had a wooden hoop over its head, with a bell which jingled all the time, and the driver was a tall Russian who flicked the horses with a long whip and kept them trotting. Some parts of the journey were very frightening, because of the deep rivers which had to be crossed, but they always came out safely on the other side, and three weeks later arrived at Chuguchak, the City of Seagulls. It was full of strange people and fine buildings, and a whole book could be written about it, but this is only " The Story of Topsy " and " What Topsy Saw " must be left for another volume.

Welcome to the Willow Cottage.

CHAPTER THIRTY

FROM Chuguchak onwards every day was a day of fresh marvels. The *britschka* and its three trotting horses was the swiftest mode of travel Topsy had ever imagined, but that was forgotten now in the excitement of the next wonder.

Here was a great big baggage-cart into which the travellers first hoisted the luggage, then climbed themselves. There was no sign of horses, yet the driver scrambled to his seat, and the next moment the whole thing rushed down the road without any horses to pull it !

This was Topsy's first introduction to the motor-lorry. It was not a very happy introduction, because there was a great deal of heavy luggage on board, and the road was very rough, so that there was a constant fight with the boxes to keep them from tumbling on to the passengers. Also, though Topsy was used to travelling all day, she was accustomed to halt at night, put up a sleeping-tent, and rest while the horses were fed; but this horseless cart did not need to rest or feed, so it carried its passengers right on through the night.

It was a hot noon-day when they first climbed into the lorry, and for the next few hours they were baked by the sun, then evening cool fell and the sun set. Later the moon rose, and still they rattled on; only now they were very cold instead of being too hot. By and bye the moon set and the sun rose again, but not until midday did that horseless and tireless cart come to a standstill and allow its stiff and bruised passengers to alight.

Then there was another wonder! After they had been standing for an hour with many other people on a long wooden pavement, a huge machine rolled up, dragging behind it

so many carts that it was as long as a desert
caravan. Everybody rushed forward, and
Topsy found herself pushed up a few steps
into a railway carriage. When the train started
she sat down near a window, and thought what
a wonderful world it was, and felt she could
never weary of looking through this window
at all the things to be seen.

Sometimes they passed through a dense
forest, where the trees pressed up close to
the railway line, and sometimes they stopped
where there were only a few low wooden
houses. The men were all so big and bearded,
the women wore bright-coloured kerchiefs over
their heads, and the children's hair was the
palest yellow—like barley when it is ripe for
cutting.

Late in the afternoon they reached a large
town, and the Grey Lady pulled out the teapot
and put some tea-leaves in it. As soon as
the train stopped, the Blue Lady seized the pot,
while the Brown Lady took the kettle, and
they both jumped out and ran down the plat-
N *

form. A lot of people got ahead of them and all stood in a long queue, everyone having a kettle in his hand. One by one they filled the kettles with boiling water at a huge tank, then the two ladies came running back with a delicious brew of tea. The travellers were all so very thirsty that they drank many cups of tea, then each lay down on a wooden seat to sleep. It was possible to let benches down from all sides of the carriage, so there was room for everyone. Each time Topsy woke up in the night she found that the train was still rolling on.

As long as they were living in the railway carriage everything was very nice, but on the third day they all got out of the train at the big crowded station of Novo-Sibirsk, the capital of Siberia, and for a whole day and half the night, sat in a waiting-room with people lying all about the floor. How tired and sleepy they all were! And what a lot of people seemed to be travelling! The next train was so crowded that they had to fight their way on to it. Here there were no nice wooden benches to lie on at night, so they had to stretch out on the floor, where horrid insects like grasshoppers jumped about.

There were so many days and nights on this train that Topsy lost count, but at last they came to an end when they reached Moscow, the capital of Russia.

To wash one's face after all those days on the train, where there was no water, was delightful for everyone; but for Topsy it was one of the thrills of life, because over the basin in the waiting room was a brass knob, and when she touched it water spurted out of the wall. She would have washed her hands fifty times a day, just for the fun of seeing the water spurt, had she been allowed to do so.

But there were more days and nights still to spend on the train, and lots of men wearing the grandest clothes wanted to see Topsy's passport, and stared at her to make sure that this really was Eileen Guy. Every time they

changed trains after leaving Moscow the
carriage seemed nicer than the last, and one
day they rolled smoothly and easily into another
big station, and this was Berlin, the capital
of Germany.

CHAPTER THIRTY-ONE

THE readers of this story of Topsy
cannot remember their first bed or their
first bath, because they have always had beds
and baths, but if you were to ask Topsy, she
would tell you that it was in Berlin that she
first saw a real bed—something so different
from the canvas sleeping-bags which her Ma-
mas used in Asia.

First she had a bath; and such a bath as
she had never dreamt of. This was no
wooden tub with Grannie Fan pouring in a

kettleful of hot water and a bucketful of cold, but a china bath like a small pond, in which she could stretch her full length and kick as she would. She came out clean and shiny, and then got into the bed to find that it rested on springs that gave to her weight and threw her into the air when she jumped about. If only she had not been so sleepy she would have loved to dance up and down all night, but unfortunately she laid her head on the cool downy pillow just for a minute or two, and behold, it was next morning, the sun was shining into the room, and she knew it was time to get up.

What fairy world days these were, when she sat on a crimson velvet chair, and ate breakfast from a table spread with a cloth that was so white that it frightened her—for what would happen if her knife and fork went wrong and jerked something off the slippery plate on to it? It was a great feat for Topsy to learn the use of such a dangerous weapon as a knife, harder even than for a little English girl to learn to handle chop-sticks, as Topsy had done so deftly since she was a tiny child.

Then there were wonderful lighting arrangements. There was now no little iron lamp with a drop of linseed oil and a hand-twisted wick, such as she and Grannie Fan used to sew by of an evening, but a button near the door which made three lights leap up all at once.

In this place which, to Topsy, seemed such a palace, there were two buttons over the wash-hand basin, and if you pressed the one cold water came, but if you touched the other steaming hot water squirted miraculously from the wall, though where it came from, who could tell? All these were wonderful things of which the little Mongolian child had never heard or dreamt.

Topsy was getting very near to the end of the journey. One more day and night and she would be in London. Very late one evening she was taken to the railway station and put to bed on a train from which she alighted next morning on to a wharf, where she saw the sea for the first time. This was a wonderful experience, and she imagined that this great stretch of water must be a river, but wider than any she had seen before, because the other bank was out of sight. The steamers looked to her like strange houses with huge white chimneys, and although she was now accustomed to things that went by themselves without being pushed by men or pulled by horses, it was difficult to think of these floating mansions as boats, for the only boat she knew was the ferry which took her across the river in Mongolia.

She walked up a gangway, and presently the ship moved slowly away from the shore, then something inside it began to throb and the Grey and Blue Ladies vanished down the stairs. Topsy did not enjoy the throbbing of the boat either, but the Brown Lady sat on deck, or walked about, and Topsy felt responsible to do her part by looking after the luggage. She was not sorry, however, when the other shore came in sight.

Presently they stepped off the floating mansion, and for the last time on this journey the luggage was taken to a Custom House. This was the eighth time that Topsy had stood by and indignantly watched unknown men open the little case which held her treasures. Some of them had looked at her doll, others had opened her precious needle-book, but when they put it back, she always counted the needles to see if any had been taken. These men, however, smiled at her, and did not even open her bundle of pieces; they only gave one glance, shut down the lid and chalked a mark on it.

She was soon in the train once more, and sat wondering if this travel would ever cease, and as she still wondered, the train drew up in Victoria Station—and that was the end of her long, long journey.

CHAPTER THIRTY-TWO

TOPSY began life as an unwanted child, then came into the hands of a woman who would have let her die of cold and hunger, but from the day of the tap, tap, tap at the Christians' door she never lacked a friend to care for her. There was kind Grandad Fan who loved her, Grannie Fan who fed her, Mandarin Lin who rescued her from the wicked woman, and Lady Lin who petted her— not to speak of the three friends who made her their own little girl.

Now she was in England, and lots of people were kind to her. One by one she recognised all those whose pictures she had seen at Spring-of-Wine. There was an Auntie who took her to her own home, where she found a delightful dog called Peggy. There was a tall, thin man with a scarlet flap hanging down his back who preached from a high pulpit, and a snowy-haired lady with lovely blue eyes who sat wrapped in a white shawl. Then there was the gentle friend who had been nurse to the Blue Lady when she was a little girl, and who came to look after Topsy when her Ma-mas went away.

There were other friends whose photographs she had never seen, and foremost among them was the lady who taught her to speak. How patient she was, teaching her little by little what talking meant, and how to push her breath out for " h " and make a jerk in her throat for " k," and press her lips together for " b." Before long Topsy loved going to her lessons, and later, when she was able to read a story to herself and write her first letter to a friend, she was very proud indeed.

Every Sunday morning Topsy went to a church, where many people had a smile for her. When they stood, she stood, and when they knelt, she also knelt. She knew when they were singing, so, of course, she wanted to sing too. Unfortunately, she did not know when to begin or when to stop, so people sitting near sometimes heard her make a joyful noise at the wrong moment, but no one seemed to mind this, and some even liked it, for though joyful, it was never too loud.

When she saw the collection taken up and everyone putting money into the plate, Topsy asked the Blue Lady about it, and whether the money was used to buy bread for the hungry, or whether it would be given to the clergyman. " If it goes to the poor," she indicated, " I will give my penny; but if not, I keep it."

One Sunday evening she was baptised by her friend the clergyman. Her belief was quite clear. She knew that the Good Shepherd had taken her to the Christians' house, had told her friends to take her in, and had brought her

out of her troubles to this happy place so full
of love.   She wanted, by this act, to tell the
Good Shepherd that she loved Him, and to let
everybody know that she belonged to Him.

There was still one important person whose
picture Topsy treasured but who had never
appeared anywhere, and that was the golden-
haired Princess.   Was she real, or was all she
had heard about her only a fairy tale after
all ?   That question was settled one day when
the Grey Lady took Topsy to Hyde Park,
where she stood and looked into a garden
where two little girls in tartan skirts were
playing, and Topsy at once realised that
the elder was actually and unmistakably her
fairy Princess !   The other was, of course, the
younger sister, Princess Margaret Rose.   As
she stood and gazed, a lady and gentleman
came into the garden, and she knew them for
the father and mother of the Princess—the
Duke and Duchess of York, who are now
King and Queen of England.

Topsy was very quiet on the way home,

but she went with a mind made up on one point—a tartan skirt she too must have. It took her many months to earn it by good conduct and long periods of perfect obedience, but in the end the tartan skirt she had.

CHAPTER THIRTY-THREE

WHEN Topsy and her Ma-mas are in England they spend the winter in a small London flat, but they never feel so much at home in the crowded city as they do in a certain stone cottage where they spend the summer. It is tucked away in the quietness of a Dorset lane, far from any railway station. The cottage is their very own, and it stands in a garden where there are roses, honeysuckle, love-in-the-mist, pansies, sweet-william, snap-dragon, jasmine and pinks. Topsy has her own piece of garden there, with a little bath where the birds play and splash.

There is an orchard full of apple trees, and all around are meadows where cows feed, and where, in the autumn, the hedges are full of blackberries. This little house is called The Willow Cottage, because willow trees grow on the bank of the stream which runs through the orchard. In Topsy's little bedroom the walls are covered with her favourite pictures. There is her precious one of the Good Shepherd, and also the coloured portrait of the little Princess, which she has treasured ever since the day when the Chinese postman brought it to Spring-of-Wine. It hangs where she can see it as she lies in bed.

Every morning Topsy is up with the sun, and after she has made her bed and tidied the room, she begins the day's work. At breakfast she says grace for the family :

" Thank you, God, for morning sun,
Thank you for the birds that sing,
Thank you for our own good breakfast,
Thank you, God, for everything."

Each morning she has lessons with the Grey

Lady in reading, writing, and brushwork, and in the afternoon she does needlework, mows the grass, weeds the garden, and does all sorts of things with her Ma-mas. She has many dear friends in the country, and is always rather sad when the day comes to move up to the great city. Town life, however, has also its joys, because in London she goes to her beloved teacher for special lessons, and sometimes has the great treat of a day at the Zoo.

People often ask whether Topsy has forgotten the sadness of her childhood. She has forgotten nothing. One day she sat with her Ma-mas, and in her own way opened her heart about the things which she had endured. She pointed to the marks on her leg where the wicked woman had tortured her, and held up the little deformed finger which hurt her so much from repeated beatings that she still uses her left hand rather than her right.

"Nobody wanted me. When I went to people's doors everyone said 'Go.' If they gave me something they still said 'Go'; but when I came to you, for the first time in my life someone said ' Come.' "

The three to whom she said it, thought with pain of the vast multitude of little lonelies in every land, to whom no one has ever yet said " Come." The Good Shepherd bids them welcome, but they cannot know this unless His missionaries go and tell them.

You may meet Topsy any day in a Dorset lane or in a London street, and you will be sure to know her if you look out for the girl with two long, black plaits and the happiest face you ever saw.

THE END